HUMAN CELL CULTURE IN DIAGNOSIS OF DISEASE

Publication Number 813
AMERICAN LECTURE SERIES®

A Monograph in
The BANNERSTONE DIVISION *of*
AMERICAN LECTURES IN LIVING CHEMISTRY

Edited by
I. NEWTON KUGELMASS, M.D., Ph.D., Sc.D.
Consultant to the Departments of Health and Hospitals
New York City

HUMAN CELL CULTURE IN DIAGNOSIS OF DISEASE

By

JEAN H. PRIEST, M.D.

University of Colorado
Medical Center
Denver, Colorado

CHARLES C THOMAS · PUBLISHER

Springfield · Illinois · U.S.A.

Published and Distributed Throughout the World by
CHARLES C THOMAS • PUBLISHER
Bannerstone House
301-327 East Lawrence Avenue, Springfield, Illinois, U.S.A.
Natchez Plantation House
735 North Atlantic Boulevard, Fort Lauderdale, Florida, U.S.A.

© 1971, by CHARLES C THOMAS • PUBLISHER

Library of Congress Catalog Number: 76-149191

With THOMAS BOOKS *careful attention is given to all details of*
manufacturing and design. It is the Publisher's desire to present books
that are satisfactory as to their physical qualities and artistic possibilities
and appropriate for their particular use. THOMAS BOOKS *will be true*
to those laws of quality that assure a good name and good will.

Printed in the United States of America
EE-11

FOREWORD

Our Living Chemistry Series was conceived by Editor and Publisher to advance the newer knowledge of chemical medicine in the cause of clinical practice. The interdependence of chemistry and medicine is so great that physicians are turning to chemistry, and chemists to medicine in order to understand the underlying basis of life processes in health and disease. Once chemical truths, proofs and convictions become sound foundations for clinical phenomena, key hybrid investigators clarify the bewildering panorama of biochemical progress for application in everyday practice, stimulation of experimental research, and extension of postgraduate instruction. Each of our monographs thus unravels the chemical mechanisms and clinical management of many diseases that have remained relatively static in the minds of medical men for three thousand years. Our new Series is charged with the *nisus élan* of chemical wisdom, supreme in choice of international authors, optimal in standards of chemical scholarship, provocative in imagination for experimental research, comprehensive in discussions of scientific medicine, and authoritative in chemical perspective of human disorders.

Dr. Priest of Denver presents the human cell in culture as the unit of life and of biological activity. It bears the basic equipment for the maintenance and continuity of life but is more than a container of "vital" machinery. It is more correctly an expression of a universal set of mechanistic principles and of a unique molecular architecture and structural pattern. The cell is truly the smallest system of the human body capable of independent function in a wide range of activities. When a cell is damaged and the damage cannot be corrected, it is only a matter of time before all activity will come to a halt and the working parts will disintegrate. Clearly, the cell can behave in many ways but a common culture type is the diploid or chromosomally normal monolayer cell line established from biopsy of human tissue. The cell thus becomes the true locus of disease that gives us precise understanding of specific departures from normal function. Every patient is sick in his cells and his metabolic defects are reflected in cell culture.

The evolution of human cell culture involves the cultivation of actively multiplying cells in a histologically undifferentiated state. The art transformed into a science in this generation has enabled investigators to concentrate on disease processes rather than on the *in vitro* establishment and maintenance of the cells themselves. Since biologic changes are reflected in cell structure, the high degree of predictability and recognition of the morphologic features and their changes form the basis of cell culture studies. By transcending descriptive morphology, the knowledgeable clinician can project it into the living image of normal or abnormal biologic processes. Our knowledge of the relationships of morphology to biologic behavior is as yet imperfect and so we must use that which we know in full realization of its limitations and capacities and extend its boundaries with investigation, thought and experience.

The author wisely recognizes islands of knowledge, communicates about them, enlarges them, builds upon them, and molds them into useful wisdom in laboratory procedures for diagnosing disease. The sharp descriptions of human cell culture are followed by established techniques for chromosome analysis, metabolic defects, antenatal diagnosis, growth disorders, hybridization, control mechanisms, cloning, virus isolation, disease processes, and aging. The presentations are comprehensive providing an evaluation of limitations, potentialities, and clinical values of the culture methods. Their application has reaped a rich harvest of clinical usefulness. Cell culture should thus be regarded as a means to an end and not as an end in itself. To grow cells is as easy an endeavor as to grow microorganisms for innumerable purposes and so this clinical panorama of techniques may be an enjoyable intellectual tour through the current understanding of human cell reactions, and be a source of pleasure for the casual tourist as well as the seasoned traveler.

I. Newton Kugelmass, M.D., Ph.D., Sc.D., *Editor*

PREFACE

This monograph is intended to emphasize the study of human cells. Such a limitation is perhaps unacceptable to the cell biologist who realizes that emphasis on humans is pure egotism and, to be sure, most important biological discoveries have been made on nonhuman material. Furthermore both inside and outside the circle of professional biologists there is general feeling against the suitability of humans for experimentation. However, techniques to grow cells removed from the living individual have now permitted experimentation on human life removed from the individual. General principles for *in vitro* culture apply to all mammalian cells, but important differences exist as well between human and other cells in culture and these differences become especially apparent to the subgroup of biologists interested in the study and prevention of human disease. The medical cell biologist has become an essential member of a medical center or diagnostic team. This book is therefore dedicated to the idea that human cell culture is certainly unique in many ways and the cell biologist with knowledge of human diseases and orientation toward them needs every manner of encouragement to pursue his field of specialization.

The White House, Washington, September 9, 1966:

Cell, Tissue and Organ Culture Research is one of the most important undertakings in the entire field of medical investigation. It advances the knowledge of physicians and scientists upon whom we rely to identify, cure and combat disease.

> Second Decennial Review Conference on Cell, Tissue and Organ Culture.
> National Cancer Institute Monograph No. 26

INTRODUCTION

Human cells in culture can behave in many ways, but a common culture type is the diploid or chromosomally normal monolayer cell line established from biopsy of human tissue. A specialized variety of short-term culture is applied to peripheral blood and is useful for the demonstration of human chromosomes. Human peripheral blood is also grown over extended periods of time, with the potential accumulation of large quantities of this human tissue. Metabolic defects of the whole individual are reflected in cell culture which then becomes useful for definitive diagnosis and detailed study of the defect. Important processes such as aging, neoplasia, differentiation, and somatic cell mating are appropriately investigated in cultures of human cells. Furthermore, the cell as a unit of biological activity continues to be an important concept in the study of human disease.

CONTENTS

HUMAN CELL CULTURE IN DIAGNOSIS OF DISEASE

SECTION I
CHARACTERISTICS OF HUMAN CELL CULTURE

Chapter One
A DESCRIPTION OF HUMAN CELL CULTURE

O ne area of human genetics, with many immediate applications to medicine and the study of disease, is concerned with cell culture techniques and may be termed somatic cell genetics (Krooth, 1969). By strict definition only the somatic or nongerm cells are properly included in these studies. However, with the development of techniques for *in vitro* growth of human germ cells, the investigation of cells in culture now includes both somatic and germ lines. Furthermore, both genetic and environmental influences are studied. Cells taken from human individuals are grown in the laboratory and in this sense a certain part of the individual is preserved for study and experimental manipulation. This simplified type of life maintained in culture preserves and expresses many of the genetic characteristics of the donor cells. Furthermore, the cells respond to environmental stimuli in specific ways determined by both the cells themselves and the type of stimulus. Methodology ranges from simple to complex and the problems investigated cover all manner of questions asked, from those of critical importance in the diagnosis of an individual patient to those concerned with universal molecular mechanisms. The unity for this field of study is furnished by the fact that the orientation is cellular and preservation of biological activity removed from the intact individual is required, as is increase in cell number outside the individual.

Human cells in culture may be studied shortly after removal from the donor or they may be grown under conditions causing them to increase many times in number. Cell culture techniques imply that conditions are supplied to permit the cells to divide. Many biochemical procedures employing tissue homogenates of various types can be said to involve preservation of biological activity removed from the intact individual; but increase in cell number does not occur. Therefore such techniques are excluded from this consideration. Also excluded or de-emphasized are investigations with the primary objective to study, not the cells themselves, but some agent which is introduced into the culture, the best example of this category being many types of viral studies.

Once a field of endeavor is firmly established and concerns large numbers of investigators, agreement regarding terminology becomes essential. Table 1-I summarizes terminology concerned with animal *in vitro* culture. The definitions are based on the recommendations of the Committee on Terminology, Tissue Culture Association (1967). Table 1-II describes the recommendations for designation of a cell line. Table 1-III lists information used to describe a new cell line and Table 1-IV specifies information used to describe a cell or a cell strain for publication. Table 1-V defines chromosome numbers. The term "culture alteration" is used to indicate a persistent change in the properties or behavior of a culture; the term should always be qualified by a precise description of the change that has occurred in the culture. "Cell transformation" should be reserved to mean heritable changes (see Chap. 8).

TABLE 1-I

TERMINOLOGY CONCERNED WITH *IN VITRO* CULTURE

Animal tissue culture	Concerns the study of cells, tissues and organs explanted from animals and maintained or grown *in vitro* for more than 24 hours.
Cell culture	Denotes the growing of cells *in vitro*, including culture of single cells. The cells are no longer organized into tissues.
Tissue or organ culture	Denotes the maintenance or growth of tissues, organ primordia or the whole or parts of an organ *in vitro* in a way that may allow preservation of the architecture or function.
Cell Types	
Epithelial cells	Refers to cells apposed to each other, forming continuous mosaic-like sheets. Epithelial origin or function should be identifiable.
Epithelial-like cells	In cell cultures epithelial cells may assume various shapes but tend to form sheets of closely

TABLE 1-I (Continued)

	adherent cells. When the only criterion for identification of such cells is their morphology, and epithelial origin or function are not identified, it is preferable to refer to the cells as epithelial-like. (See Fig. 1-1b)
Fibroblasts	Cells of spindle or irregular shape, producing fibers. In organ and tissue cultures, in which cell interrelationships are preserved, fibroblasts may be identified using accepted histologic criteria. Mesodermal origin or function should be identifiable.
Fibroblast-like cells	Cells acquiring irregular or spindle shape are referred to as fibroblast-like if their derivation or potentialities, such as production of fibers, are unknown. (See Fig. 1-1a)

Culture Types

Cell line	Arises from a primary culture at the time of the first subculture. This term implies the presence of numerous lineages of the cells originally present in the primary explant.
Cell strain	Can be derived either from a primary culture or a cell line by selection or cloning of cells having specific properties or markers. The properties or markers must persist during subsequent cultivation.
Clone	Denotes a population of cells derived from a single cell by mitosis.
Cloned strain or line	Denotes a strain or line descended directly from a clone.
Diploid cell line	Denotes a cell line in which, arbitrarily, at least 75% of the cells have the same karyotype as the normal cells of the species from which the cells were originally obtained. A description of a diploid cell line should include the actual numbers of cells examined, the percentage of diploid cells and their karyotype.
Established cell line	A cell line may be said to have become established when it demonstrates the potential to be subcultured indefinitely *in vitro*. (Based on experience with human fibroblast-like cells, a culture should exceed 70 population doublings before it is "established.")
Heteroploid (nondiploid) cell line	Denotes a cell line having less than 75% of cells with diploid chromosome constitution. In describing a heteroploid cell line, in addition to the karyotype of the stem line, the percentage of cells with such karyotype should be stated.

TABLE 1-I (Continued)

Mass culture	An uncloned culture.
Monolayer	Refers to a layer of cells growing on a surface.
Primary cloning	Implies direct cloning of single cells from a primary explant.
Primary culture	Implies a culture started from cells, tissues or organs taken directly from organisms. A primary culture may be regarded as such until it is subcultured for the first time. It then becomes a cell line (or strain).
Suspension culture	Denotes a type of culture in which cells multiply while suspended in medium.

Other Culture Terms

Absolute plating efficiency	Indicates the percentage of individual cells giving rise to colonies (clones) when inoculated into culture vessels. The total number of cells in the inoculum, type of culture vessel and the environmental conditions (medium, temperature, CO_2 atmosphere, etc.) should always be stated.
Cell generation time	Denotes the interval between consecutive divisions of a cell. (Usually determined by cinematography.) This term is not synonymous with population doubling time.
Culture alteration	Persistent change in the properties or behavior of a culture, such as altered morphology, chromosome constitution, virus susceptibility, nutritional requirements, proliferative capacity and malignant characteristics. The term should always be qualified by a precise description of the change that has occurred.
Explant	Describes an excised fragment of a tissue or an organ used to initiate an *in vitro* culture.
Population doubling time	Used when referring to an entire population of cells and indicates the interval in which for example, 1×10^6 cells increase to 2×10^6 cells. This term is not synonymous with cell generation time.
Subculture (passage)	Denotes the transplantation of cells from one culture vessel to another.
Subculture interval	Denotes the interval between subsequent subcultures of cells. This term may be unrelated to cell generation time.
Subculture number	Indicates the number of times cells have been subcultured.

TABLE 1-II

DESIGNATION OF A CELL LINE

1. Not more than four letters in series indicating the laboratory of origin
2. A series of numbers indicating the line

Example: NCL 123

TABLE 1-III

INFORMATION USED TO DESCRIBE A NEW CELL LINE

1. Whether the tissue or origin was normal or neoplastic and, if neoplastic, whether benign or malignant
2. Whether the tissue was embryonic, newborn, adult (state age)
3. The animal species of origin
4. The organ of origin
5. The cell type (if known)
6. The designation of the line
7. Whether the line has been cloned

TABLE 1-IV

INFORMATION USED TO DESCRIBE A CELL LINE OR A CELL STRAIN FOR PUBLICATION

1. History
2. Age (preferably by population doubling number)
3. Culture medium
4. Growth characteristics
5. Absolute plating efficiency
6. Morphology
7. Frequency of cells with various chromosome numbers
8. Karyotype(s) of the stem line(s)
9. Whether sterility tests for mycoplasmas, bacteria and fungi have been done
10. Whether the species of origin and the tissue of origin have been confirmed and the procedures by which this was done
11. For a cell strain include the procedure of isolation, specific properties of the cells in detail, the number of population doublings and the length of time since isolation

TABLE 1-V

DEFINITIONS CONCERNED WITH CHROMOSOME NUMBERS

Term	Definition or Description
Aneuploid	All numbers deviating from x* and exact multiples of x.*
Diploid	Double the basic number (symbol: 2x*).
Endopolyploidy	Occurrence (in a cellular population) of polyploid cells, which have originated by endomitosis.
Euploid	All exact multiples of x.*
Haploid	1. The basic number of a polyploid series (symbol: x*). Haploid in this meaning = monoploid.

TABLE 1-V (Continued)

Term	Definition or Description
	2. The chromosome number of the haplophase; the gametic reduced number (symbol: n).
Heteroploid	1. In organisms with predominating diplophase: all chromosome numbers deviating from the normal chromosome number of the diplophase.
	2. In organisms with predominating haplophase: all chromosome numbers deviating from the normal chromosome number of the haplophase.
Mixoploidy	Presence of more than one chromosome number in a cellular population. (Also termed: mosaicism.)
Polyploid	General designation for multiples of the basic number (x^*). higher than diploid.
Tetraploid	Quadruple the basic number (symbol: $4x^*$).
Triploid	Triple the basic number (symbol: $3x^*$).
Trisomic	Double the basic number, plus 1. The extra chromosome results in 3 instead of 2 chromosomes in one pair.

$*$In mammalian cell culture common usage allows the symbol n also to stand for the basic number of a somatic cell series.

MONOLAYER SERIAL CULTURE

When established from a primary explant or biopsy of fetal or adult tissue, usually one main morphologic type of human cell grows out under standard culture conditions. These cells are fibroblast-like, resembling the classical fibroblast (Fig. 1-1a), unless special conditions are provided to preserve cell, tissue or organ morphology. They usually adhere tightly to the lower surface of the culture container (Fig. 1-2a and b), as a cell monolayer. They can be separated from each other and from the container surface by enzymatic treatment, usually trypsinization, and distributed to new culture containers. By means of serial subculturings, the life of the cells is continued for at least forty to sixty generations or population doublings (Hayflick, 1965), corresponding to a total cell number of $(2n)^{40-60}$, if a single cell (n) is present originally. Maintenance of -150 to $-170°C$ in liquid nitrogen allows for prolonged storage (see Chap. 2 and Appendix on freezing of cells). This type of culture is referred to as a diploid cell line (Tables 1-I and 1-V). If the cell source is chromosomally abnormal, such as a biopsy from an individual with a trisomy syndrome, the culture is called a nondiploid cell line. It reflects the chromosome constitution of the donor cells (see Fig. 2-5, Chap. 2) although there may be *in vitro* selection for one particular chromosome cell type, if more than one is

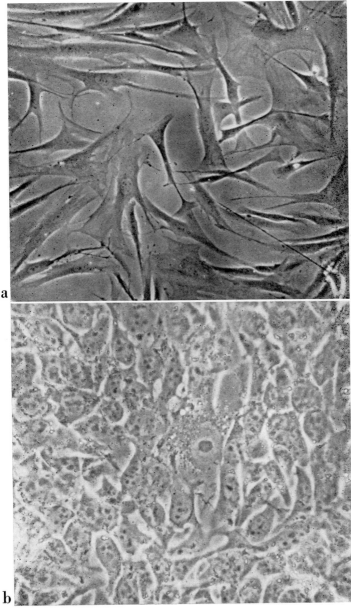

Figure 1-1. (a) Human diploid fibroblast-like cells growing in monolayer culture. Phase contrast photomicroscopy by Jane L. Showacre. (b) A non-diploid established cell line. At confluency the cells form a mosaic-like layer and may be described as epithelial-like. Phase contrast photomicroscopy by Jane L. Showacre.

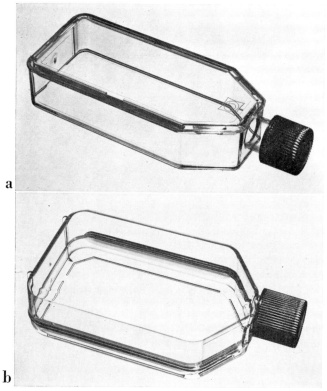

Figure 1-2a and b. Plastic, disposable flasks suitable for culturing cells in a monolayer on the lower surface. (a) 25 cm² growing surface. (b) 75 cm² growing surface. Courtesy of Falcon Plastics, Division of BioQuest.

present initially (Chang *et al.*, 1969). The culture life expectancy is finite, as for the diploid cell lines. If the cell source is neoplastic, the initial cell biopsy may produce a culture with an infinite life expectancy, called a nondiploid established cell line (Fig. 1-1b; also see Chap. 8, on cultures from tumors). The chromosome constitution is variable from cell to cell and is far different from diploid. The cells may grow in suspension rather than as mono-layers, as will be described in more detail further on in this chapter. Even as monolayers there is a tendency for nondiploid cells to grow more rapidly than diploid cells and to overgrow one another, as in neoplastic tissue *in vivo*. An example of this latter type of culture are HeLa cells started from human cervical carcinoma (Bottomley *et al.*, 1969). There are a few reports of non-neoplastic or diploid human tissues which gave rise, in culture, to established cell lines. However some of these "spontaneous" changes from diploid to nondiploid were the result of contamination, either by other cells or viruses (Gartler, 1967). Thus, contrary to initial expectations when human cell culture first became a common procedure, nondiploid established cell lines of human origin proved to be the exception rather than the rule. It is important to add that the development of defined environmental conditions in regard to pH, temperature, and growth medium has been critical to the advancement of cell culture as a useful diagnostic tool.

Monolayer cultures can be explained in more detail by protocols for handling this type of culture in the laboratory. In the appendix which is devoted to methodology, standard procedures for monolayer cell maintenance, subculture, handling of primary explants and cell storage are described. The bibliography at the end of this chapter also lists general tissue culture texts.

The term multilayer is now used to describe a monolayer culture with a tendency for the cells to grow on top of each other, nevertheless adhering strictly to the container surface. For human cells, these cultures are usually nondiploid and may have been transformed (see Chap. 8, on characteristics of transformed cells). However, special conditions may increase the tendency to form multilayers, or produce greater cell numbers as a monolayer, particularly frequent medium change (Griffiths, 1970) and perfusion techniques (Kruse *et al.*, 1969).

As of 1970 forty-seven cell lines of human origin were available from the American Type Culture Collection Repository (12301 Parklawn Drive, Rockville, Maryland 20852) (Table 1-VI); the majority of these cell lines grow as monolayer cultures. This independent nonprofit organization publishes a *Registry of Animal Cell Lines* (first edition, 1964) and supplements. The animal cells listed in the registry are preserved and distributed to the scientific community. Several commercial organizations also provide human cells.* Many investigators start their own cell lines from primary explants in order to obtain strain characteristics they want to study.

*BioQuest
Cockeysville, Maryland 21030

Cappel Laboratories Inc.
Box 156
Downington, Pennsylvania 19335

Flow Laboratories Inc.
12601 Twinbrook Parkway
Rockville, Maryland 20852

Grand Island Biological Co.
3175 Staley Road
Grand Island, New York 14072

Microbiological Associates, Inc.
P.O. Box 5970
Washington, D.C. 20014

TABLE 1-VI

CELL LINES OF HUMAN ORIGIN AVAILABLE FROM THE
AMERICAN TYPE CULTURE COLLECTION
CELL REPOSITORY

Name of Cell Line	Cell Repository Number
AV₃, Amnion	CCL 21
CCRF-CEM, Peripheral blood, acute lymphoblastic leukemia	CCL 119
CCRF-SB, Peripheral blood, acute lymphoblastic leukemia	CCL 120
CCRF-HSB-2, Human tumors in hamsters; source: peripheral blood, acute lymphoblastic leukemia	CCL 120.1
Chang Liver	CCL 13
Citrullinemia, Skin	CCL 76
Cri du Chat, Skin	CCL 90
Dempsey, Skin, Klinefelter's syndrome (XXXXY)	CCL 28
Detroit-6, Sternal marrow	CCL 3
Detroit-6, Clone 12, Sternal marrow	CCL 3.1
Detroit 98, Sternal marrow	CCL 18
D98S, Detroit 98 with biochemical markers	CCL 18.1
D98/AG, 8-azaguanine resistant	CCL 18.2
D98/AH-2, 8-azahypoxanthine resistant	CCL 18.3
D98/AH-R, 8-azahypoxanthine sensitive	CCL 18.4
Detroit 510, Skin, galactosemia	CCL 72
Detroit 525, Skin, XO plus centric fragment, Turner's syndrome	CCL 65
Detroit 529, Skin, trisomy for X and a group G chromosome, Down's syndrome	CCL 66
Detroit 532, Foreskin, Down's syndrome	CCL 54
Detroit 539, Skin, Down's syndrome, female	CCL 84
Detroit 548, Skin, partial D trisomy translocation	CCL 116
Detroit 550, Foreskin	CCL 109
Detroit 551, Embryonic skin	CCL 110
Detroit 573, Skin, B/D translocation	CCL 117
EB-3, Burkitt lymphoma	CCL 85
FL, Amnion	CCL 62

TABLE 1-VI (Continued)

Name of Cell Line	Cell Repository Number
Girardi Heart	CCL 27
HeLa, Carcinoma, cervix	CCL 2
Hela 229, Carcinoma, cervix	CCL 2.1
HEp-2, Carcinoma, larynx	CCL 23
Intestine 407, Embryonic intestine	CCL 6
J-111, Monocytic leukemia	CCL 24
JDU, Skin, galactosemic	CCL 118
Jijoye, Burkitt lymphoma, clone P-2003	CCL 87
KB-Carcinoma, oral	CCL 17
L-132, Embryonic lung	CCL 5
Minnesota-EE, Esophageal epithelium	CCL 4
NCTC 2544, Skin epithelium	CCL 19
NCTC 3075, CDM derivative of NCTC 2544	CCL 19.1
RAJI, Burkitt lumphoma	CCL 86
RPMI 2650, Quasi-Diploid Tumor	CCL 30
RPMI 6666, Leukocytes, Hodgkin's disease	CCL 113
RPMI 7666, Leukocytes, Normal	CCL 114
Tu Wi, Wilms' Tumor	CCL 31
WI-38, Diploid human lung	CCL 75
WISH, Amnion	CCL 25
Wong-Kilbourne derivative (D) of Chang Conjunctiva, Clone 1-5c-4	CCL 20.2

The importance of periodic checks for cell "purity" must not be underestimated. The problem of HeLa cell contamination of human diploid cultures has already been mentioned (Gartler, 1968). A cell strain can be monitored via the special characteristics of the strain; for instance, if an enzyme deficient strain suddenly acquires enzyme activity, cross-cell contamination with an enzyme-producing strain would be suspected. Isoenzyme analysis of cells is a significant aid in the characterization and identification of animal cell cultures from a variety of species; glucose-6-phosphate dehydrogenase (G6PD) and lactate dehydrogenase (LDH) are frequently studied in this regard (DeOca *et al.*, 1969) (also see Chap. 4, on genetic heterogeneity and enzyme variants). Chromosome analysis may be useful to monitor cell "purity" but does not help if mixing of human diploid cell lines is suspected.

The need to check for contamination with various types of microorganisms (such as viruses, mycoplasma, fungi and various bacteria) depends to some extent on how the cultured cells are to be used. Routine and frequent checks are time-consuming and may be unnecessary.

PRIMARY CULTURE

According to the definition of a primary culture (Table 1-I), the cells are derived directly from cells, tissues or organs of the donor individual and have not undergone subculture. Under the usual culture conditions for a primary explant or biopsy of human tissue, some morphologic differentiation may be present among the cells first appearing around the explant material, but eventually the fibroblast-like monolayer cells will grow to fill the culture container. Exceptions to this rule and special conditions to encourage morphologic differentiation will be considered later in this chapter and in Chapter 9, on differentiation. For instance, if a small biopsy is obtained from human skin, a tissue frequently sampled for biochemical or chromosome study, an initial outgrowth of epithelial-like (epidermal) cells is frequently seen around the primary explant (Karasek, 1966). This ring may grow in size, but the cells remain compact and mosaic-like in appearance, and close cell contact is maintained. With partial or complete media change increase in size of the epidermal primary outgrowth is apparent. Eventually growth stops entirely, subculture by usual enzymatic methods is impossible, and the fibroblast-like cell will inevitably appear and dominate the culture.

Cells in primary culture have advantages and disadvantages as summarized in Table 1-VII.

SUSPENSION CULTURE

For some purposes the ideal way to grow cells may be in suspension (Table 1-VIII). As a general rule, however, prolonged culture of individually suspended cells by standard techniques is exceptional from human material, or from primary explants of most multicellular organisms. Cells in suspension *in vivo,* such as peripheral blood cells, form prolonged suspension cultures outside the individual and this situation is considered later in this chapter. Potentially, many established suspension cultures may appear in

TABLE 1-VII

A SUMMARY OF CHARACTERISTICS OF HUMAN
CELLS IN PRIMARY CULTURE

Advantages	*Disadvantages*
Usually established in less than 7 days.	Total cell cycle time usually longer, or difficult to determine.
May retain morphologic and biochemical differentiation not preserved in serial culture.	Culture conditions and cell behavior less standardized and more variable.
Primary cloning results in cell lines descended from individual host cells that otherwise may not be retained in serial culture.	May be more difficult to reproduce from one experiment to another. Quantity of tissue is usually limited. Analyses frequently require single cell techniques.
Useful for rapid chromosome analysis in multiple tissues.	Cell storage and subsequent reinitiation may not be possible.
Cell storage and subsequent reinitiation of the culture may be possible.	
Cell selection during serial culture is avoided.	

laboratories devoting time to evaluating conditions to provide for this type of growth. The most likely human tissues sources for these cultures will probably continue to be neoplasms, cells intentionally or unintentionally infected with certain viruses, or tissues naturally in suspension *in vivo*. Presently some of the human cell lines available from the American Type Culture Collection Respository (Table 1-VI) may be grown in suspension.

Suspension cultures are usually subjected to repetitive movement to maintain the suspension and even then there may be tendency for aggregates to form, particularly at the surface of the medium. To maintain motion, tubes may be inserted on a roller-

TABLE 1-VIII

THE ADVANTAGES OF SUSPENSION CULTURES

1. Culture conditions are more uniform for individual cells.
2. Sampling is usually more accurate and easier, providing advantages for biochemical and kinetic studies.
3. A suspension system would be expected to be more efficient in terms of cell population per unit volume of medium.
4. A suspension is the most reasonable system for the production of large numbers of cells.
5. Total cell cycle time is usually relatively short (20 hrs. or less).

drum that can turn at various speeds, flasks may be swirled on a rotary shaker, stirrer vessels may be employed. Conditioning the medium to encourage suspension is accomplished by addition of methylcellulose or polyglycol (Pluronic F68), addition of dilute trypsin, or adjustment of type or amount of serum enrichment. Medium replacement is required and may be either continuous or intermittent. As a rule cells do not grow satisfactorily in suspension if the density falls below 5×10^4 to 10^5 cells per ml. Furthermore, cells in suspension frequently fail to divide again following transfer from a stationary population. Therefore medium renewal and cell number are critical for maintenance of the culture. Various devices have been designed to solve these two requirements for animal cells (Himmelfarb *et al.*, 1969; Paul, 1970).

MONOLAYER-SUSPENSION CULTURES

Some cultures combine the characteristics of monolayer and suspension. Cultures of this type are usually nondiploid and show characteristics of transformation (see Chap. 8, on transformed cells in culture). Tissue differentiation may also be present. The cells develop in a continuous cycle, which includes monolayer, multilayer and free-growing states. A culture of this type was established from human tumor astrocytes transformed by Rous sarcoma virus (Macintyre *et al.*, 1969). In this culture the transformed cells grew as a monolayer, upon which nests of rounded cells developed. From these nests, cells were shed into the medium and in turn on reinoculation formed a monolayer and repeated the cycle.

SHORT-TERM PERIPHERAL BLOOD CULTURE

A specialized kind of short-term culture is applied to peripheral blood (Nowell, 1960; Moorhead *et al.*, 1960). A sample of fresh blood is treated with a mitogenic agent such as phytohemagglutinin (PHA), an extract of the kidney bean *Phaseolus vulgaris*, to remove red cells and to stimulate division of the lymphocytes (Nowell, 1960; Robbins, 1964). Maximal mitosis is reached in a few days and the cells then fail to undergo further division, but

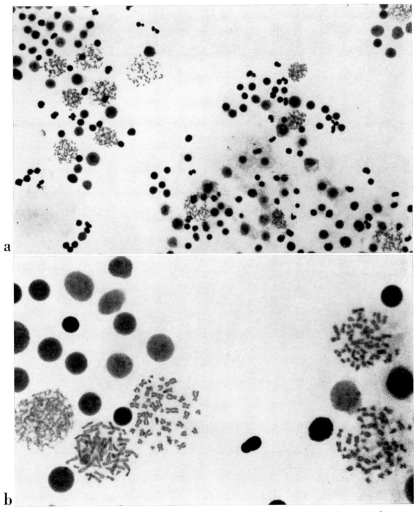

a

b

Figure 1-3a and b. Mitogenic action of phytohemagglutinin in a human peripheral blood culture. Many mitoses may be seen, representing different degrees of chromosome spreading and condensation. Giemsa stain. (a) A portion of a microscope field as viewed through lower power objective. (b) Portion of a microscope field as viewed through higher power objective.

during the short lifetime there is time for study of metaphase chromosome morphology (Fig. 1-3a, b) and other cell characteristics (Table 1-IX).

TABLE 1-IX

HUMAN SHORT-TERM PERIPHERAL BLOOD CULTURE

Uses	Examples	References
1. Analysis of metaphase chromosome morphology and number, especially for diagnosis of chromosome defects.	See Chapter 3.	
2. Evaluation of the ability of individual lymphocytes to respond to a mitogenic or antigenic agent. The agent may be phytohemagglutinin (PHA), lymphocytes from another individual, or specifically sensitized lymphocytes.	Lymphocytes from two unrelated individuals cultured in the same tube undergo morphological change to large cells and divide. There is a correlation between the degree of this response and the degree of cross-reactivity of grafts from the two individuals placed on a third unrelated recipient. Also see Chapter 6.	Bach and Hirschhorn, 1964
3. Morphological and biochemical studies of lymphocytes actively (though temporarily) synthesizing RNA and protein.	The lymphocytes changed by PHA have granular, basophilic cytoplasm staining with pyronin Y (indicating RNA). Electron micrographs suggest cytoplasmic ribosomes, lipid inclusions and active pinocytosis.	Marshall and Roberts, 1963
	When lymphocytes are stimulated to enlarge and divide by treatment with PHA, most of the rapidly synthesized RNA is nonribosomal (possibly messenger RNA).	Cooper and Rubin, 1966
	Human blood lymphocytes stimulated *in vitro* with phytohemagglutin (PHA) and nonviral antigens (such as purified protein derivative of tuberculin, tetanus toxoid and diphtheria) produce an antiviral substance resembling interferon.	Green *et al.*, 1969

TABLE 1-IX (Continued)

Uses	Examples	References
4. Study of the *in vivo* and *in vitro* effects of various agents on chromosomes, lymphocyte morphology and short-term growth in subsequent culture.	The effects of PHA and Xrays on peripheral blood short-term cultures suggested that addition of PHA protected lymphocytes against the cytotoxic effects of irradiation.	Schrek and Stefani, 1964
	Ribosomal RNA extracted from peripheral lymphocytes, recently stimulated by specific antigens to which the donor was sensitized, was capable of promoting mitosis and "blastoid" changes when added to cultures of autologous unstimulated lymphocytes.	Hashem, 1965
	Response to PHA by lymphocytes from patients with congenital rubella was inhibited. The response of normal lymphocytes infected *in vitro* was also inhibited. These results suggest that early association of lymphocytes with virus inhibits the function of the cell and contributes to persistent carrying of virus in congenital rubella. This phenomenon may be a means of detecting viruses not now recognizable by routine methods of tissue culture.	Montgomery et al, 1967
	An alpha globulin fraction prepared from normal plasma prevents homologous lymphocyte change and DNA and protein stimulation by PHA and specific antigens. A normal circulating immunosuppressant factor that prevents lymphoid cell proliferation is suggested.	Cooperband et al, 1968

TABLE 1-IX (Continued)

Uses	Examples	References
	Leukocytes from 17 A-bomb-exposed survivors and 10 control persons were cultured for 2 and 3 days. Among controls 0.6%–0.8% of cells showed chromosome aberrations while among exposed, 7.0%–8.7% showed aberrations.	Honda et al., 1969
5. Detection and study of genetic and acquired diseases in the lymphocyte donor.	Normal WBCs were cultured in plasma obtained from leukemic subjects during active disease and during remission. The results suggested the presence, in leukemic plasma during active stages of disease, of factor(s) capable of inducing mitoses in normal WBCs.	Wills and Gross, 1965
	Cultures of white blood cells derived from peripheral blood provide a simple screening procedure to detect cellular metachromasia in mucopolysaccharidoses.	Foley et al., 1969
	In familial deficiency of lysosomal acid phosphatase, heterozygotes could not be distinguished from normals in untreated lymphocytes, whereas marked differences were found after short-term peripheral blood culture with phytohemagglutinin.	Nadler and Egan, 1970
6. Preparation of large quantities of diploid human chromosomes.	A simple method for isolating and zonal fractionation of chromosomes from peripheral lymphocytes has been developed. The chromosome fractions represent separation according to chromosome size.	Schneider and Salzman, 1970

The usual methodology for short-term peripheral blood culture to study chromosomes is described in the appendix. Modifications of the usual methods may suit special purposes: the cultures can be handled as near-monolayers; leukocyte cell suspension can be frozen and stored in liquid nitrogen (Brody *et al.*, 1968). Culture kits are available from several commercial firms to facilitate processing, especially if the volume of culturing is small.* Lymphocyte rich cultures may be prepared in various ways. Bach and Hirschhorn (1964) suspend the supernatant plasma from heparinized blood in medium in a flint-glass prescription bottle, allow the polymorphonuclear leukocytes to attach to the lower surface, and pour off the lymphocytes in suspension. When short-term peripheral cultures are used to study the lymphocyte response to phytohemagglutinin (PHA) in different disease states (see Chap. 6), additional special modifications may be introduced.

In vivo, human peripheral lymphocytes do not show appreciable mitotic activity or synthesize protein, DNA or RNA. Following PHA stimulation in culture they will enlarge, synthesize DNA and RNA, and divide. The degree of response of the lymphocytes is usually measured by percent of cells in mitosis, percent of large cells with the morphological appearance of primitive "blast" cells (Fig. 1-4b through d; Fig. 1-5b), or quantitative analysis of incorporation of labeled thymidine into DNA (Caron *et al.*, 1965). When the cells are placed in culture with PHA there is a delay of about forty hours before incorporation of labeled thymidine starts (Bender and Prescott, 1962). The ability to incorporate thymidine into DNA is paralleled by increase in DNA polymerase activity (Loeb *et al.*, 1968). There may be some variability in the time between PHA stimulation and entrance into the first *in vitro* DNA synthesis period (Steffen and Stolzmann, 1969).

The mechanism of action of PHA is presently unclear. It is known that certain enzymes acting on cell membrane, such as

*Grand Island Biological Co.
Grand Island, New York

Difco Lab.
Detroit, Michigan

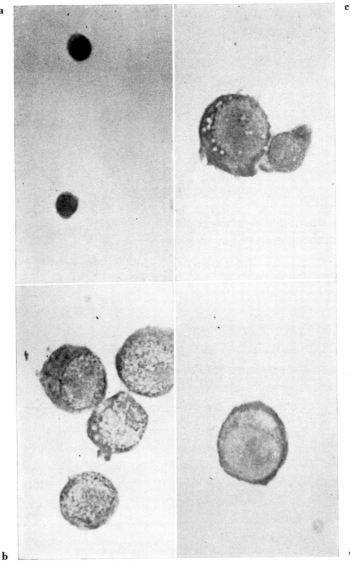

Figure 1-4. Photomicrographs of human lymphocytes in peripheral blood culture. (a) Small lymphocyte, unstimulated. Note small size and dense staining of the nucleus. (b) through (d) Examples of stimulated or "blast" cells. Note increased size and less dense nucleus. Courtesy of Dr. Kurt Hirschhorn, Mount Sinai School of Medicine, New York.

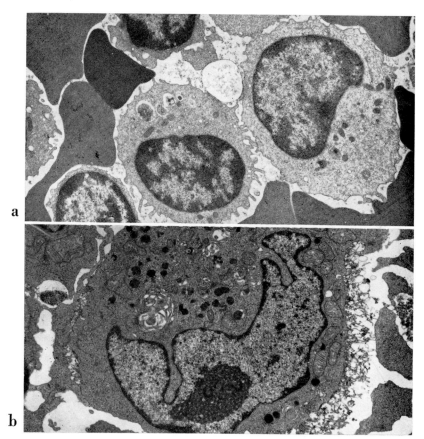

Figure 1-5. Electron micrographs of lymphocyte cultures. (a) Untreated control culture, normal small lymphocyte. Three-day culture. X5500. (b) Culture treated with phytohemagglutinin (PHA). Large blast-like cell with more dispersed chromatin in nucleus. Three-day culture. X6000. Courtesy of Dr. Steven D. Douglas, *Med Clin N Amer*, 53:917, 1969.

trypsin and neuraminidase, will make the lymphocytes temporarily refractory to PHA (Lindahl-Kiessling and Peterson, 1969, II). Cells treated with trypsin are refractory to PHA but not to stimulation by allogenic cells, termed mixed lymphocyte reaction (Lindahl-Kiessling and Peterson, 1969, III). It is not known if PHA acts as an antigen, if it acts nonspecifically to decrease stability of lysosomal membranes, if it precipitates some inhibitory factor in serum, or if it acts as an adhesive agent to combine cells with the proper stimulus such as other cells or a glass surface (also see Chap. 6, consideration of PHA action).

LONG-TERM PERIPHERAL BLOOD CULTURE

Permanent human lymphocytoid cell lines have been established from patients with various malignant and nonmalignant diseases and from normal persons (Moore *et al.*, 1966a; Moore *et al.*, 1967). Initially it was observed that peripheral blood had to be maintained in culture for at least forty to one hundred days before sustained rapid growth of the cells began (Moore *et al.*, 1966). During this initial stage the cells were noted to "hover" in the culture vessel under the stationary conditions provided for short-term peripheral blood cultures. The cells did not attach firmly to the bottom or go into suspension as single cells. Hence the term "hover" was used. The eventual formation of cell clumps and evidence of rapid growth was considered to signal establishment of a permanent cell line. The uses of these established cultures are described in Table 1-X, and methodology to establish them is in the appendix. It has become apparent that human hematopoietic cell lines can maintain the donors' chromosome constitutions as well as rapid growth rates for long periods and hundreds of cell generations *in vitro* (Huang and Moore, 1969). Isoenzyme activity is maintained (Canover *et al.*, 1970).

HUMAN GERM CELLS

Human oocytes, when released from ovarian follicles at laparotomy and cultured in medium of various types, progress through the first meiotic metaphase (metaphase I) to metaphase II with formation of the first polar body (Edwards, 1965). This maturation process normally occurs *in vivo* at the time of ovulation. The number of oocytes obtained for culture may range from zero to sixty or seventy per ovary, depending on a number of factors such as patient's age and pelvic pathology. The short *in vitro* culture period of approximately two days results in maturation regardless of stage in the menstrual cycle of the origi-

TABLE 1-X

HUMAN LONG-TERM PERIPHERAL BLOOD CULTURE

Uses	Examples	References
1. Production of large quantities of established cell lines for storage, chromosome analysis, biochemical studies.	Bence Jones protein continues to be produced by a lymphocytoid cell line from a patient with multiple myeloma.	Matsuoka et al., 1967
	A characteristic chromosomal marker (long arm secondary constriction) in No. 10 chromosome occurs in high frequency in cell lines established from peripheral leukocytes of 3 patients with acute infectious mononucleosis, and in low frequency in lines from 4 healthy donors.	Kohn et al., 1968
	Twelve lines of human leukocytes from patients with leukemia and 2 from patients without neoplastic disease showed diploid or very near-diploid karyotypes. All but one showed occasional No. 10 chromosome with near terminal secondary constriction. Nine lines showed accentuation of secondary constrictions in usual sites. Exchanges could occur at these sites. Some cells in various lines showed multiple secondary constrictions or chromosome pulverization.	Miles et al., 1968
	Permanent lymphocytoid cell lines are available from patients with XYY and XXY chromosome constitutions.	Moore et al., 1969a
	A permanent lymphoid cell line with 46 chromosomes and one small marker chromosome was established from a "normal human" female. The abnormal karyotype was also present in short-term peripheral blood culture and appeared to be a persistent feature of the donor's mosaic karyotype. It persisted in the oldest culture line as a marker chromosome two years after establishment.	Moore et al., 1969

TABLE 1-X (Continued)

Uses	Examples	References
2. To study the characteristics of peripheral blood lymphocytes in long-term culture and to relate these characteristics to the condition of the donor individual.	The design of practical automated units for continuous culture of leukemia cells was accomplished. Some of the nutritional requirements of these cells were studied. No cells showed the Ph chromosome but electron microscopy showed virus-like particles in several cell lines.	Moore et al., 1966a
	The comparative sensitivity of several established cell lines (derived from the buffy coats of normal humans and patients with neoplastic diseases) to treatment with various antimetabolites, was tested. Levels of sensitivity fell into different discrete classes, possibly related to genetic differences between the cell lines.	Aoki and Moore, 1969
	A leukocyte cell line derived from peripheral blood of a healthy female individual was cultivated for over 20 months. The cells maintained a high degree of diploidy, and they were not neoplastic, as tested by implantation into hamster cheek pouch.	Christofinis, 1969
	An established suspension culture lymphoid cell line from peripheral blood of a patient with Chediak-Higashi syndrome showed large lysosome-like organelles by electron microscopy, pathognomonic of this syndrome. The organelles were also present in a small percentage of lymphoid cells from heterozygotes.	Douglas et al., 1969
3. To study growth of inoculated viruses and other microorganisms.	Long-term lymphoid suspension cultures were established from peripheral blood of patients with viral hepatitis. These cell systems may be the ideal tissue for isolation and propagation of the etiologic agent of viral hepatitis.	Glade et al., 1968
	The presence of virus may or may not be a necessary factor for continued growth in culture of peripheral blood from "normal" individuals; virus particles were not seen in a line of peripheral blood cells from a healthy donor.	Dunham et al., 1969

nal donor. Maturation to metaphase I or II occurs in mammalian cell media such as 199 or Ham's F-10 supplemented with approximately 15 percent fetal calf serum. Completely defined medium consisting of F-10 supplemented with bovine serum albumin is also successful, as is less complex completely defined medium such as pyruvate or oxaloacetate in Krebs-Ringer salt solution plus bovine serum albumin. Human oocytes also resume meiosis in microdroplets of medium under paraffin oil (Kennedy and Donahue, 1969). Fertilization of primate eggs *in vitro* still presents major problems and our control over culture of mammalian embryos is far from complete. Nevertheless, control of preimplantation human development *in vitro* appears to be possible (Edwards, 1969).

Human male meiosis is usually studied directly from testicular biopsy material without intervening culture. Organized growth of mammalian testicular tissue has not included successful human tissue in reported literature to date. However, testes of fourteen day old rats were grown as organ cultures for periods of up to six months (Steinberger *et al.*, 1964). Tubular structures with healthy Sertoli cells and mitoses were maintained; spermatocytes survived approximately four weeks, without differentiating into spermatids, however.

Present and potential uses of culture of human germ cells and preimplantation embryos are summarized in Table 1-XI.

AGAR CULTURE

Agar culture may provide selective growth advantage to certain cells not well studied by conventional monolayer or suspension techniques (Table 1-XII). Agar may be added in different concentrations to provide media layers of varying consistencies; thus, more than one culture phase can be established within a single culture to separate various cell types in the different agar concentrations. The feeder-layer technique employs "feeder" cells of one type that may be separated in agar from cells to be "nourished" and grown for study. Relative immobilization of cells may be used to facilitate separation and isolation of clones or colonies derived from single cells. Agar also permits control

TABLE 1-XI

PRESENT AND POTENTIAL USES OF CULTURE OF GERM CELLS
AND PREIMPLANTATION EMBRYOS

1. Analysis of meiotic chromosomes in oocytes or spermatocytes, or of mitotic
   chromosomes in cleaving embryos.
   a. To diagnose chromosome abnormalities and the possibility of transmission
      to offspring.
   b. To study the etiology of chromosome defects.
   c. To evaluate chromosomal causes for infertility.
   d. To study the effects of aging of germ cells or of delayed fertilization on
      chromosomes.
2. Analysis and treatment of infertility.
   a. Treatment of certain types of infertility by transfer of fertilized eggs into
      the uterus of the mother.
   b. To study "capacitation" of spermatozoa.
3. Evaluation of prevention of genetic disorders in man.
   a. Potential sexing of blastocysts before transfer into a recipient female.
   b. To evaluate the advisability of *in vitro* development of selected germ cells.
4. Study of the factors which affect completion of meiosis, fertilization, and growth
   of the preimplantation embryo.
   a. Identification of substrates required for metabolism of germ cells and early
      embryos.
   b. Study of the synthesis of DNA, RNA and protein before and after fertilization.
   c. Manipulation of early embryonic development such as fusion of different
      embryos; disassociation and reaggregation of early embryonic cells; intro-
      duction of environmental agents to study effects on development.

of CO_2 or O_2 gradients to support specialized growth within the
culture.

ORGAN CULTURE AND MORPHOLOGICALLY DIFFERENTIATED TISSUE CULTURE

The object of organ culture is to maintain architecture of a
small piece of tissue or organ and direct it towards development
such as occurs *in vivo*. Agar culture has already been considered
and may support tissue differentiation. Testicular organ culture
has also been mentioned. Techniques of organ culture may be
divided into those using a solid medium (such as agar or plasma
clots) and those using a standard fluid medium plus modifications
to encourage tissue differentiation. Rafts, grids (Fig. 1-6), and
nets of inert materials have been used to support tissues in fluid
media. Special chambers may perfuse fluid or gas to maintain
constant fluid or gas phases. "Feeder" or inducing cells may be
supported separately in semisolid solid media or separated from

TABLE 1-XII

EXAMPLES OF AGAR CULTURE

The colony forming ability of cells from various types of human marrow was investigated by placing appropriate numbers of cells in soft-agar gel (0.3% agar) over "feeder" cells in 0.5% agar.	Senn *et al.*, 1967
Explants from various solid tumors of children formed colonies in soft agar. The histologic characteristics of the colonies in many of the tumor cultures were similar to those of the tumor from which they were derived. It was concluded that the culture method gave selective growth advantage to cancer cells and was potentially useful for *in vitro* studies of human cancer.	McAllister and Reed, 1968
The fate of individual lymphocytes in tissue culture and the possible role of cell-to-cell contact can be directly analyzed by suspending the lymphocytes in agar before stimulation with antigen or mitogen.	Coulson *et al.*, 1968
Colonies from aspirated human bone marrow cells in the presence of "feeder" cells (in two-layer agar) can be studied in regard to radiation sensitivity, and compared to other mammalian cells in the same test situation.	Senn and McCulloch, 1970
With active disease, the leukemic cells from human marrow fail to form colonies in soft agar. With suppression of leukemic cells by chemotherapy, the "normal" cell population is once more able to produce colonies. Ability of marrow to form myeloid colonies in soft agar thus provides a functional means of distinguishing between "normal" and leukemic cell lines, and of evaluating remission.	Harris and Freireich, 1970

the differentiated culture by filters of various pore sizes. Embryonic tissues and organs are by far the easiest materials for starting organ or morphologically differentiated tissue culture. However, many types of adult tissues are now showing morphologic differentiation *in vitro*. Culture conditions are not the only factors contributing to the production of a specialized culture. Dissection and selection of tissue types prior to culture will influence the subsequent result. Some of the uses of human cells in organ culture or morphologically differentiated tissue culture are considered in Chapter 9, on differentiation.

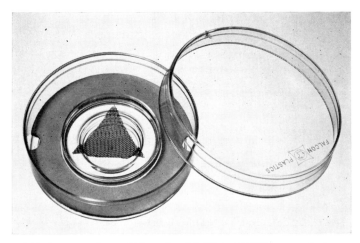

Figure 1-6. Organ culture dish and grid. This 60X15 mm polystyrene dish is equipped with a triangular grid of stainless steel cloth, designed to provide a substrate for organ culture, and to allow diffusion of nutrient medium. Courtesy of Falcon Plastics, Division of BioQuest.

REFERENCES

General

Merchant, D. J.; Kahn, R. H., and Murphy, W. H., Jr.: *Handbook of Cell and Organ Culture.* Minneapolis, Burgess, 1964.

National Cancer Institute: *Second Decennial Review Conference on Cell, Tissue and Organ Culture.* NCI Monograph No. 26, 1967.

National Cancer Institute: *Cell Cultures for Virus Vaccine Production.* NCI Monograph No. 29, 1968.

Paul, John: *Cell and Tissue Culture,* 4th ed. Edinburgh, Livingston, 1970.

Priest, Jean H.: *Medical Technology Series: Cytogenetics.* Philadelphia, Lea & Febiger, 1969.

White, Philip R.: *The Cultivation of Animal and Plant Cells,* 2nd ed. New York, Ronald Press, 1963.

Willmer, E. N. (Ed.): *Cells and Tissues in Culture: Methods, Biology and Physiology.* New York, Academic Press, 1965.

Specific

Aoki, Y., and Moore, G. E.; Comparative sensitivity to various antimetabolites of several established cell lines derived from the buffy coat of normal humans and patients with neoplastic diseases. *Cancer Res, 29:* 1307, 1969.

Bach, F., and Hirschhorn, K.: Lymphocyte interaction: A potential histocompatibility test *in vitro. Science, 143*:813, 1964.

Bender, M. A., and Prescott, D. M.: DNA synthesis and mitosis in cultures of human peripheral leukocytes. *Exp Cell Res, 27*:221, 1962.

Bottomley, R. H.; Trainer, A. L., and Griffen, M. J.: Enzymatic and chromosomal characterization of HeLa variants. *J Cell Biol, 41*:806, 1969.

Brody, J. A.; Harlem, M. M.; Plank, C. R., and White, L. R.: Freezing human peripheral lymphocytes and a technique for culture in monolayers. *Proc Soc Exp Biol Med, 129*:968, 1968.

Canover, J. H.; Hatheway, P.; Glade, P. R., and Hirschhorn, K.: Persistence of phosphoglucomutase (PGM) polymorphism in long-term lymphoid lines. *Proc Soc Exp Biol Med, 133*:750, 1970.

Caron, G. A.; Sarkany, I.; Williams, H. S.; Todd, A. P., and Gell, H. M. C.: Radioactive method for the measurement of lymphocyte transformation *in vitro. Lancet, 2*:1266, 1965.

Chang, T. D.; Niewczas-Late, V., and Uchida, I. A.: Selection for trisomic cells in a mosaic fibroblast culture. *Cytogenetics (Basel), 8*:410, 1969.

Christofinis, G. J.: Chromosome and transplantation results of a human leukocyte cell line derived from a healthy individual. *Cancer, 24*:649, 1969.

Committee on Terminology, Tissue Culture Association: Proposed usage of animal tissue culture terms. *Cytogenetics (Basel), 6*:161, 1967.

Cooper, H. L., and Rubin, A. D.: Synthesis of nonribosomal RNA by lymphocytes: A response to phytohemagglutinin treatment. *Science, 152*:516, 1966.

Cooperband, S. R.; Bondevik, H.; Schmid, K., and Mannick, J. A.: Transformation of human lymphocytes: Inhibition by homologous alpha globulin. *Science, 159*:1243, 1968.

Coulson, A. S.; Turk, A.; Glade, P. R., and Chessin, L. N.: Lymphocyte culture in agar. *Lancet, 1*:89, 1968.

DeOca, F. M.; Macy, M. L., and Shannon, J. E.: Isoenzyme characterization of animal cell cultures. *Proc Soc Exp Biol Med, 132*:462, 1969.

Douglas, S. D.; Blume, R. S., and Wolff, S. M.: Fine structural studies of leukocytes from patients and heterozygotes with the Chediak-Higashi syndrome. *Blood, 33*:527, 1969.

Dunham, W. B.; Vinson, W. E.; Parker, M. V., and Clark, I. D.: Prolonged culture of human leukocytes in an isolated environment. *Proc Soc Exp Biol Med, 130*:370, 1969.

Edwards, R. G.: Maturation *in vitro* of human ovarian oocytes. *Lancet, 2*: 926, 1965.

Edwards, R. G.: The culture of pre-implantation mammalian embryos. *Proc Roy Soc Med, 62*:143, 1969.

Foley, K. M.; Danes, B. S., and Bearn, A. G.: White blood cell cultures in genetic studies on the human mucopolysaccharidoses. *Science, 164*: 424, 1969.

Gartler, S. M.: Genetic markers as tracers in cell culture. *Nat Cancer Inst Monogr, 26*:167, 1967.

Gartler, S. M.: Apparent HeLa cell contamination of human heteroploid cell lines. *Nature (London), 217*:750, 1968.

Glade, P. R.; Hirshaut, Y.; Douglas, S. D., and Hirschhorn, K.: Lymphoid suspension cultures from patients with viral hepatitis. *Lancet, 2*:1273, 1968.

Green, J. A.; Cooperband, S. R., and Kibrick, S.: Immune specific induction of interferon production in cultures of human blood lymphocytes. *Science, 164*:1415, 1969.

Griffiths, J. B.: The quantitative utilization of amino acids and glucose and contact inhibition of growth in cultures of the human diploid cell, WI-38. *J Cell Sci, 6*:739, 1970.

Harris, J., and Freireich, E. J.: *In vitro* growth of myeloid colonies from bone marrow of patients with acute leukemia in remission. *Blood, 35*:61, 1970.

Hashem, N.: Mitosis: Induction by cultures of human peripheral lymphocytes. *Science, 150*:1460, 1965.

Hayflick, L.: The limited *in vitro* lifetime of human diploid cell strains. *Exp Cell Res, 37*:614, 1965.

Himmelfarb, P.; Thayer, P. S., and Martin, H. E.: Spin filter culture: The propagation of mammalian cells in suspension. *Science, 164*:555, 1969.

Honda, T.; Kamada, N., and Bloom, A. D.: Chromosome aberrations and culture time. *Cytogenetics (Basel), 8*:117, 1969.

Huang, C. C., and Moore, G. E.: Chromosomes of 14 hematopoietic cell lines derived from peripheral blood of persons with and without chromosome abnormalities. *J Nat Cancer Inst, 43*:1119, 1969.

Karasek, M. A.: *In vitro* culture of human skin epithelial cells. *J Invest Derm, 47*:533, 1966.

Kennedy, J. F., and Donahue, R. P.: Human oocytes: Maturation in chemically defined media. *Science, 164*:1292, 1969.

Kohn, G.; Diehl, V.; Mellman, W. J.; Henle, W., and Henle, G.: C-group chromosome marker in long-term leukocyte cultures. *J Nat Cancer Inst, 41*:795, 1968.

Krooth, R. S.: Genetics of cultured somatic cells. *Med Clin N Amer, 53*: 795, 1969.

Kruse, P. F.; Whittle, W., and Miedema, E.: Mitotic and nonmitotic multiple-layered perfusion cultures. *J Cell Biol, 42*:113, 1969.

Lindahl-Kiessling, K., and Peterson, R. D. A.: The mechanism of phytohemagglutinin (PHA) action. II. The effect of certain enzymes and sugars. III. Stimulation of lymphocytes by allogenic lymphocytes and phytohemagglutinin. *Exp Cell Res, 55*:81, 1969.

Loeb, L. A.; Agarwal, S. S., and Woodside, A. M.: Induction of DNA polymerase in human lymphocytes by phytohemagglutinin. *Proc Nat Acad Sci USA, 61*:827, 1968.

Macintyre, E. H.; Grimes, R. A., and Vatter, A. E.: Cytology and growth characteristics of human tumor astrocytes transformed by Rous sarcoma virus. *J Cell Sci, 5*:583, 1969.

Marshall, W. H., and Roberts, K. B.: The growth and mitosis of human small lymphocytes after incubation with a phytohaemagglutinin. *Quart J Exp Physiol, 48*:146, 1963.

Matsuoka, Y.; Moore, G. E.; Yagi, Y., and Pressman, D.: Production of free light chains of immunoglobin by a hematopoietic cell line derived from a patient with multiple myeloma. *Proc Soc Exp Biol Med, 125*:1246, 1967.

McAllister, R. M., and Reed, G.: Colonial growth in agar of cells derived from neoplastic and non-neoplastic tissues of children. *Pediat Res, 2*: 356, 1968.

Miles, C. P.; O'Neill, F.; Armstrong, D.; Clarkson, B., and Keane, J.: Chromosome patterns of human leukocyte established cell lines. *Cancer Res, 28*:481, 1968.

Montgomery, J. R.; South, M. A.; Rawls, W. E.; Melnick, J. L.; Olson, G. B.; Dent, P. B., and Good, R. A.: Viral inhibition of lymphocyte response to phytohemagglutinin. *Science, 157*:1068, 1967.

Moore, G. E.; Grace, J. T.; Citron, P.; Gerner, R., and Burns, A.: Leukocyte cultures of patients with leukemia and lymphomas. *New York J Med, 66*:2757, 1966.

Moore, G. E.; Ito, E.; Ulrich, K., and Sandberg, A. A.: Culture of human leukemia cells. *Cancer, 19*:713, 1966a.

Moore, G. E.; Gerner, R. E., and Franklin, H. A.: Culture of normal human leukocytes. *JAMA, 199*:87, 1967.

Moore, G. E.; Fjelde, A., and Huang, C. C.: Established hyperdiploid hematopoietic cell line with a minute marker chromosome persisting both in culture and in the "normal" donor. *Cytogenetics (Basel), 8*: 332, 1969.

Moore, G. E.; Porter, I. H., and Huang, C. C.: Lymphocytoid lines from persons with sex chromosome anomalies. *Science, 163*:1453, 1969a.

Moorhead, P. S.; Nowell, P. C.; Mellman, W. J.; Battips, D. M., and Hungerford, D. A.: Chromosome preparations of leukocytes cultured from human peripheral blood. *Exp Cell Res, 20*:613, 1960.

Nadler, H. L., and Egan, T. J.: Deficiency of lysosomal acid phosphatase. *New Eng J Med, 282*:302, 1970.

Nowell, P. C.: Phytohemagglutinin An initiator of mitosis in cultures of normal human leukocytes. *Cancer Res, 20*:462, 1960.

Paul, John: *Cell and Tissue Culture,* 4th ed. Edinburgh, Livingston, 1970.

Robbins, J. H.: Tissue culture studies of the human lymphocyte. *Science,* *146*:1648, 1964.

Schneider, E. L., and Salzman, N. P.: Isolation and zonal fractionation of metaphase chromosomes from human diploid cells. *Science, 167*:1141, 1970.

Schrek, R., and Stefani, S.: Radioresistance of phytohemagglutinin-treated normal and leukemic lymphocytes. *J Nat Cancer Inst, 32*:507, 1964.

Senn, J. S.; McCulloch, E. A., and Till, J. E.: Comparison of colony-forming ability of normal and leukaemic human marrow in cell culture. *Lancet, 2*:597, 1967.

Senn, J. S., and McCulloch, E. A.: Radiation sensitivity of human bone marrow cells measured by a cell culture method. *Blood, 35*:56, 1970.

Steffen, J. A., and Stolzmann, W. M.: Studies on *in vitro* lymphocyte proliferation in cultures synchronized by the inhibition of DNA synthesis. I. Variability of S plus G2 periods of first generation cells. *Exp Cell Res, 56*:453, 1969.

Steinberger, A.; Steinberger, E., and Perloff, W. H.: Mammalian testes in organ culture. *Exp Cell Res, 36*:19, 1964.

Wills, J. M., and Gross, S.: The mitogenic activity of leukemic plasma. *J Pediat, 67*:29, 1965.

Chapter Two

A DESCRIPTION OF SPECIAL PROCEDURES IN CELL CULTURE

CLONING

S election of a cell population derived from a single cell, by the process of cloning, is sometimes necessary for the study of certain cell functions (Table 2-I) (Puck, 1957). Cloning is performed much as in microbiology when a single colony representing growth from a single bacterial cell is selected and subcultured. In the case of mammalian cells, single cells can be inoculated at low density into a culture container; a cell settles to the lower surface of the container and divides to form a clone or individual colony (Fig. 2-1). This colony is then selected, subcultured and grown to a large number of cells, all derived from the same original cell. Such a culture is properly called a cell strain, pro-

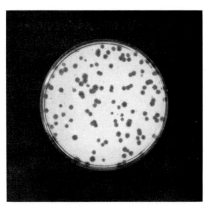

Figure 2-1. A petri dish containing macroscopic clones or colonies of cells each derived from a single mammalian cell. The clones are stained to make them easily visible. Courtesy Dr. Fa-Ten Kao, Department of Biophysics, University of Colorado Medical Center, Denver.

vided some specific property of the culture has been identified and maintained (see terminology, Table 1-I, Chap. 1). The entire culture may have properties or markers of the single ancestral cell, although cloning by no means guarantees preservation of specific properties of specific cells, since selective factors are immediately active at the cellular level to make the culture heterogenous.

TABLE 2-I

EXAMPLES OF THE USE OF CLONING FOR
STUDIES OF CELL FUNCTIONS*

HeLa cells (derived from human cervical carcinoma) were cloned for the purpose of isolating mutant colonies, and to obtain greater uniformity of behavior as compared to mass (uncloned) cultures. Different clonal strains exhibited differences in growth characteristics (plating efficiency) persisting for more than 20 generations. However cells from the same clones were found to show entirely different morphology depending on the character of the serum present in the nutrient medium.	Puck *et al.*, 1956
Clones derived from single skin cells from females heterozygous for X-linked glucose-6-phosphate dehydrogenase deficiency were analyzed for activity of this enzyme. Two distinct populations of cells were present, with and without enzyme deficiency, providing evidence that in each single cell only one X chromosome was functional for this X-linked gene.	Davidson *et al.*, 1963
Single cell plating technique was used to develop four clonal strains that performed organ-specific functions for prolonged periods in culture. These mammalian strains included steroid secreting Leydig cells, melanoma cells that form pigment, and two hormone secreting strains from a pituitary tumor.	Yasumura *et al.*, 1966
Clones from a fibroblast-like mass culture from a mosaic mongol infant provide evidence for the repeated occurrences of *in vitro* mitotic nondisjunction for chromosome 21 or 22. The majority of clones were primarily G trisomic, but there were also some normal diploid and G quadrisomic cells.	Martin, 1966

*Examples in this table are chosen for their theoretical importance in study of biological principles.

TABLE 2-I (Continued)

The glucose-6-phosphate dehydrogenase (G6PD) types of erythrocytes, granulocytes, and skin cells in chronic myelogenous leukemia (CML) were determined. The patients were heterozygous at the G6PD locus, so that two enzyme types were found in cultured skin cells. The fact that only one type was found in erythrocytes and granulocytes was interpreted as strong evidence that erythrocytes and granulocytes have a common stem cell and that CML has a clonal origin. It appears most likely that this malignancy arises as a consequence of a rare event in a single stem cell.	Fialkow *et al.*, 1967
Tetraploid cells regularly occurred in mass diploid human cultures and within clones of diploid cultured cells. Diploid cells again appeared within cultures of the tetraploid clones. This cycle of 2n to 4n to 2n, with recombination of entire linkage groups (chromosomes) in the final 2n cells could form the basis of formal genetic analysis in man.	Martin and Sprague, 1969
Cloned human diploid and tetraploid cells show a direct relationship between ploidy and collagen production in culture. (Cells with twice as many chromosomes make twice as much collagen.)	Priest and Priest, 1969
Cell cultures derived from human sarcomas differed from those derived from normal adult tissue in that they formed colonies when inoculated as single cells onto monolayers of contact-inhibited cells. The system provided a method of selecting cells with decreased contact inhibition of cell division and may be used to select tumor cell from a population containing a large excess of normal cells.	Aaronson *et al.*, 1970

TABLE 2-II

VARIOUS WAYS TO CLONE MAMMALIAN CELLS

Type of Method	General Procedure	Reference
Single cell plating followed by clone isolation	A known number of single cells are inoculated into a tissue culture container, usually a petri dish. Each cell is allowed to grow to a macroscopic colony (Fig. 2-1). This clone is then isolated, usually by placing a ring around it and the cells contained within the ring are removed.	Puck *et al.*, 1956
Capillary technique	A suspension of single cells is drawn into a capillary pipette. Under the microscope a single cell is located and that portion of the pipette is cut off and placed in medium for culture.	Sanford *et al.*, 1961

TABLE 2-II (Continued)

Type of Method	General Procedure	Reference
Coverslip method for selecting single cells	Single cells are inoculated at low density into a petri dish containing many small coverslip pieces. The cells are allowed to attach and coverslip pieces with one attached cell (as determined under the microscope) are placed in medium for culture.	Martin and Tuan, 1966
Soft agar technique	Single cells are suspended in medium containing dilute agar. They divide to form colonies and can be counted and sized by means of a particle counter.	Macdonald and Bruce, 1968
Microculture plate method	Single lymphocytes are isolated and cultivated in individual wells of microculture plates, either after a 48 hr. short-term peripheral blood culture or after establishment of a lymphocyte cell line.	Choi and Bloom, 1970

Various ways to clone mammalian cells are described in Table 2-II. Detailed description of a modified method of single cell plating and clone isolation is given in the appendix. Methods to isolate clones rapidly (up to 500 clones per hour) have been described (Goldsby and Zipper, 1969).

The techniques of primary cloning are unquestionably important for future investigations on human cell cultures; single cells are produced from the primary explant by various dispersion methods and grown as clones (Pious *et al.*, 1964; Ham and Murray, 1967). One important potential for primary cloning is to obtain differentiated functions in the subsequent clones, not preserved in the usual monolayer mass cultures (see Chap. 9 on differentiation).

The plating efficiency of single cells may be used as a quantitative measure of either the quality of the medium or the growing capacity of the cultured cells at low density (Ham, 1963). If, say, one hundred cells are placed in a petri dish and seventy-five clones form, the plating efficiency of the cells is 75 percent in the culture conditions provided. Human cells do not reach 100 percent plating efficiency under the best of culture conditions, and human diploid cells may be in the range of 10 percent (Goldstein *et al.*, 1969). Culture medium or serum of poor quality will not support single growth of human diploid cells at all.

CELL CYCLE ANALYSIS

Methods to study divisions of the cell life cycle are summarized in Table 2-III. The significance of these cell cycle divisions or phases is discussed further in Chapter 12. Most studies on cultured cells require some knowledge of the length of the various phases—synthesis (S), mitosis (M), the time between M and S (G1), and the time between S and M (G2) (see Fig. 12-1 in Chap. 12). For instance, analysis of metaphase chromosomes in cultured human cells requires knowledge of cell cycle divisions so that maximal numbers of mitoses may be accumulated for study. Mean cell cycle time and lengths of S and G2 of human monolayer cells are frequently studied by the methods illustrated in Figures 2-2 and 2-3; then, if mitosis is assumed to be not more than one hour, G1 represents the remainder of the total cell cycle, once S and G2 are determined. Length of S phase is also studied by determining the percentage of labeled cells right after a pulse of H_3-thymidine; the fraction of cells thus labeled must be converted to duration of the S phase by means of further calculations (Cleaver, 1965).

TABLE 2-III

METHODS OF ESTIMATING THE GENERATION TIME AND PHASES
OF THE CELL LIFE CYCLE IN VARIOUS POPULATIONS OF CELLS
(Modified from Nachtwey and Cameron, 1968)

Method	*Reference**
A. *Generation Time*	
1. Time for cell number to double, (a) obtained from counts of periodic samples by Coulter counter or hemocytometer (see Fig. 2-2); or (b) obtained from direct repeated counts of entire population of cells in microchambers.	(a) Merchant *et al.*, 1964 (b) Prescott, 1957

*References in this table describe the method in detail but are not necessarily the original description.

TABLE 2-III (Continued)

Method	Reference*
2. Mean time for one cell division, obtained from number of divisions per unit time in cells originally isolated in (a) hanging drops; (b) drops under oil; or (c) attached to glass or plastic.	(a) Christensen and Giese, 1956 (b) Nachtwey and Cameron, 1968
3. Time between 50% points of two consecutive ascending portions of the curve formed by plotting % of labeled mitoses (ordinant) against time (abscissa) after H_3-thymidine pulse labeling. (See Fig. 2-3).	Sisken, 1964
4. Metaphase accumulation rate in cells treated with colchicine of Colcemid.	Puck and Steffen, 1963
5. Time between two successive divisions of individual cells as determined by time-lapse cinematography.	Sisken, 1964
B. *Mitotic phase (M)*	
1. Time spent in mitosis by individual cells determined by time-lapse cinematography or direct observation.	Sisken and Morasca, 1965
2. Time for mitotic index to decrease to zero after X-irradiation.	Kim and Evans, 1963
3. †Percentage of cells in mitosis.	Merchant *et al.,* 1964
C. *G1 phase*	
1. Time between cell division and appearance of H_3-thymidine labeled cells, (a) by combining time-lapse cinematography and autoradiography; or (b) by selecting dividing cells with a micropipette and pulsing the cells at intervals with H_3-thymidine.	(a) Sisken, 1964 (b) Stone and Cameron, 1964
2. Time required for the percentage of H_3-thymidine labeled cells to reach a plateau after treatment with Colcemid or colchicine in a continuously labeled cell population.	Puck and Steffen, 1963
3. †The fraction of nonlabeled cells with low DNA content, by the combined use of autoradiography and microspectrophotometry.	Mak, 1965
4. When the generation time is known, G1 represents the remaining time after S, G2 and M are determined.	(See Fig. 2-3)
5. Time required for the percentage of H_3-thymidine labeled cells to reach first plateau after X-irradiation in a continuously labeled cell population. (Gives G2+M+G1; M and G2 must be known to obtain G1.)	Kim and Evans, 1963

†These methods are used to determine the fraction of the cell population in a particular phase of the cell cycle. This fraction can then be converted to the duration of the phase by further analysis.

TABLE 2-III (Continued)

Method	*Reference**
D. S phase	
1. Time between the midpoints of first increase and subsequent decrease of labeled mitotic cells after H_3-thymidine pulse labeling (see Fig. 2-3).	Sisken, 1964
2. Rate of accumulation of H_3-thymidine labeled cells after Colcemid or colchicine treatment in a continuously labeled cell population.	Puck and Steffen, 1963
3. Difference in percentage of cells labeled with C_{14}-thymidine and percentage of cells labeled with H_3-thymidine after sequential, separate pulsing.	Thrasher, 1966
4. Time required for grain counts over labeled metaphase cells to reach a plateau after a pulse of H_3-thymidine.	Stanners and Till, 1960
5. †Percentage of labeled cells sampled right after a pulse of H_3-thymidine.	Stanners and Till, 1960
E. G2 phase	
1. Time between start of H_3-thymidine labeling and the time of appearance of labeled mitotic cells (usually the first point when half of maximal percent of mitotic labeling is obtained; see Fig. 2-3).	Defendi and Manson, 1963
2. Time between accumulation of mitotic cells and accumulation of H_3-thymidine labeled mitotic cells after Colcemid treatment in a continuously labeled cell population.	Puck and Steffen, 1963
3. †Difference between the percentage of H_3-thymidine labeled cells at the plateau of nonirradiated cells and the percentage at the plateau of X-irradiated cells in a continuously labeled population.	Kim and Evans, 1963
4. †The fraction of interphase cells not labeled with H_3-thymidine and with high DNA content.	Mak, 1965

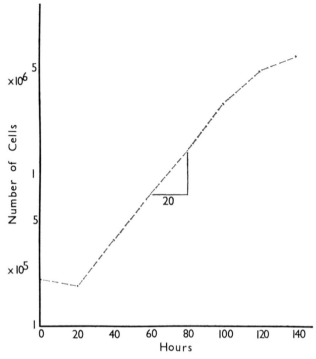

Figure 2-2. A method to determine mean cell cycle time (generation time). Cell counts are made at intervals following inoculation of 2-3 x 10^5 human diploid cells into a culture container. Cell number is plotted on a logarithmic scale. Twenty hours (the mean total cell cycle time) is the time taken for the cell number to double during logarithmic growth. For the first day after subculture, human diploid cells usually do not increase in number.

CELL SYNCHRONIZATION

Study of events at specific times during the cell cycle is facilitated by methods for culture synchronization, such that cells can be induced to proceed through the cell cycle together (see Fig. 12-1, Chap. 12). There are many ways to synchronize cultured cells and the method to choose depends on what cells are used and what events are to be studied. Table 2-IV lists some of the synchronization methods applicable to mammalian cell cultures (Stubblefield, 1968). The methods of choice for human diploid cells are noted in Table 2-V, along with the usefulness of each technique. It is important to remember that synchrony of

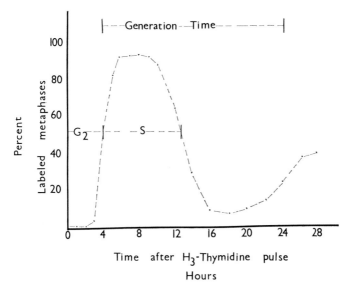

Figure 2-3. A method to determine generation time, and lengths of S and G2. Percent of labeled human diploid metaphases (ordinant) is plotted against time after onset of a 10 min. pulse of H_3-thymidine (abscissa). The time between 50% points of two consecutive ascending portions of the curve represents mean length of the cell cycle (generation time). Time between the mid-points of the first increase and subsequent decrease in percent of labeled mitotic cells represents mean length of S phase. G2 length is the time from start of H_3-thymidine labeling to the first point when half of maximal percent of mitotic labeling is obtained.

these diploid cells is short-lived, usually much less than the mean cell cycle time, and never complete. Human nondiploid established lines, such as HeLa cell, may be said to respond to any of the methods generally applicable to mammalian cells and synchrony may be more successful and lasting. All considerations of cell synchronization and its usefulness depend on knowledge of divisions in the cell life cycle and their significance (see section this chapter on cell cycle analysis and also Chap. 12, Significance of Cell Cycle Events).

A striking difference between human diploid monolayer cells and other types of mammalian monolayer cells is related to the behavior of mitotic cells. Human diploid cells in mitosis are more firmly attached to their substrate and there-

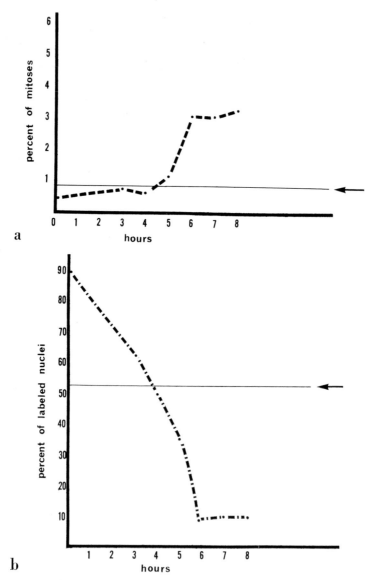

Figure 2-4. (a) Percent of mitoses and (b) percent of labeled interphase nuclei at intervals after reversal of FUdR block with thymidine (nondiploid Chinese hamster cells). A sharp mitotic peak is not obtained; nor is a sharp exit of cells from S (as represented by a sudden fall in percent of labeled interphases). The percent of mitoses and the percent of labeled nuclei for asynchronous cells are also indicated by straight lines (arrows).

fore are not easily removed mechanically and separated from cells in other cell cycle phases; methods to select human diploid mitotic cells by shaking or by brief trypsanization are less or not at all successful.

LABELING OF CELLS WITH TRITIATED COMPOUNDS; AUTORADIOGRAPHY

One of the most useful methods for studying *in situ* biochemical reactions on the level of the individual cell is autoradiography. In this technique a specimen containing radioactive material is covered with a layer of photographic film of a type designed particularly for this purpose. The specimen and film are in contact for a certain exposure period during which the radioactive atoms decay. The emitted radiation (β-rays, in the case of tritium) strikes the photographic emulsion and activates silver halide grains, forming a latent image which, upon development of the emulsion, will depict the distribution of radioactive material within the specimen. The developed image contains two distinct elements of information: first, its location relative to certain observable structures in the specimen, and second, its intensity, which bears a definite relationship to the amount of radioactivity present (Perry, 1964, p. 305-306).

H_3-thymidine labels DNA specifically and is therefore particularly useful to study patterns of DNA replication in chromosomes (see Fig. 2-5). Administration of H_3-thymidine to human cells is hazardous *in vivo* and well-controlled conditions of application also require cell culture techniques (Priest, 1969). Cell growth in culture may be inhibited by H_3-thymidine; the lethal action is a function of both the dose and specific activity, and is reasonably attributed to nuclear damage by beta-radiation (Drew and Painter, 1959). The labeling of chromosomes with H_3-uridine requires special precautions to insure specific labeling (Comings, 1966).

An interesting use of whole cell autoradiography to study the behavior of human X-linked genes in single cells involves fibroblast-like cells from individuals who have or carry the syndrome of cerebral palsy with automutilation and excessive synthesis of uric acid (Rosenbloom *et al.*, 1967). Cells from an affected child were labeled by H_3-adenine but not by H_3-hypo-

TABLE 2-IV

METHODS TO SYNCHRONIZE CULTURED MAMMALIAN CELLS

Method*	Explanation	Examples
A. Analysis of cell life cycle events (Stubblefield, 1968)	An asynchronous culture is used but only those cells in a particular part of the cell cycle are included in the analysis.	See Figure 2-3. Only the cells in S phase are labeled with a pulse of H_3-thymidine. The morphologic marker of mitosis is used as a reference point and mitotic labeling is analyzed at intervals following the pulse.
B. Inhibition and release of DNA synthesis 1. Amethopterin (Petersen, 1964) 2. 5-fluoro-2′-deoxyuridine (FUdR) (Priest et al., 1967) 3. Excess thymidine (Bootsma et al., 1964)	Flow of cells around the cell cycle is interrupted by agents that block DNA synthesis. Cells enter S phase synchronously when the block is relieved either by removal of the agent or by addition of a missing essential metabolite.	Both amethopterin and FUdR blocks are relieved by addition of thymidine. Cells enter and proceed together through S phase but may not show a sharp mitotic peak if synchrony is already lost by the next mitosis (Fig. 2-4 a and b).
C. Inhibition of mitosis 1. Colchicine (Taylor, 1965) 2. Colcemid (Stubblefield, 1964) 3. Vinblastin sulfate (Malawista et al., 1968)	Agents interfering with mitotic spindle formation will accumulate cells in metaphase.	To obtain enough metaphases for karyotyping, metaphase arresting agents are applied for periods usually not exceeding 6 hours. Cells are sampled when the percent of metaphases is high.

*References describe the method in more detail but are not necessarily the first or most complete description.

TABLE 2-IV (Continued)

Method*	Explanation	Examples
D. Selection of mitotic cells (Robbins and Marcus, 1964)	Cells from a brief phase of the cell cycle (M) are selected mechanically. Serial collections may increase the yield. Applicable only to monolayer cells.	Mitotic cells in a monolayer culture are not as firmly attached to the container surface as are interphase cells. Mitoses may be removed selectively by shaking or brief trypsinization.
C. Inhibition of mitosis + D. and selection of mitotic cells (Stubblefield, 1968)	Methods C and D may be combined to select mitotic cells.	Mitotic cells accumulated and selected are recultured in the absence of metaphase inhibitor; cells will then proceed together into G1.
E. Reproductive killing of cells in S phase (Whitmore and Gulyas, 1966)	Short exposure to H_3-thymidine of high specific activity destroys the proliferative capacity of the cells in S phase at time of tritium exposure.	H_3-thymidine label is applied to leave viable cells in only a narrow phase interval at the end of G1. These viable cells constitute a partially synchronized population when unlabeled thymidine is supplied.
F. Multiple synchronization 1. "Phased" subculturing (Stubblefield, 1968) 2. Double excess thymidine (Puck, 1964) 3. FUdR and metaphase shake (Priest, unpublished) 4. Nitrous oxide followed by excess thymidine (Rao, 1968) 5. Amethopterin + adenosine, FUdR or excess TdR (Steffen and Stolzmann, 1969)	Since the effect of a synchronizing agent varies because of position of cells in the cell cycle and differences between individual cells, multiple synchronization may be desirable to achieve a high degree of synchrony.	Excess thymidine is applied and removed so as to leave behind a culture with most cells *not* in S phase. Excess thymidine is again added; almost all cells will then proceed to the end of G1. Removal of excess thymidine a second time to these G1 cells results in a high degree of synchrony of entrance into S.

TABLE 2-IV (Continued)

Method*	Explanation	Examples
G. Production of reversible G2 lag (Puck, 1964) 1. Small doses of irradiation 2. Chemical agents such as streptonigrin	When G2 lag (delay in G2) is induced and relieved a high degree of synchrony is not achieved. However, this technique is useful to trace the kinetics of the lag produced by different agents.	Cells in which DNA replicates in the presence of streptonigrin exhibit a large delay in reaching mitosis similar to that produced by X-irradiation.
H. Inhibition of protein synthesis 1. Amino acid analog: fluorophenylalanine (Puck, 1964)	Progress of cells can be halted at various points in the cell cycle, depending on the concentration of inhibitor employed.	Fluorophenylalanine is shown to arrest cells in S and G1, while G2 is more resistant.
I. Temperature change (Miura and Utakoji, 1961)	Chilling of the cell culture causes lag and then "burst" of division occurs following return to 37°C.	Length of the lag period varies from one cell type to another. However, after preliminary tests on the cells to be studied, both methods I. and J. may be used to obtain a reasonable mitotic peak. Some phasing in other parts of the cell cycle may also be useful.
J. Media change	Media change causes lag and then "burst" of cell division.	
K. Reversal of in vivo G1 arrest (Bender and Prescott, 1962)	Some varieties of cells removed from the intact animal and provided with suitable culture conditions, after a lag period will proceed through S and on to M together.	In fresh human peripheral blood the level of DNA synthesis is low and mitoses undetectable. In cultured peripheral leukocytes treated with phytohemagglutinin, a first wave of mitosis occurs by about 40 hr., preceded by an in vitro DNA duplication. Individual cells undergo at least 4 mitoses and the cultures have a life span of about 2 weeks.

TABLE 2-V

SYNCHRONIZATION METHODS KNOWN TO BE APPLICABLE
TO HUMAN DIPLOID CELLS

(See Table 2-IV for additional references concerning methodology)

Method	Some Uses
Inhibition and release of DNA synthesis	1. H_3-thymidine labeling patterns of chromosomes at various times during S (Fig. 2-5) (Priest, 1968).
	2. Study of metabolic events and cell characteristics at specific times during S (Davies *et al.*, 1968).
	3. Collection of S phase cells to study if they will respond specifically to chemotherapeutic agents (Lampkin *et al.*, 1969).
	4. Incorporation of H_3-thymidine into a high proportion of cells (and to produce high specific activity label in DNA fibers) (Huberman and Riggs, 1966).
	5. To obtain large numbers of mitoses without use of metaphase arresting agents (Fig. 2-6).
Inhibition of mitosis	1. Accumulation of enough suitable metaphases for karyotyping. (See Fig. 1-3 a and b, Chap. 1.)
	2. Accumulation of mitotic cells for other studies such as isolation and fractionation of metaphase chromosomes (Salzman and Mendelsohn, 1968).
	3. Accumulation of enough suitable metaphases for autoradiography (Fig. 2-5).
Reversal of *in vivo* G1 arrest	1. To obtain optimal numbers of metaphases for karyotyping of peripheral blood cultures. (See Fig. 1-3 a and b, Chap. 1.)
	2. To follow chromosome labeling patterns in peripheral blood cultures at 1st, 2nd, 3rd and 4th metaphases after a pulse of H_3-thymidine (Prescott and Bender, 1963).

xanthine while normal cells incorporated both labeled compounds in RNA. Since HGPRT (hypoxanthine-guanine phosphoribosyl transferase) is required to convert hypoxanthine to the ribonucleotide necessary for subsequent incorporation into nucleic acids, absence of the enzyme from single cells of the affected child was confirmed by autoradiography. Furthermore, virtually all the mother's fibroblast-like cells studied were able to incorporate H_3-adenine but only slightly more than half incorporated H_3-hypoxanthine. Thus two cell populations, enzyme sufficient and enzyme deficient, were demonstrated in an obligatory carrier of

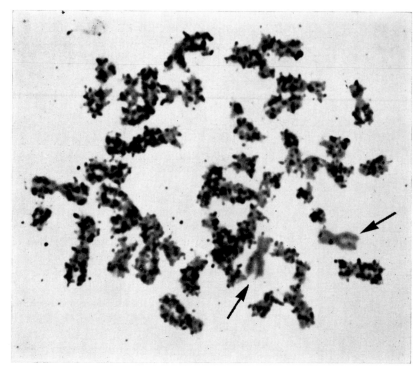

Figure 2-5. Autoradiograph of metaphase in a serial monolayer culture originating from a human female with an extra X chromosome. The extra chromosome was present in all the cultured cells karyotyped. This culture was treated with FUdR and thymidine to inhibit and release DNA synthesis (see Tables 2-IV and 2-V). When a majority of the cells were just entering S phase, H_3-thymidine was applied to label the replicating chromosomes at the beginning of S. The cell was prepared for autoradiography at next metaphase after label. Two C group chromosomes (X chromosomes) are seen to be unlabeled (arrows); human X chromosomes in excess of one are delayed in onset of replication. (Ilford L-4 emulsion, Giemsa stain, 100X oil emersion objective).

X-linked enzyme deficiency, lending further support to X chromosome inactivation in some cells of XX carrier females (see Chaps. 13 and 14).

ASSAYS OF THE EFFECTS OF ENVIRONMENTAL AGENTS

Human peripheral blood and monolayer cultures are frequently used to test the effects of irradiation, viruses, chemicals

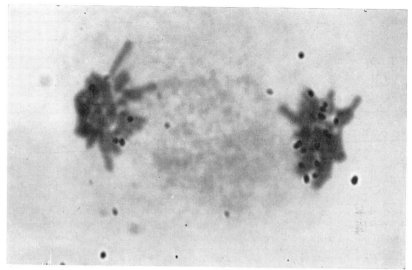

Figure 2-6. Autoradiograph of a human diploid anaphase obtained during the mitotic peak following inhibition and release of DNA synthesis. This particular cell was labeled with H_3-thymidine two S phases previously, and the distribution of a light label is unequal between the two sets of daughter chromosomes. Metaphase arresting agents will not allow progression of mitosis to anaphase; furthermore, since anaphase occupies so short a period of time, synchronization is needed to obtain large numbers of mitoses and enough anaphase figures for analysis. (NTB-2 emulsion, Giemsa stain, 100X oil emersion objective).

and various biological compounds such as steroids and antimetabolites (Table 2-VI; also see Chap. 3 on effects of environmental agents on chromosomes). Culture conditions must be standardized and cellular effects must be measurable directly, as for instance changes in chromosome morphology or cell growth rate. Cytotoxic effects may be scored quantitatively (Barile and Hardegree, 1970). Correlation between dose directly to individual cells and dose to an intact individual is never easy; the amount of environmental agent at the level of measurable *in vitro* cellular effect may have no relation to the dose causing changes in the intact individual. This problem is important to bear in mind when cultured cells are used to evaluate teratogenicity of certain drugs. Table 2-VI gives a few examples of culture assays, of both practical and theoretical interest.

TABLE 2-VI

EXAMPLES OF ASSAYS OF ENVIRONMENTAL AGENTS
ON CULTURED HUMAN CELLS

Environmental Agents Tested	Results and Interpretation	Reference
	Peripheral blood cultures	
Streptonigrin; X-ray	Chromosome breaks from X-ray are randomly distributed. Streptonigrin causes nonrandom breaks, some in areas of secondary constrictions.	Cohen, 1963
Lysergic acid diethylamide	The incidence of chromosome abnormalities is increased.	Cohen *et al.*, 1967
Cytochalasin B (isolated from moulds)	Multinucleated cells are produced.	Ridler and Smith, 1968
Busulfan (Myleran®)	Chromosome abnormalities and reduced mitotic indices are proportional to the drug concentration.	Richmond and Kaufmann, 1969
Bacitracin; 5-fluorouracil; fluorodeoxyuridine; mitomycin C	Mitotic index is measured to assay the cytotoxicity of various chemicals.	Amata *et al.*, 1969
	Diploid monolayer cell lines	
Oncogenic DNA virus, SV40; human adenovirus type 12	Certain cell strains are much more susceptible to transformation by both viruses. These cells may offer the best chance of detecting viruses possibly involved in human neoplasia.	Todaro and Aaronson, 1968
DNA isolated from SV40 (simian virus)	Cells are transformed, contain SV40 T-antigen and infectious virus can be recovered.	Aaronson and Todaro, 1969
Sodium and calcium cyclamate	Chromosome breaks are induced *in vitro* (in both leukocyte and monolayer cultures).	Stone *et al.*, 1969
	Nondiploid Established Cell Lines	
Thyroid hormones: L-thyroxine (T4); 3, 5, 3'-L-tri-iodothyronine (T3)	T3 is 5 to 10 times more potent than T4. Both hormones can enhance cell plating efficiency and induce or accelerate morphologic differentiation.	Siegel and Tobias, 1966
Environmental Agents Tested	*Results and Interpretation*	*Reference*
Cortisone	Virus induced cytotoxicity and acid phosphatase activation are both inhibited by cortisone, lending support	Walker and Pumper, 1968

TABLE 2-VI (Continued)

	to the stabilizing effect of cortisone on lysosomes.	
Aminonucleoside of puromycin (structurally analogous to adenosine)	Nondiploid cells have a greater capacity to proliferate than do diploid cells, when rate of ribosomal RNA synthesis is depressed by aminonucleoside.	Studzinski and Ellem, 1968
Antitumor drugs	Cultured cells from a human thyroid cancer were used to screen the effect of specific anticancer drugs.	Hirose, 1968
Inorganic water pollutants, herbicides and pesticides	Plating efficiency tests of growth of discrete macroscopic colonies from single cells were used to titrate toxicity of environmental agents.	Fisher *et al.*, 1969

PRODUCTION OF VACCINES AND VIRUS ISOLATION

The importance of human cell cultures for vaccine production and virus isolation is increasing. Field trials of live virus vaccines (against poliomyelitis, adenovirus type 4, measles and rubella) produced in human diploid cell lines indicate good epidemiological results and negligible vaccinal reactions (Andzaparidze, 1968). Nevertheless the problem always arises, do undesirable or unnecessary viruses also contaminate these vaccines? A battery of control tests must be performed on uninoculated cultured cells, viral harvest from the cultured cells and final filtered vaccine product (Tint and Rosanoff, 1969). The usual human cells for vaccine production are standard monolayer cell lines, such as diploid WI-38. However, specially isolated human cells may be useful to support growth of certain viruses, not only for production of vaccines but also for diagnosis and study of various disease-producing viruses that grow best in certain types of cells (see Table 2-IV for several examples of viral studies in cultured human cells; also see Chap. 8, on relation of viruses to transformation and neoplasia). As an example of special human cells used to grow viruses for diagnosis of respiratory disease, organ cultures of tracheas from fresh human embryos were prepared in glass tubes (Harnett and Hooper, 1968). These cultures increased the isolation rate of respiratory viruses over that obtained with standard monolayer cell cultures.

HISTOCHEMICAL TECHNIQUES

Histochemistry remains of great value for the study of cells outside the individual, in culture. It has been proposed to use histochemical techniques on *in vitro* cells for (a) identification of outgrowth components that may acquire ambiguous morphologic properties in the course of *in vitro* adaptation; (b) determination of degree of differentiated function and metabolic patterns in cultured cells; (c) definition of extents of diversity in *in vitro* cell populations (Farnes, 1967).

Chromogenic reactions may be used to identify specific cellular enzymes (Maio and De Carli, 1962). These enzymes may in turn serve as genetic markers at the cellular level. The choice of which enzymatic reaction to use depends on such factors as the sensitivity of the indicator and whether it can be used on intact cells; the effect on viability of the cells, if they are to survive for further analysis and recovery of variants; and whether or not spontaneous deficient variants exist for the enzymatic reaction under consideration.

Various staining techniques may be used to identify more complex metabolic products in intact cells, intra- or extra-cellular structures or differentiated morphology. Table 2-VII lists some types of studies in this category.

CINEMICROGRAPHY

Techniques to study the living cell and to record its movements must be considered in any discussion of cell culture. Time-lapse photomicrography includes motion picture camera, microscope with phase contrast optics, and cell culture container that can be mounted on a microscope stage in a way to preserve conditions for continued cell growth. The speed of photography may vary from one study to another but is often at the rate of one frame per minute. The dynamic behavior of a living cell may be very startling to someone accustomed to fixed material (Fig. 2-7). The constant movements recorded on motion picture film may be reproduced as still photographs for further study (Fig. 2-8; also see Fig. 1-1a and b in Chap. 1). Table 2-VIII summarizes the behavior of various human cells as recorded on time-lapse motion

TABLE 2-VII

STUDIES INVOLVING STAINING REACTIONS TO
IDENTIFY VARIOUS CHARACTERISTICS OF
INTACT HUMAN CULTURED CELLS

Cell Type	Staining Technique	Results and Interpretation	Reference
Epithelial-like mono- layer nondiploid cells derived from human embryonic epithelium	α-Naphthol phosphate coupled to Fast Blue R R	Clones possessing alkaline phospha- tase activity can be detected.	Maio and De Carli, 1962
Fibroblast-like monolayer diploid cells and peripheral blood cells from patients with mucopolysaccharide storage syndromes	Toluidine blue	Storage cells are present in culture and contain metachromatic material. The presence of these cells may be used to detect the carrier state.	Danes and Bearn, 1965 (See Chap. 4 on metabolic abnormalities in cell structure and function)
Fibroblast-like monolayer diploid cells	Mallory trichrome and Gomori trichrome stain	Extracellular col- lagen production may be detected by its affinity for aniline blue of Mallory stain and light green of Gomori stain.	Priest and Priest, 1964 and unpublished data
Fibroblast-like monolayer diploid cells	Various DNA stains such as Feulgen and orcein	Cultured cells may be examined for presence or absence of sex chromatin.	See Chap. 13, on heterochromatin

picture film (Rose, 1965). Although terminology may change and the reasons for all this behavior are often disputed, there can be no disputing the existence of complex and dynamic behavior patterns. Cinematography is also an important tool for the study of cell life cycle events (see earlier in this chapter).

ISOLATION OF CELL STRUCTURES

Culture conditions may provide reasonably uniform samples of human cells in large numbers for the isolation of various cell structures and organelles for further study (Table 2-IX).

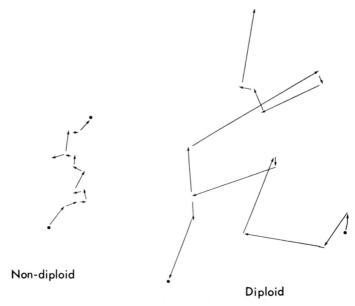

Non-diploid

Diploid

Figure 2-7. The movement of a cell from each of two different cell lines is followed by time-lapse photography and represented diagramatically. Both cultures were at the same cell density but one cell moved further between direction changes and also covered more territory during the same period of time. The cell labeled diploid is human and the cell labeled non-diploid is Chinese hamster.

STUDIES OF CELL SIZE AND VOLUME

The sizes of cells and nuclei are used to characterize cell populations in culture. In a diploid/triploid culture of human fibroblast-like cells from an individual with mosaicism, nuclear volume was found to correlate directly with DNA content and chromosome number (Mittwoch, 1968). Normal human diploid cells also change volume during the cell cycle, during changes in growth rate and during the degenerative phase of the culture (Simons, 1967).

FREEZING OF CELLS FOR PROLONGED STORAGE

A method to freeze monolayer cultured cells for prolonged storage in liquid nitrogen is detailed in the appendix. It is gen-

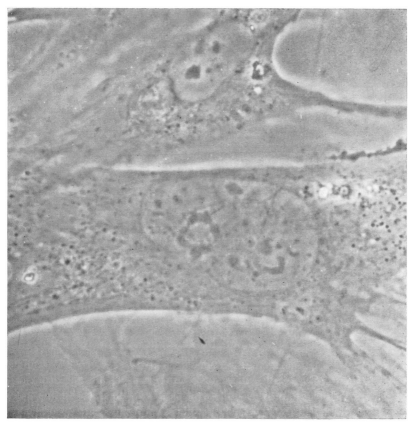

Figure 2-8. High power phase contrast photomicrograph of a human diploid cell in monolayer culture. Cytoplasmic stretching on the surface of the culture container is visible as well as refractile and dense cytoplastic inclusions. Some nuclear detail can be seen, particularly the multiple nucleoli. Photography by Jane L. Showacre.

erally agreed that some type of slow "programed" freeze (controlled rate of freezing) is important for subsequent cell viability on retrieval but the rate of thawing can be extremely rapid. Retrieved human diploid cells do not have altered *in vitro* life span (Jacobs *et al.*, 1970).

According to Mazur (1970) the molecular bases of freezing damage are not understood. During freezing (a) water is removed as ice, (b) solutes of high and low molecular weight

TABLE 2-VIII

A SUMMARY OF THE BEHAVIOR OF VARIOUS HUMAN CELLS
RECORDED ON TIME-LAPSE MOTION PICTURE FILM (Rose, 1965)

Cells Studied: KB established line (from oral carcinoma)
HeLa established line (from cervical carcinoma)
Melanoma line
Primary culture from fetal thyroid
Primary culture from skin

A. *Cell Membrane*
1. *Pinocytosis* involves:
   a. ruffling of the cell membrane and engulfment of phase-white fluid drop-
      lets that become membrane-bound.
   b. fusions and distortions of several droplets close to the cell membrane.
   c. contripetal direction of droplet travel toward the cell nucleus.
   d. contact with small phase-dark cytoplasmic bodies (microkinetospheres)
      during this transit.
   e. gradual rounding of these fluid droplets (pinosomes).
   f. continuous encirclement of these fluid droplets by other microkineto-
      spheres.
   g. shrinkage and spherical rounding of pinosomes as they approach the
      nucleus.
   h. ultimate shrinkage to total disappearance or to small phase-black granules
      near the nucleus.
2. *Ze'osis* involves a boiling and bubbling motion of the cell membrane.
   a. Cytoplasm fills the blebs and is withdrawn from them.
   b. Occasionally the blebs become separated from the cell to remain un-
      attached and even motile for a while, and the cell can proceed without
      any apparent distress.
   c. Cell organelles may be ejected into a zeiotic bleb.
3. Usually, multinucleated giant cells in cell cultures are observed to have
   especially active membranes. The outward migration of part of the membrane and the return of part of the membrane, simultaneously, is termed
   reciprocating activity. A primary function of giant cells appears to be their
   accumulation of large quantities of the fluid medium and cellular debris.

B. *Cytoplasm*
1. *Fat inclusions:*
   a. are identified by their multicolored interference patterns (by interference
      microscopy).
   b. are occasionally observed to coalesce.
2. *Mosaic patterns* in the cytoplasm undergo constant change in some areas of
   the cell; stable in other areas.
3. *Golgi complex*
   a. Phase-white droplets originate from the Golgi complex or from the area
      between the nucleus and the Golgi complex.
   b. They pass into the cytoplasm or under certain conditions they pass
      through the cell membrane into the cellular environment.

C. *Nucleus*
1. *Nuclear rotation occurs.*

2. *Nuclear membrane folds* appear.
3. *Intranuclear inclusions* are produced by invaginations of the nuclear membrane. The inclusions:
   a. are bound by double membrane.
   b. may include various cytoplasmic fragments from endoplasmic reticulum, mitochondria, myelin, Golgi complex; often the fragments are digested and therefore distorted.
4. The *nucleolus* is a plastic body confined to the nucleus.
   a. It is molded and reshaped in association with the changing patterns of nuclear folds.
   b. Phase-white droplets either leave the nucleolus through a small tract or disappear abruptly.

TABLE 2-IX

A SUMMARY OF SOME OF THE REASONS FOR ISOLATION OF
SPECIAL COMPONENTS FROM HUMAN CELLS IN CULTURE

Structure Isolated	Purpose	Reference
Metaphase chromosomes	To preserve in separate and distinct structures the DNA sequences corresponding to genetic linkage groups; to study the association of specific types of histone and RNA with specific chromosomes.	Maio and Schildkraut, 1966 Mirsky *et al.*, 1968
Interphase chromatin	To compare the characteristics of genetically active and inactive chromatin.	Comings, 1967
Nuclei	To assay synthesis of RNA, DNA and protein in mass preparations of nuclei; and to relate to stages of differentiation and disease.	Prescott *et al.*, 1966 Takakusu *et al.*, 1968 Munro *et al.*, 1969
Lysosomes	To characterize the contents and action of lysosomes; and to relate to disease states involving lysosomes.	Thacore and Wolff, 1968
Mitochondria	To study activity of mitochondrial enzyme (cytochrome oxidase) when isolated mitochondria are treated directly by environmental manipulation (change in pO_2).	Hakami and Pious, 1967
Microsomes	To synthesize proteins (histones) in a cell-free system derived from synchronized cultures of HeLa cells; to study the nature of the coupling between histone synthesis and DNA replication.	Gallwitz and Mueller, 1969

concentrate, (c) cell volume decreases, and (d) solutes pre-
cipitate. Rapid cooling produces small intracellular crystals which
are likely to enlarge during warming. If cells are cooled slowly or
if their permeability to water is high, they will equilibrate by
dehydration. Since cooling velocity affects the physical-chemical
events in cells during freezing it is not surprising that it also
affects their survival.

Various compounds are used to "protect" living cells during
freezing, so that they are viable when thawed and recultured.
These compounds include (a) glycerol and dimethyl sulphoxide,
nonelectrolytes that penetrate readily into cells; (b) sucrose and
glucose, that do not penetrate cells easily; (c) polyvinylpyrrolidone (PVP), a polymer that remains in extracellular position;
(d) ammonium acetate, a low molecular weight, weak electrolyte.
Many theories have evolved to explain why such a divergent
group should be effective. It has been shown that the action of
glycerol in protecting cells against damage during freezing is
probably associated with "buffering" the concentrations of salt
(NaCl) produced in the liquid phase as ice forms. All the
various types of compounds mentioned above are shown to reduce
the temperature at which a particular mole fraction of sodium
chloride will be reached as ice forms (Farrant, 1969). According
to Mazur (1970) most additives appear to protect against solution
effects rather than against intracellular freezing. However, ability
of a cell to survive freezing may depend more on protection of the
cell surface than on protection of the cell interior. Perhaps the
cell interior is protected by the high concentration of macro-
molecules normally within it. In any case, many major questions
remain unsolved.

TESTS OF CELL VIABILITY

The ability of a cell to reproduce is a test of it viability.
On the other hand, the failure of a cell to duplicate itself need not
necessarily mean the cell is dead. Hence, tests of biochemical or
physiological function have been used to determine whether or not
a nondividing cell is viable. A direct test for the viability of the
cultured mammalian cell based on its ability to form colonies *in
vitro* or to initiate tumors *in vivo* has not been sufficiently developed

to make it practical for all but a few cell lines. Therefore, an indirect test, based on the preservation of a selective membrane and the concomitant ability to exclude certain dyes as an index of viability, has become the assay of choice as a matter of convenience (DeLuca, 1965 p. 186).

Various dyes are used for this purpose, notably trypan blue. Another method to indicate cell viability employs the principal that trypsin (in concentration not greater than about 0.25%) is cytolytic to "damaged" cells but does not itself cause reproductive cell death in a healthy cell population, otherwise it could not be used for routine subculturing. Trypsin is therefore administered to a population of cells and its cytotoxic effect measured by cell counts at intervals after administration (DeLuca, 1965). Another method to test cell function (viability) is to measure uptake by the cell, of various substances such as nigrosin. It becomes obvious that the choice of what test to use depends on what cell functions are under investigation. How one defines cell "death" is also important; for instance, if reproductive death is to be measured, then some test of subsequent cell division is indicated.

MICROSURGICAL METHODOLOGY

A methodology for micromanipulating human cells of normal and malignant origin has evolved from study of about two-thousand nondiploid HeLa and diploid embryonic lung cells during interphase and mitosis (Diacumakos *et al.*, 1970). Various possible procedures are summarized in Table 2-X. The potential for these procedures is indeed great, since diseased or abnormal states can be produced directly in an individual cell.

Another technique to introduce micropathology to cells is with laser microirradiation of particular cell structures, such as chromosomes (Berns *et al.*, 1970).

TABLE 2-X

VARIOUS POSSIBLE MICROSURGICAL PROCEDURES
ON INDIVIDUAL HUMAN CELLS

1. Intracytoplasmic injection of interphase cells with aqueous and nonaqueous fluids.
2. Transplantation of chromosomes from one cell to another and subsequent retrieval

TABLE 2-IX (Continued)

of viable clones; production of predictable derangements of mitotic cells.
3. Intranuclear injection of silicone oil, DNA and sodium chloride, with survival of the cells.
4. Introduction of subcellular fractions into nucleus or cytoplasm of other cells.
5. Introduction of virus suspensions into nuclei of other cells without killing them.

REFERENCES

General

Cloning

Puck, T. T.: Single human cells *in vitro. Sci Amer, 197*:91, 1957.

Cell Cycle Analysis

Nachtwey, D. S., and Cameron, I. L.: Cell cycle analysis. In Prescott, D. M. (Ed.): *Methods in Cell Physiology.* New York, Academic Press, 1968, vol. III, chap. 10.
Puck, T. T.: Studies of the life cycle of mammalian cells. *Cold Spring Harbor Symp Quant Biol, XXIX*:167, 1964.

Synchronization

Newton, A. A.: Synchronous division of animal cells in culture. In Zeuthen, E. (Ed.): *Synchrony in Cell Division and Growth.* New York, Inter-science, 1964, chap. 17.
Petersen, D. F.; Tobey, R. A., and Anderson, E. C.: Synchronously dividing mammalian cells. *Fed Proc, 28*:1771, 1969.
Stubblefield, E.: Synchronization methods for mammalian cell cultures. In Prescott, D. M. (Ed.): *Methods in Cell Physiology.* New York, Academic Press, 1968, vol. III, chap. 2.

Tritiated Thymidine Labeling

Cleaver, J. E.: *Thymidine Metabolism and Cell Kinetics.* New York, Wiley, 1967.
Prescott, D. M. (Ed.): *Methods in Cell Physiology.* New York, Academic Press, 1964, vol. I, chap. 15-19.

Production of Vaccines and Virus Isolation

Cell cultures for virus vaccine production. *Nat Cancer Inst Monogr, 29*: 1968.

Histochemical Techniques

Farnes, P.: Histochemical approaches to cell characterization *in vitro. Nat Cancer Inst Monogr, 26*:199, 1967.

Gurr, E.: *Staining: Practical and Theoretical.* Baltimore, Williams and Wilkins, 1962.

Cinemicrography

Showacre, J. L.: Staging of the cell cycle with time-lapse photography. In Prescott, D. M. (Ed.): *Methods in Cell Physiology.* New York, Academic Press, 1968, vol. III, chap. 7.

Sisken, J. E.: Methods for measuring the length of the mitotic cycle and the timing of DNA synthesis for mammalian cells in culture. In Prescott, D. M. (Ed.): *Methods in Cell Physiology.* New York, Academic Press, 1964, vol. I, chap. 20.

Isolation of Cell Structures

Frenster, J. H.; Allfrey, V. G., and Mirsky, A. E.: Repressed and active chromatin isolated from interphase lymphocytes. *Proc Nat Acad Sci USA, 50:*1026, 1963.

Maio, J. J., and Schildkraut, C. L.: A method for the isolation of mammalian metaphase chromosomes. In Prescott, D. M. (Ed.): *Methods in Cell Physiology.* New York, Academic Press, 1966, vol. II, chap. 5.

Prescott, D. M.; Rao, M. V. N.; Evenson, D. P.; Stone, G. E., and Thrasher, J. D.: Isolation of single nuclei and mass preparations of nuclei from several cell types. In Prescott, D. M. (Ed.): *Methods in Cell Physiology.* New York, Academic Press, 1966, vol. II, chap. 6.

Schneider, E. L., and Salzman, N. P.: Isolation and zonal fractionation of metaphase chromosomes from human diploid cells. *Science, 167:*1141, 1970.

Studies of Cell Size and Volume

Harvey, R. J. Measurement of cell volumes by electric sensing zone instruments. In Prescott, D. M. (Ed.): *Methods in Cell Physiology.* New York, Academic Press, 1968, vol. III, chap. 1.

Freezing of Cells

Mazur, P.: Cryobiology: The freezing of biological systems. *Science, 168:*939, 1970.

Specific

Aaronson, S. A., and Todaro, G. J.: Human diploid cell transformation by DNA extracted from the tumor virus SV40. *Science, 166:*390, 1969.

Aaronson, S. A.; Todaro, G. J., and Freeman, A. E.: Human sarcoma cells in culture. *Exp Cell Res, 61:*1, 1970.

Amato, R. S.; Mitra, J., and Antopol, W. A.: Cytotoxicity assessed by mitotic activity of lymphocyte cultures. *J. Cell Biol, 43:*6a, 1969.

Andzaparidze, O. G.: Clinical experience with vaccines produced in the human diploid cell line WI-38. *Nat Cancer Inst Monogr, 29*:477, 1968.

Barile, M. F., and Hardegree, M. C.: A cell culture assay to evaluate the toxicity of Arlacel A (34444). *Proc Soc Exp Biol Med, 133*:222, 1970.

Bender, M. A., and Prescott, D. M.: DNA synthesis and mitosis in cultures of human peripheral leukocytes. *Exp Cell Res, 27*:221, 1962.

Berns, M. W.; Ohnuki, Y.; Rounds, D. E., and Olson, R. S.: Modification of nucleolar expression following laser micro-irradiation of chromosomes. *Exp Cell Res, 60*:133, 1970.

Bootsma, D.; Budke, L., and Vos, O.: Studies on synchronous division of tissue culture cells initiated by excess thymidine. *Exp Cell Res, 33*: 301, 1964.

Choi, K. W., and Bloom, A. D.: Cloning human lymphocytes *in vitro*. *Nature (London), 227*:171, 1970.

Christensen, E., and Giese, A. C.: Increased photoreversal of ultraviolet injury by flashing light. *J Gen Physiol, 39*:513, 1956.

Cleaver, J. E.: The relationship between the duration of the S phase and the fraction of cells which incorporate ^{3}H-thymidine during exponential growth. *Exp Cell Res, 39*:697, 1965.

Cohen, M. M.: The specific effects of streptonigrin activity on human chromosomes in culture. *Cytogenetics (Basel), 2*:271, 1963.

Cohen, M. M.; Marinello, M. J., and Back, N.: Chromosome damage in human leukocytes induced by lysergic acid diethylamide. *Science, 155*: 1417, 1967.

Comings, D. E.: H^3-uridine autoradiography of human chromosomes. *Cytogenetics (Basel), 5*:247, 1966.

Comings, D. E.: Histones of genetically active and inactive chromatin. *J Cell Biol, 35*:699, 1967.

Danes, B. S., and Bearn, A. G.: Hurler's syndrome: Demonstration of an inherited disorder of connective tissue in cell culture. *Science, 149*:987, 1965.

Davidson, R. G.; Nitowsky, H. M., and Childs, B.: Demonstration of two populations of cells in the human female heterozygous for glucose-6-phosphate dehydrogenase variants. *Proc Nat Acad Sci USA, 50*:481, 1963.

Davies, L. M.; Priest, J. H., and Priest, R. E.: Collagen synthesis by cells synchronously replicating DNA. *Science, 159*:91, 1968.

DeLuca, C.: The use of trypsin for the determination of cellular viability. *Exp Cell Res, 40*:186, 1965.

Defendi, V., and Manson, L. A.: Analysis of the life-cycle in mammalian cells. *Nature (London), 198*:359, 1963.

Diacumakos, E. G.; Holland, S., and Pecora, P.: A microsurgical methodology for human cells *in vitro*: Evolution and applications. *Proc Nat Acad Sci USA, 65*:911, 1970.

Drew, R. M., and Painter, R. B.: Action of tritiated thymidine on the clonal growth of mammalian cells. *Radiat Res, 11*:535, 1959.

Farnes, P.: Histochemical approaches to cell characterization *in vitro. Nat Cancer Inst Monogr, 26*:199, 1967.

Farrant, J.: Is there a common mechanism of protection of living cells by polyvinylpyrrolidone and glycerol during freezing? *Nature (London), 222*: 1175, 1969.

Fialkow, P. J.; Gartler, S. M., and Yoshida, A.: Clonal origin of chronic myelocytic leukemia in man. *Proc Nat Acad Sci USA, 58*:1468, 1967.

Fisher, H. W.; McManus, A. T., and Malcolm, A. R.: Bioassay of water pollutants with cultured mammalian cells. *J Cell Biol, 43*:37a, 1969.

Gallwitz, D., and Mueller, G. C.: Histone synthesis *in vitro* by cytoplasmic microsomes from HeLa cells. *Science, 163*:1351, 1969.

Goldsby, R. A., and Zipser, E.: The isolation and replica plating of mammalian cell clones. *Exp Cell Res, 54*:271, 1969.

Goldstein, S.; Littlefield, J. W., and Soeldner, J. S.: Diabetes mellitus and aging: Diminished plating efficiency of cultured human fibroblasts. *Proc Nat Acad Sci USA, 64*:155, 1969.

Hakami, N., and Pious, D. A.: Regulation of cytochrome oxidase in human cells in culture. *Nature (London), 216*:1087, 1967.

Ham, R. G.: An improved nutrient solution for diploid Chinese hamster and human cell lines. *Exp Cell Res, 29*:515, 1963.

Ham, R. G., and Murray, L. W.: Clonal growth of cells taken directly from adult rabbits. *J Cell Physiol, 70*:275, 1967.

Harnett, G. B., and Hooper, W. L.: Test-tube organ cultures of ciliated epithelium for the isolation of respiratory viruses. *Lancet, 1*:339, 1968.

Hirose, M.: Tissue culture of human thyroid cancer. *Acta Med Okayama, 22*:185, 1968.

Huberman, J. A., and Riggs, A. D.: Autoradiography of chromosomal DNA fibers from Chinese hamster cells. *Proc Nat Acad Sci USA, 55*:599, 1966.

Jacobs, J. P.; Jones, C. M., and Baille, J. P.: Characteristics of a human diploid cell designated MRC-5. *Nature (London), 227*:168, 1970.

Kim, J. H., and Evans, T. C.: Effects of x-irradiation on the mitotic cycle of Ehrlich ascites tumor cells. *Radiat Res, 21*:129, 1963.

Lampkin, B. C.; Nagao, T., and Mauer, A. M.: Synchronization of the mitotic cycle in acute leukemia. *Nature (London), 222*:1274, 1969.

Macdonald, K. B., and Bruce, W. R.: A minicolony assay for the viability of mammalian cells *in vitro. Exp Cell Res, 50*:471, 1968.

Maio, J. J., and De Carli, L.: The use of chromogenic reactions for the study of enzymic markers in populations of mammalian cells cultured *in vitro. Cytogenetics (Basel), 1*:353, 1962.

Maio, J. J., and Schildkraut, C. L.: A method for the isolation of mammalian metaphase chromosomes. In Prescott, D. M. (Ed.): *Methods in Cell Physiology.* New York, Academic Press, 1966, vol. II, chap. 5.

Mak, S.: Mammalian cell cycle analysis using microspectrophotometry combined with autoradiography. *Exp Cell Res, 39*:286, 1965.

Malawista, S. E.; Sato, H., and Bensch, K. G.: Vinblastine and Griseofulvin reversibly disrupt the living mitotic spindle. *Science, 160*:770, 1968.

Martin, G. M.: Clonal variation of derepressed phosphatase in chromosomally mosaic cell cultures from a child with Down's syndrome. *Exp Cell Res, 44*:341, 1966.

Martin, G. M., and Sprague, C. A.: Parasexual cycle in cultivated human somatic cells. *Science, 166*:761, 1969.

Martin, G. M., and Tuan, A.: A definitive coloning technique for human fibroblast cultures. *Proc Soc Exp Biol Med, 123*:138, 1966.

Mazur, P.: Cryobiology: The freezing of biological systems. *Science, 168*: 939, 1970.

Merchant, D. J.; Kahn, R. H., and Murphy, W. H., Jr.: *Handbook of Cell and Organ Culture.* Minneapolis, Burgess, 1964.

Mirsky, A. E.; Burdick, C. J.; Davidson, E. H., and Littau, V. C.: The role of lysine-rich histone in the maintenance of chromatin structure in metaphase chromosomes. *Proc Nat Acad Sci USA, 61*:592, 1968.

Mittwoch, U.: Nuclear sizes in a human diploid/triploid cell culture. *Nature (London), 219*:1074, 1968.

Miura, T., and Utakoji, T.: Studies on synchronous division of FL cells by chilling. *Exp Cell Res, 23*:452, 1961.

Munro, G. F.; Daunce, A. L., and Lerman, S.: Nucleic acid and protein composition of HeLa cell nuclei isolated by three methods. *Exp Cell Res, 55*:46, 1969.

Nachtwey, D. S., and Cameron, I. L.: Cell cycle analysis. In Prescott, D. M. (Ed.): *Methods in Cell Physiology.* New York, Academic Press, 1968, vol. III, chap. 10.

Perry, R. P.: Quantitative autoradiography. In Prescott, D. M. (Ed.): *Methods in Cell Physiology.* New York, Academic Press, 1964, vol. I, chap. 15.

Petersen, A. J.: DNA synthesis and chromosomal asynchrony. *J Cell Biol, 23*:651, 1964.

Pious, D. A.; Hamburger, R. N., and Mills, S. E.: Clonal growth of primary human cell cultures. *Exp Cell Res, 33*:495, 1964.

Prescott, D. M.: Change in the physiological state of a cell population as a function of culture growth and age. *Exp Cell Res, 12*:126, 1957.

Prescott, D. M., and Bender, M. A.: Autoradiographic study of chromatid distribution of labeled DNA in two types of mammalian cells *in vitro. Exp Cell Res, 29*:430, 1963.

Prescott, D. M.; Rao, M. V. N.; Evenson, D. P.; Stone, G. E., and Thrasher, J. D.: Isolation of single nuclei and mass preparations of nuclei from several cell types. In Prescott, D. M. (Ed.): *Methods in Cell Physiology.* New York, Academic Press, 1966, vol. II, chap. 6.

Priest, J. H.: The replication of human heterochromatin in serial culture. *Chromosoma, 24*:438, 1968.

Priest, J. H.: *Medical Technology Series: Cytogenetics.* Philadelphia, Lea & Febiger, 1969, chap. 9.

Priest, J. H.; Heady, J. E., and Priest, R. E.: Synchronization of human cells by fluorodeoxyuridine. The first ten minutes of synthesis in female cells. *J. Nat Cancer Inst, 38*:61, 1967.

Priest, R. E., and Priest, J. H.: Redifferentiation of connective tissue cells in serial culture. *Science, 145*:1053, 1964.

Priest, R. E., and Priest, J. H.: Diploid and tetraploid clonal cells in culture: Gene ploidy and synthesis of collagen. *Biochem Gen, 3*:371, 1969.

Puck, T. T.: Single human cells *in vitro. Sci Amer, 197*:91, 1957.

Puck, T. T.: Studies of the life cycle of mammalian cells. *Cold Spring Harbor Symp Quant Biol, XXIX*:167, 1964.

Puck, T. T.; Marcus, P. I., and Cieciura, S. J.: Clonal growth of mammalian cells *in vitro.* Growth characteristics of colonies from single HeLa cells with and without a "feeder" layer. *J Exp Med, 103*:273, 1956.

Puck, T. T., and Steffen, J.: Life cycle analysis of mammalian cells. I. A. method for localizing metabolic events within the life cycle, and its application to the action of colcemide and sublethal doses of X-irradiation. *Biophys J, 3*:379, 1963.

Rao, P. H.: Mitotic synchrony in mammalian cells treated with nitrous oxide at high pressure. *Science, 160*:774, 1968.

Richmond, J. Y., and Kaufmann, B. N.: Studies on Busulfan (Myleran) treated leukocyte cultures. I. Cytological observations. *Exp Cell Res, 54*: 377, 1969.

Ridler, M. A. C., and Smith, G. F.: The response of human cultured lymphocytes to cytochalasin B. *J Cell Sci, 3*:595, 1968.

Robbins, E., and Marcus, P. I.: Mitotically synchronized mammalian cells: A simple method for obtaining large populations. *Science, 144*:1152, 1964.

Rose, G. G.: Time-lapse cinemicrography of cells in tissue culture. *Bull Hopkins Hosp, 116*:33, 1965.

Rosenbloom, F. M.; Kelley, W. H.; Henderson, J. F., and Seegmiller, J. E.: Lyon Hypothesis and X-linked disease. *Lancet, 2*:305, 1967.

Salzman, N. P., and Mendelsohn, J.: Isolation and fractionation of metaphase chromosomes. In Prescott, D. M. (Ed.): *Methods in Cell Physiology.* New York, Academic Press, 1968, vol. III, chap. 12.

Sanford, K. K.; Covalesky, A. B.; Dupree, L. T., and Earle, W. R.: Cloning of mammalian cells by a simplified capillary technique. *Exp Cell Res, 23*: 361, 1961.

Siegel, E., and Tobias, C. A.: Actions of thyroid hormones on cultured human cells. *Nature (London), 212*:1318, 1966.

Simons, J. W. I. M.: The use of frequency distributions of cell diameters to characterize cell populations in tissue culture. *Exp Cell Res, 45*:336, 1967.

Sisken, J. E.: Methods for measuring the length of the mitotic cycle and the timing of DNA synthesis for mammalian cells in culture. In Prescott, D. M., (Ed.): *Methods in Cell Physiology.* New York, Academic Press, 1964, vol. I, chap. 20.

Sisken, J. E., and Morasca, L.: Intrapopulation kinetics of the mitotic cycle. *J Cell Biol, 25*:179,1965.

Stanners, C. P., and Till, J. E.: DNA synthesis in individual L-strain mouse cells. *Biochim Biophys Acta, 37*:406, 1960.

Steffen, J. A., and Stolzmann, W. M.: Studies on *in vitro* lymphocyte proliferation in cultures synchronized by the inhibition of DNA synthesis. I. Variability of S plus G2 periods of first generation cells. *Exp Cell Res, 56*:453, 1969.

Stone, D.; Lamson, E.; Chang, Y. S., and Pickering, K. W.: Cytogenetic effects of cyclamates on human cells *in vitro*. *Science, 164*:568, 1969.

Stone, G. E., and Cameron, I. L.: Methods for using *Tetrahymena* in studies of the normal cell cycle. In Prescott, D. M. (Ed.): *Methods in Cell Physiology.* New York, Academic Press, 1964, vol. I, chap. 8.

Stubblefield, E.: DNA synthesis and chromosomal morphology of Chinese hamster cells cultured in media containing N-deacetyl-N-methylcolchine (Colcemid). In Harris, R. J. C. (Ed.): *Cytogenetics of Cells in Culture.* New York, Academic Press, 1964, pp. 223-248.

Stubblefield, E.: Synchronization methods for mammalian cell cultures. In Prescott, D. M. (Ed.): *Methods in Cell Physiology.* New York, Academic Press, 1968, vol. III, chap. 2.

Studzinski, G. P., and Ellem, K. A. O.: Differences between diploid and heteroploid cultured mammalian cells in their response to puromycin aminonucleoside. *Cancer Res, 28*:1773, 1968.

Takakusu, A.; Lazarus, H.; Levine, M.; McCoy, T. A., and Foley, G. E.: Studies on the nuclei of cultured human leukemic lymphoblasts (CCRF-CEM cells). Method of isolation. *Exp Cell Res, 49*:226, 1968.

Taylor, E. W.: The mechanism of colchicine inhibition of mitosis. I. Kinetics of inhibition and the binding of H^3-colchicine. *J Cell Biol, 25*:145, 1965.

Thacore, H., and Wolff, D. A.: Isolation and characterization of lysosome-rich fractions from cultured cells. *Exp Cell Res, 49*:266, 1968.

Thrasher, J. D.: Analysis of renewing epithelial cell populations. In Prescott, D. M. (Ed.): *Methods in Cell Physiology,* New York, Academic Press, 1966, vol. II, chap. 12.

Tint, H., and Rosanoff, E. I.: Production and testing of rubella virus vaccine. *Amer J Dis Child, 118*:367, 1969.

Todaro, G. J., and Aaronson, S. A.: Human cell strains susceptible to focus formation by human adenovirus type 12. *Proc Nat Acad Sci USA, 61*:1272, 1968.

Walker, W. E., Jr., and Pumper, R. W.: Lysosome response of virus infected serum and serum-free mammalian cells cultured *in vitro*. *Exp Cell Res, 49*:441, 1968.

Whitmore, G. F., and Gulyas, S.: Synchronization of mammalian cells with tritiated thymidine. *Science, 151*:691, 1966.

Yasumura, Y.; Tashjian, A. H., and Sato, G. H.: Establishment of four functional, clonal strains of animal cells in culture. *Science, 154*:1186, 1966.

SECTION II

THE DIAGNOSIS OF HUMAN DISEASE

Chapter Three

CHROMOSOME ANALYSIS

CHROMOSOME ABNORMALITY SYNDROMES

M ost requests from clinicians for cell culture are to confirm abnormalities of mitotic chromosome morphology and number in patients suspected of having certain well-defined syndromes. These include Klinefelter, Turner and multiple-X syndromes, D, E, and G trisomies, and B chromosome deletion (Table 3-I and 3-II). In Chapter 1, Table 1-V lists definitions concerned with chromosome numbers. In addition, the glossary at the end of this chapter summarizes some of the definitions useful in clinical cytogenetics. Although chromosome analysis is not an emergency procedure, it frequently becomes essential for prognosis in the syndromes just mentioned, and for genetic counseling. Definitive identification of a chromosome abnormality also allows the physician to be on guard for certain aspects of the syndrome, particularly major internal malformations. However, standard maternal age-dependent G trisomy resulting in classical mongolism clinically usually does not need cytologic confirmation.

TABLE 3-I

NEW NOMENCLATURE SYMBOLS

The first item to be recorded is the total number of chromosomes, including the sex chromosomes, followed by a comma. The sex chromosome constitution is given next. The autosomes are specified only when there is an abnormality present.

A-G	the chromosome groups
1-22	the autosome numbers (Denver system)
X, Y	the sex chromosomes
diagonal (/)	separates cell lines in describing mosaicism

TABLE 3-I (Continued)

plus sign (+) or minus sign (−)	when placed immediately after the autosome number or group letter designation indicates that the particular chromosome is extra or missing; when placed immediately after the arm or structural designation indicates that the particular arm or structure is larger or smaller than normal
question mark (?)	indicates questionable identification when placed before chromosome symbol
asterisk (*)	designates a chromosome or chromosome structure explained in text or footnote, when placed after the symbol
ace	acentric (no centromere)
cen	indicates centromere when placed after the chromosome symbol
dic	dicentric (2 centromeres)
end	indicates an endoreduplicated metaphase when placed before the karyotype designation
h	indicates secondary constriction or negatively staining region when placed after the chromosome symbol
i	indicates isochromosome when placed after the chromosome arm involved
inv	indicates an inversion when placed before the chromosome arms involved
inv (p+q−) or inv (p−q+)	pericentric inversion
mar	marker chromosome
mat	maternal origin
p	indicates short arm of chromosome when placed after the chromosome symbol
pat	paternal origin
q	indicates long arm of chromosome when placed after the chromosome symbol
r	indicates a ring chromosome when placed after the chromosome symbol
s	indicates satellite when placed after the chromosome or chromosome structure symbol
t	indicates translocation when placed before the symbols for the involved chromosomes enclosed in parentheses
tri	tricentric (3 centromeres)
repeated symbols	duplication of chromosome structure

TABLE 3-II

SOME OF THE VIABLE CHROMOSOME DEFECTS ASSOCIATED WITH
HUMAN DISEASE STATES

(The prototype in each syndrome category is underlined.)
(Nomenclature symbols are defined further in Table 3-I.)

Syndrome Name	New Nomenclature	Chromosome Abnormality
		Description of Nomenclature

A. Abnormalities of sex chromosomes. The number of sex chromatin bodies in each case is one less than the number of X chromosomes. There is some clinical overlap between syndrome categories.

1. Conditions in which a Y chromosome is present	47,XXY (Klinefelter syndrome)	47 chromosomes, XXY sex chromosomes
	48,XXXY	48 chromosomes, XXXY sex chromosomes
	49,XXXXY	49 chromosomes, XXXXY sex chromosomes
	47,XYY	47 chromosomes, XYY sex chromosomes
	48,XXYY	48 chromosomes, XXYY sex chromosomes
	49,XXXYY	49 chromosomes, XXXYY sex chromosomes
	46,XY/47,XXY	
	46,XX/47,XXY	2 cell types
	47,XXY/48,XXXY	
	48,XXXY/49,XXXXY	
	46,XY/47,XXY/48,XXXY	3 cell types
2. Conditions in which a Y chromosome is absent	45,X (Turner syndrome)	45 chromosomes, one X chromosome
	46,XXqi	46 chromosomes, one X is an isochromosome for the long arm

TABLE 3-II (Continued)

46,XXp−	46 chromosomes, one X has a deleted short arm
46,XrX	46 chromosomes, one abnormal chromosome is suspected to be an X
46,XXr	46 chromosomes, one X is a ring
45,X/46,XX 45,X/47,XXX 45,X/46XXp−	2 cell types
45,X/46,XX/47,XXX	3 cell types
47,XXX (Triple X female)	47 chromosomes, XXX sex chromosomes
48,XXXX	48 chromosomes, XXXX sex chromosomes
49,XXXXX	49 chromosomes, XXXXX sex chromosomes
46,XX/47,XXX 45,X/47,XXX 45,X/48,XXXX	2 cell types

3. Conditions in which both X and Y chromosomes are present

46,XX/46,XY	46 chromosomes, XX and XY sex chromosomes
45,X/46,XY 45,X/47,XYY	2 cell types
45,X/46,XX/46,XY 46,XX/47,XYY/49,XXYYY	3 cell types

B. Abnormalities of autosomes. There are rare reports of combinations of the autosomal syndromes in one individual. XX or XY sex chromosomes may be present.

1. D group trisomy or 13-15 trisomy

46,XX,D+	47 chromosomes, an additional D group chromosome
46,XY/47,XX,D+	2 cell types are present, one normal and one trisomic

TABLE 3-II (Continued)

2. E group trisomy or 18 trisomy	47,XY,E+ or 47,XY,18+	47 chromosomes, an additional E group or number 18 chromosome is present
	46,XX/47,XX,18+ 47,XX,?E+	2 cell types, one normal and one trisomic 47 chromosomes, an additional chromosome is suspected to be an E
3. G group trisomy, Down's syndrome or mongolism	47,XX,G+ or 47,XX,21+	47 chromosomes, an additional G group or number 21 is present
	46,XX/47,XX,G+ 46,XX,D—,t(DqDq)+	2 cell types, one normal and one trisomic D/G translocation mongolism—46 chromosomes, one chromosome missing from the D group. The long arm of this chromosome is united with the long arm of a G chromosome. Since there are 4 normal G chromosomes, part of a G is present in triplicate.
	46,XY,G—,t(GqGq)+	G/G translocation mongolism—46 chromosomes, one chromosome missing from the G group. The long arm of this chromosome is united with the long arm of a G chromosome. Since there are 3 normal G chromosomes, part of a G is present in triplicate.
	46,XX/47,XX,G+/48,XX,G+G+	3 cell types, one normal, one trisomic and one tetrasomic
4. B chromosome deletion*	46,XX,Bp—	46 chromosomes, decrease in length of the short arm of a B chromosome
5. Some of the less clearly defined syndromes	a. —	a. Mixed group of translocations involving C group chromosomes.

*Deletion of No. 4 chromosome may be distinguished clinically from deletion of No. 5 (Arias et al., 1970).

TABLE 3-II (Continued)

b. 45,XY,D−D−,t(DqDq)+   b. D/D translocation—45 chromosomes, 2 D chromosomes missing, the long arms of 2 D chromosomes are united.

c. 46,XY,18−,18r+   c. 18 deletion—46 chromosomes, one 18 chromosome missing, one 18 chromosome is a ring.

or

46XY/46,XY,18−,18r+   2 cell types, one normal and one with a ring 18 chromosome.

d. 47,XX,22+   d. Trisomy 22—47 chromosomes, an extra 22 chromosome is present.

e. 46,XY/46,XY,?Gq−   e. G deletion—2 cell types, one normal, one with a suspected long arm deletion of a G chromosome.

C. Abnormalities of sex chromosomes and autosomes. Occurrence is rare.

1. Klinefelter-mongol   48,XXY,G+   48 chromosomes, XXY sex chromosomes, an additional G group chromosome is present.

2. Multiple-X-mongol   48,XXX,G+   48 chromosomes, XXX sex chromosomes, an additional G chromosome is present.

3. D trisomy-mongol   48,XX,D+,G+   48 chromosomes, additional D and G chromosomes are present.

4. Klinefelter-
D translocation   46,XXY,D−D−,t(DqDq)+   46 chromosomes, XXY sex chromosomes, 2 D chromosomes missing, the long arms of these chromosomes are united.

5. E trisomy-mongol   48,XX,E+,G+   48 chromosomes, additional E and G chromosomes are present.

6. Some of the less clearly defined syndromes include translocations between sex chromosomes and autosomes.

The short-term peripheral blood culture technique (Chap. 1) is used for chromosome analysis because of the ease of obtaining a specimen by venipuncture and the relative ease of laboratory processing. If initial studies on peripheral blood suggest more than one chromosomal cell type (mosaicism), analysis may be performed on other tissues in order to evaluate the extent of the mosaicism. In such a situation the tissue usually employed is skin obtained by pinch biopsy; and in certain instances autopsy or surgical tissue may be sources for chromosome analysis. These tissue sources require some type of primary or serial culture method, usually monolayer culture of fibroblast-like cells to provide enough dividing cells for analysis of metaphase chromosomes. Long-term human hematopoietic cell lines can maintain the donors' chromosome constitutions for long periods and hundreds of cell generations. Both XXY and XYY karyotypes have been maintained in long-term peripheral blood culture for ten to twelve months (Huang and Moore, 1969). In another report a permanent human lymphoid cell line with normal chromosomes and one minute marker chromosome was established from a normal female (Moore *et al.*, 1969). The abnormal karyotype was also present in short-term peripheral blood culture and a second permanent cell line derived from a later sampling of the donor's leukocytes. The abnormality appeared to be a feature of the donor's mosaic karyotype and persisted in the oldest culture line as a marker chromosome two years after establishment. Some of the culture methods used to study human chromosome abnormality syndromes and indications for selecting these methods are summarized in Table 3-III (also see Chap. 1 and Appendix).

Autoradiography may be helpful to identify abnormal chromosomes (Table 3-IV). The section in Chapter 2, on labeling of cells with tritiated compounds explains why conditions of cell culture are required to label human chromosomes with tritiated thymidine.

The consequences of chromosome defects to the individual have been investigated outside the individual in cultures of his cells. One type of study centers on the biochemical effects of, say, the presence of an entire extra chromosome. If a third gene

TABLE 3-III

INDICATIONS FOR SELECTING VARIOUS CELL CULTURE METHODS
TO STUDY HUMAN MITOTIC CHROMOSOMES

Peripheral Blood Culture—Short Term

1. Specimen is easy to obtain. No special consent forms are needed from the patient.
2. Mitotic chromosomes are available for study within 3-4 days.
3. Culture methodology is easy and investment in laboratory supplies and equipment is minimal.
4. This is the method of choice for routine cytogenetic analysis in a clinical laboratory.

Peripheral Blood Culture—Long Term

1. Indicated when a large number of cells are needed for biochemical, histochemical, or other analyses in connection with cytogenetic defects.
2. Cells may be stored on a long-term basis and retrieved when needed.
3. Indicated for long-term cytogenetic studies of cell selection *in vitro*.
4. Permits serial sampling of the same culture.

Fibroblast-like Monolayer Culture

1. Indicated when multi-tissue sampling for chromosome analysis is required.
2. Indicated for most surgical and autopsy specimens.
3. Indicated when a reasonably large number of cells are needed for biochemical, histochemical, or other biochemical analyses in connection with cytogenetic defects.
4. Permits reanalysis without returning to the patient for another specimen.
5. Cells may be stored on a long-term basis and retrieved when needed.
6. Cells may be grown directly on cover-slips and processed for chromosome analysis.

Primary Culture

1. Indicated when multi-tissue sampling for chromosome analysis is required.
2. Mitotic chromosomes are available for study within about 2-3 weeks (occasionally in less time).
3. Decreases the risk of cell selection occurring during serial culture.
4. Cells may be grown directly on slides or coverslips and processed for chromosome analysis.

is present in the homologous set, will there be effect on measurable genetic products such as enzymes or other types of proteins? Is more protein made? The congenital defects in many of the chromosomal syndromes are presently poorly understood and explanations take the form of general statements such as "genetic imbalance." If more precise mechanisms could be defined, other types of treatment become conceivable short of restoring the normal karyotype. A variety of enzymes have been studied in

TABLE 3-IV

THE USE OF AUTORADIOGRAPHY TO IDENTIFY ABNORMAL CHROMOSOMES
(from Priest, 1969, p50)

1. No. 4 chromosome is later to replicate over the long arm than No. 5 and is less commonly deleted in the B chromosome deletion syndrome than is No. 5.*

2. No. 13 (D_1) chromosome is later to replicate over the distal long arm than are Nos. 14 (D_2) and 15 (D_3) and is commonly trisomic in D trisomy syndrome.

3. No. 21 (G_1) is found, by some investigators, to replicate later than No. 22 and is trisomic in Down's syndrome (mongolism). However, other investigators report difficulty in distinguishing No. 21 and No. 22 by their terminal labeling patterns.

4. As a rule, structurally abnormal X chromosomes (rings, isochromosomes, or deleted) are late to replicate as compared to the entire chromosome complement.

5. The most common D/G translocation chromosome associated with Down's syndrome is 14/21. Less commonly it is 15/21. The distinction between Nos. 14 and 15 is possible because No. 14 chromosome is later to finish replication near the centromere than is No. 15.

cultured fibroblast-like cells derived from humans with and without autosomal trisomy syndromes (Table 3-V). No consistent differences have been found between the two groups although inconsistent differences have been noted in biochemical studies of tissues taken directly from the individuals, usually peripheral blood (Hsia *et al.*, 1968). This negative type of evidence has several possible explanations. In the situations studied there may be no simple, direct relationship between number of autosomes present and amount of enzyme produced. In addition, we do not have gene maps for human autosomes and we often lack appropriate measurements of specific gene functions.

TABLE 3-V

ENZYMES STUDIED IN CULTURED FIBROBLAST-LIKE CELLS FROM CONTROLS AND AUTOSOMAL TRISOMY SYNDROMES

Alkaline phosphatase
Acid phosphatase
Glucose-6-phosphate dehydrogenase
Galactose-1-phosphate uridyl transferase
Beta-glucuronidase
UDPG-4-epimerase

---

*Deletion of No. 4 chromosome (short arm) may be distinguished clinically from deletion of No. 5 short arm (Arias *et al.*, 1970).

MEIOTIC CHROMOSOMES

Direct handling of germ cells is presently the most useful technique for studying meiotic chromosomes (Ohno, 1965, pp 75-90). However, because of the limitations inherent in *in vivo* studies of both male and female meiosis, continued development of *in vitro* techniques is extremely important. Limitations to direct handling of human germ cells include the difficulty of obtaining specimens from both sexes, unless surgical or autopsy specimens are readily available. Furthermore, the desirable stage of meiosis for cytogenetic study is not necessarily present once the specimen is obtained, particularly in the female. Tissue culture techniques do not circumvent the need to biopsy an initial tissue specimen but they can facilitate obtaining suitable stages of female meiosis for study and can make the tissue available for continued study (see Chap. 1, on culture of human germ cells). It should be stressed that the *in vivo* timing of human male meiosis is considerably different from female meiosis. Male meiosis occurs throughout the period of sexual maturity. In female meiosis the entire process of first meiotic prophase is completed before the end of fetal life. When the estrus cycle begins, one or more oocytes at a time resume meiosis I shortly before being ovulated into the Fallopian tube. *In vivo*, meiosis II is usually completed only after an ovum has been fertilized (Ohno *et al.*, 1962). *In vitro*, resumption of meiosis I and progression to meiosis II may be accomplished in appropriate culture conditions (Edwards, 1966).

Some of the uses of germ cell culture have been presented in Table 1-XI in Chapter 1. Some of the conclusions about human meiosis, obtained from these germ cell studies, are listed in this chapter in Table 3-VI.

Ovarian and testicular tissue is also used to establish fibroblast-like cells in monolayer culture. In this situation mitosis rather than meiosis is studied for the purpose of evaluating the presence or absence of abnormal mitotic chromosomes in gonadal tissue. It should be re-emphasized that these techniques to support division of somatic cells do not at present support the events necessary for initiation of meiosis I.

TABLE 3-VI

SOME OBSERVATIONS ABOUT HUMAN MEIOSIS, OBTAINED FROM
STUDIES ON GERM CELL CULTURE

Observations	*Reference*
Short term incubation of oocytes obtained at laparotomy revealed some metaphase II figures with many more than 23 chromosomes, suggesting fusion of the first polar body with the egg, under the conditions provided.	Edwards, 1965
Cells in culture from testicular biopsies were exposed to labeled DNA precursor (tritiated thymidine). Autoradiographic analysis revealed that DNA synthesis takes place during the interphase preceding meiosis and extends into the leptotene and zygotene stages of meiosis.	Lima-de-Faria *et al.*, 1966
Oocytes obtained from ovaries at laparotomy were incubated for periods up to 60 hours to obtain metaphase I and II figures. Chiasma counts were made as well as identification of the number and configuration of the bivalents (paired homologous chromosomes).	Yuncken, 1968

STUDY OF ABORTIONS, STERILITY, AND INFERTILITY

Gross chromosomal aberration is established as a major factor associated with early spontaneous abortion. The common abnormalities of karyotype are 45,X; various trisomies; triploidy and tetraploidy. Tissue culture techniques have been essential for production of enough dividing cells for chromosome analysis of fetal, embryonic or trophoblastic tissue. One puzzling fact from these studies is that many specimens fail to grow in culture. This high failure rate has raised the question of sampling bias in all cytogenetic studies on spontaneous abortions. A study of the effect of tissue culture techniques on success or failure of cell growth is summarized in Table 3-VII (Smith *et al.*, 1969). The results suggest that culture techniques are of critical importance for a high success rate in chromosomal diagnosis of abortions. The question has also been raised if the karyotype of fetal membranes is representative of other fetal tissues. A study of primary cultures from full-term fetal membranes revealed correspondence between karyotype of the fetal membrane and karyotype in infants' peripheral blood cultures (Book *et al.*, 1968).

TABLE 3-VII

AN EVALUATION OF CULTURE TECHNIQUES FOR
CYTOGENETIC STUDY OF ABORTIONS

Tissue Material	Culture Method	Results
Identifiable fetal or embryonic tissue	Multiple tissue fragments are placed in culture. The first outgrowth is carried through 3 or 4 subcultures before chromosome studies.	This technique was the most successful and also provided cells suitable for long-term storage.
Trophoblastic tissue	Multiple tissue fragments are placed in culture on coverslips. The primary outgrowth on the coverslips is examined cytogenetically after about 3 weeks.	This was the method of choice when fetal tissue could not be identified. Maintenance of cellular growth from trophoblastic tissue was found to present a major problem, however.

CHROMOSOMES IN NEOPLASMS

Chromosome analysis of bone marrow is useful for the diagnosis of chronic myelogenous leukemia when a deleted G group chromosome (Philadelphia or Ph^1 chromosome) may be found to precede definitive clinical diagnosis by other tests (Nowell and Hungerford, 1960). No other specific chromosome abnormalities are found to be associated consistently with leukemias. However, marrow chromosome changes of more than one type have been useful in the diagnosis of preleukemia (Nowell, 1965). Chromosome abnormalities of different types may be present in direct tissue specimens or in tissue cultures from various types of human solid tumors (Gottleib, 1969). It has been suggested that tumor cells in culture may be useful as an *in vitro* assay system for the effectiveness of antitumor drugs, much as bacterial cells in culture are useful for testing their sensitivity to antibiotics (see Chap. 8, on tests of antitumor agents).

In some instances direct tissue examination without *in vitro* culture is the method of choice for chromosome analysis of neoplasms since it may be argued that direct tissue examination, without tissue incubation or mitotic stimulant, may reduce any selective effect of culture on the cell population. For instance, cells resembling fibroblasts in bone marrow cultures from patients with granulocytic leukemia were found not to contain the Ph[1] chromosome; it was concluded that these fibroblast-like cells did not derive from leukemic cells or their precursors, otherwise the Ph[1] chromosome should be present (Maniatis *et al.,* 1969) However, culture may be extremely useful (as summarized in Table 3-VIII), one main advantage being to increase the number of analyzable mitoses. Bone marrow and some neoplastic tissues may have high enough *in vivo* mitotic rates for direct analysis, but frequently the natural mitotic rate in neoplasms is too low. In a study to compare direct and short-term tissue culture techniques in determining solid tumor karyotypes, Kotler and Lubs (1967) concluded that culture provided increased numbers and quality of metaphase mitoses for study and was applicable to a wide variety of tumors. In Chapter 8, on neoplasia, cultures from tumors are considered in more detail.

TABLE 3-VIII

INDICATIONS FOR THE USE OF TISSUE CULTURE TO STUDY CHROMOSOMES IN HUMAN NEOPLASMS

Indication	*Example*	*Reference*
1. To increase the number of analyzable mitoses, in tissues likely to reflect the cytogenetic status of the original neoplastic cell line.	Chromosomes were analyzed in cells cultured from cerebrospinal fluid and ascitic fluid for the purpose of diagnosing abnormalities suggesting neoplasia.	Baughman and Hirsch, 1963
	Lymph node tissue was suspended in tissue culture medium at 37°C for 14-16 hrs. This brief period of culture greatly increased the number of analyzable metaphases in cases of lymphosarcoma, Hodgkin's disease, reticulum-cell sarcoma and follicular lymphomas.	Spiers and Baikie, 1966
2. To increase the number of analyzable mitoses, in multiple tissue studies.	Serial chromosome studies directly on bone marrow were compared to studies of cultured peripheral blood and skin in different types of human leukemia.	Baikie *et al.,* 1959
	In a serial study of 40 cases of Ph[1]-positive myelogenous leukemia, either in the chronic state or during exacerbation, eight examples of karyotype	de Grouchy *et al.,* 1966

TABLE 3-VIII (Continued)

Indication	Example	Reference
	evolution were observed. These chromosome changes were compared between direct examination and tissue culture specimens.	
3. To follow karyotype changes in tumor tissue in long term culture.	Long-term cultivation of tumor cells from several poorly differentiated carcinomas of the cervix produced two established hypodiploid human cell lines.	Auersperg, 1964
	Near hexaploid cultures were isolated from a human carcinoma. During prolonged culture there was gradual chromosome loss.	Auersperg, 1966
	Human anaplastic thyroid carcinoma in tissue culture maintained the ability to produce anaplastic carcinoma nodules when injected into rats. Chromosomes in cultured cells showed a high degree of aneuploidy and polyploidy with numerous abnormalities of chromosome morphology.	Jones *et al.*, 1967
	Two cell lines were derived from an embryonal rhabdomyosarcoma. Line No. 1 had a stem-line of 51 chromosomes with consistent karyotype; in line No. 2 no main chromosomal cell line was noted and counts ranged from 45 to 170.	McAllister *et al.*, 1969

EFFECTS OF ENVIRONMENTAL AGENTS ON CHROMOSOMES*

Well controlled studies of the effects of environmental agents on chromosomes usually require conditions provided by cell culture. As examples, some of the effects of viruses on human chromosomes in cultured cells are summarized in Table 3-IX. These studies and many more have established beyond reasonable doubt that viruses are agents capable of producing chromosome changes. The same conclusion, from similar kinds of studies, is also true for other infectious agents (Stanbridge *et al.*, 1969), various drugs or chemicals (Kato, 1968), and ionizing irradiation

---

*Also see Chap. 2, assays of the effects of environmental agents.

TABLE 3-IX

SOME EXAMPLES OF THE EFFECTS OF VIRUSES ON HUMAN
CHROMOSOMES IN CULTURED CELLS*

Type of Culture

Peripheral blood, short-term culture	Increased single *breaks* (without tendency for reunion) are found in cultures from patients with rubeola. Identical changes are also seen in chicken pox and mumps.
Peripheral blood, short-term culture	Increased single *breaks* are seen following administration of live attenuated vaccines to patients, including rubeola vaccines.
Peripheral blood, short-term culture	The Schmidt-Ruppin strain of Rous virus that causes tumors in a large number of mammals causes inhibition of mitosis when added to cultures at the time they are established. When added at 36 hours, after DNA synthesis has already begun, *chromosome breaks* occur. Similar results occur with the oncogenic adenovirus-12.
Peripheral blood, short-term culture; some diploid and heteroploid long-term monolayer cultures	*Chromosome pulverization* occurs when rubeola virus is added to cultures in large concentrations or for prolonged periods. Sendai, NDV and mumps virus (myxoviruses) also cause chromosome pulverization. Virus fractions or UV-inactivated virus may be active.

*Summarized from the review article by Aula, Nichols and Levan, 1968.

(Puck, 1960). Nevertheless, at present it remains difficult to answer the question: what are the immediate or ultimate effects of environmentally induced chromosome changes on the individual?

Some of the long-term chromosome changes, as well as the other growth changes induced in human diploid cell cultures by various environmental agents, are considered to provide a cellular model *in vitro* for malignant changes *in vivo*. This concept of a cellular model for neoplasia will be considered further in Chapter 8. Further questions concerning the relation of exogenously induced chromosomal breakage to disease processes such as teratogenesis, aplastic anemia and autoimmunity must be answered by future investigations.

SINGLE GENE DEFECTS ASSOCIATED WITH CHROMOSOME ABNORMALITIES

The relationship of genetics to chromosome defects is raised by certain well established inherited syndromes associated with

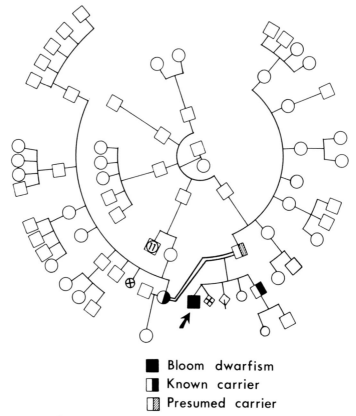

■ Bloom dwarfism
▯ Known carrier
▨ Presumed carrier

Figure 3-1. Pedigree of an individual with Bloom syndrome (arrow) showing recessive inheritance. The patient's parents were related as first cousins
once removed. In this syndrome chromosome abnormalities seen in the
affected individual (see Table 3-X and Figure 3-2) are also seen in the
carriers.

chromosome defects. The two best studied syndromes, from the
point of view of chromosomes in cultured cells, are Bloom syndrome (German, 1969) and Fanconi anemia (Bloom *et al.*, 1966;
Swift and Hirschhorn, 1966). Both are inherited as autosomal
recessive single gene defects (Fig. 3-1). Table 3-X summarizes
the clinical and cytogenetic findings in these two syndromes. The
chromosome changes are present in short-term peripheral blood
cultures and in diploid cell lines established from affected in-

TABLE 3-X

CLINICAL CHARACTERISTICS OF TWO HUMAN SYNDROMES, WITH
AUTOSOMAL RECESSIVE INHERITANCE, AND ASSOCIATED
WITH CHROMOSOME CHANGES IN CULTURED CELLS

Bloom Syndrome (Congenital telangiectatic erythema and stunted growth)	*Fanconi Anemia* (Constitutional aplastic anemia; hypoplastic anemia with multiple congenital anomalies)
Telangiectatic skin lesions, aggravated by exposure to sun	Aplastic anemia
Stunted growth from birth	Dwarfism
Typical facies	Microcephaly
Other congenital defects may be present	Skin pigmentation
	Hypogenitalism
	Strabismus
	Anomalies of ears, limbs, kidneys, heart

Chromosome Changes

Chromatid breaks (Fig. 3-2a)
Exchange figures (Fig. 3-2b)
Multicentric chromosomes (Fig. 3-2c)
Acentric fragments
Complex rearrangements
Transverse centromeric breakage
Chromatin at metaphase may appear segmented, shadowy and deteriorated, or pulverized
Abnormal mitotic figures with chromatin bridges (Fig. 3-2d), lagging chromosomes or chromosomal fragments

dividuals (Fig. 3-2a through d) (German *et al.,* 1965; German and Pugliatti Crippa, 1966; Schmid, 1967). An interesting finding is the fact that diploid fibroblast-like cultures (cell lines) from patients with Fanconi anemia provide cells highly susceptible to transformation by SV40 (Todaro *et al.,* 1966). Transformation is defined in this context as heritable change in the cultural characteristics of the cells such that the growth in monolayers is more dense and disorganized. Karyotypic abnormalities also appear and the culture lifetime becomes infinite (see Chap. 8, on neoplasia and transformation, and Fig. 8-1).

Several interpretations are given to the cytogenetic and cultural changes found in cells from individuals with Bloom syndrome and Fanconi anemia. The changes might reflect an inherited increased susceptibility to chromosomal breakage by environmental agents such as viruses. Alternatively, the chromosome changes could be explained by the more frequent infections

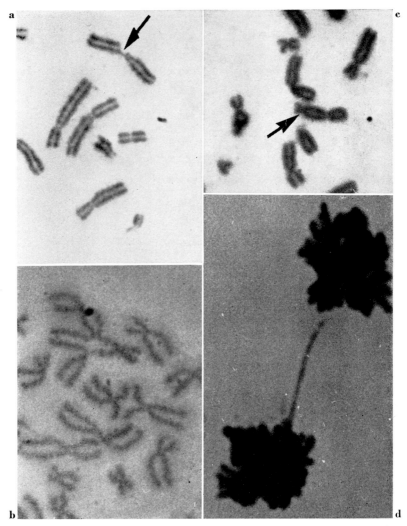

Figure 3-2. Chromosome abnormalities seen in Bloom syndrome. (a) chromatid break (arrow) with loss of chromatid alignment on either side of the break. (b) Two exchange figures are present, representing associations of mitotic chromosomes not seen in normal human metaphases. (c) A dicentric chromosome is present. A second centromere is indicated by the arrow. (d) A chromatin bridge is seen in this abnormal mitotic figure (anaphase).

occurring in the affected individuals. Both (or other) explanations could also be operating.

Xeroderma pigmentosum (XP) is a recessively transmitted disorder characterized by increased sensitivity to ultraviolet light, followed by skin cancers. A tissue culture line derived from an affected individual was studied in regard to sensitivity of cellular DNA to damage by ultraviolet-irradiation (production of UV-induced primidine dimers) and subsequent repair (excision of UV-induced dimers) (Setlow *et al.*, 1969). A much higher percentage of dimers were excised following UV-irradiation of cells from normal individuals as compared to XP cells; thus XP cells apparently fail to start the excision process. These findings also raise the possibility that unexcised pyrimidine dimers can be implicated in the oncogenicity of UV-irradiation.

CHROMOSOME ALTERATIONS IN "ACQUIRED" DISEASE STATES

Chromosome abnormalities are found in association with "acquired" pathologic states, in some cases with unclear relation to the disease; nevertheless the associations are consistent enough to warrant further investigations. An example is the high rate of chromosome alteration (breakage and pulverization) found in leukocytes of patients with subacute sclerosing panencephalitis (Szirtes *et al.*, 1969). Further investigation revealed high antibody concentrations to measles virus, suggesting a prolonged persistence of virus in human cells and a viral etiology for both the chromosome changes and the disease. Another example is the reported relationship between association of acrocentric chromosomes in metaphases, and aging of the cell donor (Prokofieva-Belgovskaya *et al.*, 1968). Lower numbers of acrocentric associations were found in primary cultures from human embryos. The highest numbers were found in cells from individuals age twenty-six to forty, although some decrease occurred in the group aged fifty-one to ninety years. Chromosome aneuploidy has been shown to increase with age of the cell donor (Jacobs *et al.*, 1963).

REFERENCES

General

Bartolos, M., and Baramki, T. A.: *Medical Cytogenetics.* Baltimore, Williams and Wilkins, 1967.

Bearn, A. G., and German, J. L.: Chromosomes and disease. *Sci Amer, 205:* 66, 1961.

Priest, J. H.: *Medical Technology Series: Cytogenetics.* Philadelphia, Lea & Febiger, 1969.

Swanson, C. P.; Merz, T., and Young, W. J.: *Cytogenetics.* Englewood Cliffs, N. J., Prentice-Hall, 1967.

Thompson, J. S., and Thompson, M. W.: *Genetics in Medicine.* Philadelphia, Saunders, 1966.

Yunis, J. J. (Ed.): *Human Chromosome Methodology.* New York, Academic Press, 1965.

Specific

Arias, D.; Passarge, E.; Engle, M. A., and German, J.: Human chromosomal deletion: Two patients with the 4p-syndrome. *J Pediat,* 76:82, 1970.

Auersperg, N.: Long-term cultivation of hypodiploid human tumor cells. *J Nat Cancer Inst,* 32:135, 1964.

Auersperg, N.: Karyotype changes of near hexaploid carcinoma cells during adaptation in culture. *Nature (London),* 212:635, 1966.

Aula, P.; Nichols, W. W., and Levan, A.: Virus-induced chromosome changes. *Ann NY Acad Sci,* 155:737, 1968.

Baikie, A. G.; Court Brown, W. M.; Jacobs, P. A., and Milne, J. S.: Chromosome studies in human leukemia. *Lancet,* 2:425, 1959.

Baughman, F. A., Jr., and Hirsch, B.: Karyotyping of cells from cerebrospinal fluid. *Lancet,* 2:417, 1963.

Bloom, G. E.; Warner, S.; Gerald, P. S., and Diamond, L. K.: Chromosome abnormalities in constitutional aplastic anemia. *New Eng J Med,* 274:8, 1966.

Book, J. A.; Kjessler, B., and Santesson, B.: Karyotypes of cultured cells from foetal membranes of normal newborns. *J Med Genet,* 5:224, 1968.

Edwards, R. G.: Maturation *in vitro* of human ovarian oocytes. *Lancet,* 2:926, 1965.

Edwards, R. G.: Mammalian eggs in the laboratory. *Sci Amer,* 215:72, 1966.

German, J.: Bloom's syndrome. I. Genetical and clinical observations in the first twenty-seven patients. *Amer J Hum Genet,* 21:196, 1969.

German, J.; Archibald, R., and Bloom, D.: Chromosomal breakage in a rare and probably genetically determined syndrome of man. *Science,* 148:506, 1965.

German, J., and Pugliatti Crippa, L.: Chromosome breakage in diploid cell lines from Bloom's syndrome and Fanconi's anemia. *Ann Genet (Paris),* 9:143, 1966.

Gottlieb, S. K.: Chromosomal abnormalities in certain human malignancies. *JAMA, 209*:1063, 1969.

de Grouchy, J.; de Nava, C.; Cantu, J.; Bilski-Pasquire, G., and Bousser, J.: Models for clonal evolutions: A study of chronic myelogeous leukemia. *Amer J Hum Genet, 18*:485, 1966.

Hsia, D. Y.; Nadler, H. L., and Shih, L.: Biochemical changes in chromosomal abnormalities. *Ann NY Acad Sci, 155*:716, 1968.

Huang, C. C., and Moore, G. E.: Chromosomes of 14 hematopoietic cell lines derived from peripheral blood of persons with and without chromosome abnormalities. *J Nat Cancer Inst, 43*:1119, 1969.

Jacobs, P. A.; Brunton, M.; Court Brown, W. M.; Doll, R., and Goldstein, H.: Change of human chromosome count distributions with age: Evidence for a sex difference. *Nature (London), 197*:1080, 1963.

Jones, G. W.; Simkovic, D.; Biedler, J. L., and Southam, C. M.: Human anaplastic thyroid carcinoma in tissue culture. *Proc Soc Exp Biol Med, 126*:426, 1967.

Kato, R.: Chromosome breakage induced by a carcinogenic hydrocarbon in Chinese hamster cells and human leukocytes *in vitro. Hereditas (Lund),* 59:120, 1968.

Kotler, S., and Lubs, H. A.: Comparisons of direct and short-term tissue culture techniques in determining solid tumor karyotypes. *Cancer Res,* 27:1861, 1967.

Lima-de-Faria, A.; German, J.; Ghatnekar, M.; McGovern, J.; and Anderson, L.: DNA synthesis in the meiotic chromosomes of man. A preliminary report. *Hereditas (Lund), 56*:398, 1966.

McAllister, R. M.; Melnyk, J.; Finklestein, J. S.; Adams, E. C., and Gardner, M. B.: Cultivation *in vitro* of cells derived from a human rhabdomyosarcoma. *Cancer, 24*:529, 1969.

Maniatis, A. K.; Amsel, S.; Mitus, W. J., and Coleman, N.: Chromosome pattern of bone marrow fibroblasts in patients with chronic granulocytic leukaemia. *Nature (London), 222*:1278, 1969.

Moore, G. E.; Fjelde, A., and Huang, C. C.: Established hyperdiploid hematopoietic cell line with a minute marker chromosome persisting both in culture and in the "normal" donor. *Cytogenetics (Basel),* 8:332, 1969.

Nowell, P. C.: Prognostic value of marrow chromosome studies in human "preleukemia." *Arch Path, 80*:205, 1965.

Nowell, P. C., and Hungerford, D. A.: Chromosome studies on normal and leukemic human leukocytes. *J Nat Cancer Inst, 25*:85, 1960.

Ohno, S.: Direct handling of germ cells. In Yunis, J. J. (Ed.): *Human Chromosome Methodology.* New York, Academic Press, 1965.

Ohno, S.; Klinger, H. P., and Atkin, N. B.: Human oogenesis. *Cytogenetics (Basel)*, 1:42, 1962.

Priest, J. H.: *Medical Technology Series: Cytogenetics.* Philadelphia, Lea & Febiger, 1969.

Prokofieva-Belgovskaya, A. A.; Gindilid, V. M.; Grinberg, K. N.; Bogomasov, E. A.; Podugolnikova, O. A.; Isaeva, I. I.; Radjabli, S. I.; Cellurius, S. PH., and Veschneva, I. V.: Association of acrocentric chromosomes in relation to cell type and age of individuals. *Exp Cell Res, 49*:612, 1968.

Puck, T. T.: Radiation and the human cell. *Sci Amer, 202*:142, 1960.

Schmid, W.: Familial constitutional panmyelocytopathy, Fanconi's anemia (F.A.). II. A discussion of the cytogenetic findings in Fanconi's anemia. *Seminars Hemat, 4*:241, 1967.

Setlow, R. B.; Regan, J. D.; German, J., and Carrier, W. L.: Evidence that xeroderma pigmentosum cells do not perform the first step in the repair of ultraviolet damage to their DNA. *Proc Nat Acad Sci USA, 64*:1035, 1969.

Smith, M.; Macnab, J., and Ferguson-Smith, M. A.: Cell culture techniques for cytogenetic investigation of human abortus material. *Obstet Gynec, 33*:313, 1969.

Spiers, A. S. D., and Baikie, A. G.: Cytogenetic studies in the malignant lymphomas. *Lancet, 1*:506, 1966.

Stanbridge, E.; Onen, M.; Perkins, F. T., and Hayflick, L.: Karyological and morphological characteristics of human diploid cell strain WI-38 infected with mycoplasmas. *Exp Cell Res, 57*:397, 1969.

Swift, M. R., and Hirschhorn, K.: Fanconi's anemia. Inherited susceptibility to chromosome breakage in various tissues. *Ann Intern Med, 65*:496, 1966.

Szirtes, G.; Csonka, E., and Lipcsak, M.: Chromosome alterations in leukocytes from subacute sclerosing panencephalitis patients. *Nature (London), 222*:692, 1969.

Todaro, G. J.; Green, H., and Swift, M. R.: Susceptibility of human diploid fibroblast strains to transformation by SV40 virus. *Science, 153*:1252, 1966.

Yuncken, C.: Meiosis in the human female. *Cytogenetics (Basel), 7*:234, 1968.

GLOSSARY OF TERMS USEFUL IN CLINICAL CYTOGENETICS

Arm (chromosome): The portion of a chromatid on one side of the centromere of a metaphase chromosome.

Arm ratio: The length of the longer arm of a metaphase chromosome relative to the shorter arm.

Association (chromosome): Proximity of certain portions of different chromosomes, often used to refer to proximity of satellites of D and G chromosomes.

Autoradiography: From auto, meaning self, and radiography, meaning the practice of producing a picture upon a sensitive surface, by some form of radiation, usually other than light. Chromosomes labeled with tritiated thymidine will expose photographic emulsion and produce an autoradiogram.

Autosomes: Non-sex chromosomes (22 pairs in humans).

"Balanced" structural rearrangement (chromosome): Rearrangement of chromosome material, without genetic effect.

Bivalent: Two paired homologous chromosomes during meiosis.

"Blastoid" reaction: The process by which a small lymphocyte is transformed *in vitro* into a large, morphologically primitive, "blast-like" cell capable of undergoing mitosis.

Break (chromosome): Interruption in staining of chromosome arm, with disturbance of alignment of the portions on either side of the interruption.

Cell cycle (or cell life cycle): The cycle in the life of a cell which includes mitosis (M) and interphase. The cell progresses from M to G1, to S, to G2, and on to M again.

Centromere (kinetochore, or primary constriction): A nonstaining area on a chromosome, separating the chromosome arms; the point of attachment of the chromosome to the mitotic spindle.

Centromere index: The ratio of the length of the shorter arm to the length of the whole chromosome.

Chromatid: One of two structurally distinguishable longitudinal subunits (by light miscroscopy) of a metaphase chromosome.

Chromatin: Areas of a cell nucleus that stain in some manner with a DNA stain.

Chromomere: "Beadlike," darker staining regions on meiotic prophase chromosome, constant in size and position.

Cinemicroscopy: Motion picture microscopy.

Daughter cell: One of the two products of mitosis.

DNA: Deoxyribonucleic acid.

Duplication (chromosome): Repetition of part of a chromosome.

Endoreduplication (or endopolyploidy): Result of mitosis involving doubling of chromosome number without division of nucleus or cytoplasm.

Euchromatic: Relating to areas of the nucleus that do not stain "differently" with DNA stains. (See heterochromatic.)

Exchange (chromosome): Transfer, morphologically, of chromosome material between chromosomes.

Exchange figure (chromosome): Partial pairing of chromosomes at mitosis.

Fragment (chromosome): A portion of a chromosome.

Gamete: Mature male or female germ cell.

Gap (chromosome): Interruption in staining of chromosome arm, without disturbance of alignment of the portions on either side of the interruption.

Genotype: The genetic constitution.

Hermaphrodite: Both male and female gonadal tissue in the same individual.

Heterochromatin: Nuclear areas that stain "differently" with DNA stains.

Homologous (chromosomes, genes): Paired or allelic (chromosomes, genes).

Intersex: Phenotypes of both sexes in one individual.

Isochromosome: Chromosome consisting of identical arms on either side of the centromere.

Karyotype: Systematized array of chromosomes of a single cell prepared either by drawing or photography, with the extension in meaning that the chromosomes of a single cell can typify the chromosomes of an individual or even a species.

Length (chromosome): Total distance between the opposite ends of a metaphase chromosome.

Map (chromosome): A linear diagram of the location of genes on a chromosome.

Meiosis I, II: 1st and 2nd meiotic division.

Metaphase I, II: 1st and 2nd meiotic metaphases.

Mitogenic: Capable of inducing mitosis.

Mitotic index: Number of mitoses per total number of cells in a given sample, expressed as a percent.

Mosaicism (chromosomal): A situation with more than one chromosomal cell type.

Nucleolus: Nuclear structure that stains with both DNA and RNA stains.

Oocyte: Immature female germ cell.

Oogonium: Primordial female germ cell.

Ovum: Mature female germ cell.

Phenotype: External appearance or constitution of an individual.

Pulverization (chromosome): Loss of metaphase chromosome morphology, with preservation of enough chromosome material to stain with a DNA stain.

Replication (DNA): Process by which new DNA is made from a DNA template.

Ring (chromosome): Attachment of opposite ends of a chromosome to form a ring (loss of chromosome material is implied).

RNA: Ribonucleic acid.

Satellite: DNA staining structure on the distal end of a chromosome arm and separated from it by a secondary constriction.

Secondary constriction: Nonstaining area on a chromosome arm.

Segregation (chromosome): Distribution of chromosomes to daughter cells.

Sex chromatin (or Barr body): Characteristic area of heterochromatin in the nucleus, composed of X chromosome material that stains heavily with a DNA stain.

Sex chromatin negative (or chromatin negative): Sex chromatin body is not present in cell nucleus.

Sex chromatin positive (or chromatin positive): Sex chromatin body is present in cell nucleus.

Sex chromosomes: XX in human female; XY in male; one pair normally present in each individual.

Somatic: Pertaining to cells other than germ cells.

Spermatocyte: Immature male germ cell.

Synthesis period (or S period): Period during interphase when DNA is replicated.

Transcription: Process by which messenger RNA is coded from DNA.

Translation: Process by which amino acids are coded from RNA.

Translocation (chromosome): Portion of a chromosome located on a chromosome other than the normal one.

Tritiated thymidine. Thymidine containing tritium, one of the isotopes of hydrogen, which is unstable and decays with emssion of a weak beta-particle.

Watson-Crick double helix: Model for the molecular structure of DNA.

Zygote: First product of union of sperm and egg.

Chapter Four

METABOLIC DEFECTS IN SOMATIC CELLS

SPECIFICALLY IDENTIFIED ENZYME DEFECTS

C ells in culture may preserve the enzyme defect or defects that cause the whole individual to be affected (Table 4-IA). An enzyme present in multiple tissues of the body is usually readily accessible for study; peripheral blood and skin are tissues easily biopsied from the living individual. Furthermore, enzymatic activity with wide *in vivo* tissue distribution is, as a rule, found in the usual type of human cell culture—the monolayer fibroblast-like culture (see Chap. 1). In addition to providing definitive diagnosis of the full metabolic defect, cell culture can be used for diagnosis of the heterozygous state, when enzyme function may be found to be intermediate between normal homozygote individuals and homozygote defectives. Maintenance of enzyme markers in culture also provides experimental models for the study of enzyme controls and effects at the cellular level, inasmuch as the cells of the affected human can be used rather than a more remote type of cell system. The fact that a single enzyme can exist in several different forms or isoenzymes within a single tissue, and between tissues, suggests that isoenzymes could cause different clinical diseases or a spectrum of involvement within one disease group; or the same clinical signs of an enzyme deficiency could result from multiple types of molecular defect. Thus the patient's own defective enzyme frequently needs to be studied both qualitatively and quantitatively in order to understand and treat his disease effectively. The diagnosis of an enzymatic defect rests upon demonstration of defective enzymatic activity. This demonstration may be possible only on cultured cells from the involved individual.

The intensive investigation of enzyme controls in cultured human cells and changes with environmental conditions, includ-

101

ing substrate induction will also be considered in Chapter 14 (Control Mechanisms) since human metabolic disease cannot be understood merely by identification of defective enzymes.

ABNORMALITIES IN CELL STRUCTURE AND FUNCTION

This group of metabolic defects reflected in cell culture (Table 4-IB) includes some diseases that will, no doubt, soon or eventu-

TABLE 4-IA

EXAMPLES OF ENZYME DEFECTS OF THE WHOLE INDIVIDUAL
REFLECTED IN SERIAL CELL CULTURE

Disease State	Defective Enzyme	Reference
Acatalasemias	Catalase	Krooth et al., 1962
Argininosuccinic aciduria	Argininosuccinase	Shih et al., 1969
Branched chain ketonurias	Decarboxylating enzymes for keto acids of leucine, isoleucine and valine	Dancis et al., 1969b
Citrullinemia	Argininosuccinic acid synthetase is abnormal (has a high K_m for citrulline)	Tedesco and Mellman, 1967
Deficiency of lysosomal acid phosphatase	Acid phosphatase in lysosomal fractions of cultured cells	Nadler and Egan, 1970
Fabry's lipidosis	Alpha-galactosidase (cleaves galactose from ceramide trihexoside)	Romeo and Migeon, 1970
Galactosemias	Galactose-1-phosphate uridyl transferase (G-1-PUT)	Russell and DeMars, 1967
Gaucher's disease	Glucocerebrosidase	Uhlendorf and Brady, Unpublished
G_{M1} gangliosidoses	G_{M1}-Beta-galactosidases[*]	Sloan et al., 1969
Glucose-6-phosphate dehydrogenase deficiencies	Glucose-6-phosphate dehydrogenase (G6PD)	Nitowsky et al. 1965
Glycogenosis type 2 (Pompe's disease)	Alpha-1, 4-glucosidase (acid maltase)	Dancis et al, 1969c

[*]Subtypes are now described but are not fully evaluated in cultured cells (O'Brien, 1969).

TABLE 4-IA (Continued)

Disease State	Defective Enzyme	Reference
Hyperuricemia (with hereditary choreoathetosis and self-mutilation)	Hypoxanthine-quanine phosphoribosyl transferase (HGPRT)	Seegmiller *et al.*, 1967
Homocystinuria	Cystathionine synthase	Uhlendorf and Mudd, 1968
Metachromatic leukodystrophy		
Late infantile	Arylsulfatase-A	Porter *et al.*, 1969
Juvenile	Arylsulfatase-A	Leroy *et al.*, 1970
Orotic aciduria	Orotidine-5′-monophosphate (OMP) pyrophosphorylase and OMP decarboxylase, two sequentially acting enzymes in biosynthesis of uridine-5′-monophosphate	Wuu and Krooth, 1968
Phytanic acid storage disease (Refsum's disease; heredopathia atactica polyneuritiformis)	A single enzyme involved in the alpha-hydroxylation of phytanate	Herndon *et al*, 1969
Tay-Sachs gangliosidosis	Hexosaminidase component A	Okada and O'Brien, 1969

TABLE 4-IB

EXAMPLES OF METABOLIC DEFECTS OF THE WHOLE INDIVIDUAL
REFLECTED IN SERIAL CULTURE BY THE PRESENCE OF
ABNORMAL CELLULAR STRUCTURE AND FUNCTION

Disease State	Abnormal Metabolism	Reference
Cystic fibrosis	Increased total acid mucopolysaccharide in fibroblast-like cells	Matalon and Dorfman, 1969
	Increased lysosomes by EM	Bartman *et al.*, 1970
Cystinosis	Increased free cystine content of fibroblast-like cells	Schneider *et al.*, 1967
	EM evidence of cystine stored in amorphous form compartmentalized in cell organelles resembling lysosomes	Hummeler *et al.*, 1970
Fabry's lipidosis (Glycolipid lipidosis)	A trihexosyl ceramide (GL-3) and mucopolysaccharide material accumulate in fibroblast-like cells	Matalon *et al.*, 1969

TABLE 4-IB (Continued)

Disease State	Abnormal Metabolism	Reference
Gaucher's disease (Cerebroside lipidosis)	Increased acid phosphatase in spleen cultured cells of juvenile form of Gaucher's	Perona et al., 1968
	Increased total acid mucopolysaccharide in fibroblast-like cells	Matalon and Dorfman, 1969
Gout	In two cell lines of fibroblast-like cells the rate of purine biosynthesis de novo was increased; in another the rate of catabolism of adenine nucleotides to hypoxanthine and inosine was increased	Henderson et al., 1968
Krabbe's disease	Increased total acid mucopolysaccharide in fibroblast-like cells	Matalon and Dorfman, 1969
Marfan syndrome	Hyaluronic acid is increased in fibroblast-like cells	Matalon and Dorfman, 1969
Methylmalonic acidemia	Fibroblast-like cultured cells accumulate methylmalonate and fail to convert the C label of proprionate-2-^{14}C readily into CO_2, aspartate and glutamate	Morrow et al., 1969
Mucopolysaccharidoses Hurler-Hunter	Defective degradation of sulfated mucopolysaccharide; aberrant metabolism in fibroblast-like cells can be corrected by secretions of non-Hurler-Hunter cells.	Fratantoni et al., 1969
Hurler, Hunter, Sanfilippo	Dermatan sulfate (chondroitin sulfate B) accumulates in fibroblast-like cells	Matalon and Dorfman, 1969
Morquio	Increased total acid mucopolysaccharide	Matalon and Dorfman, 1969
Variant (lipomucopolysaccharidosis)	Increased ganglioside as well as total acid mucopolysaccharide	Matalon et al., 1968
Xeroderma pigmentosum	Cultured fibroblast-like cells do not perform the first step in the repair of ultraviolet damage to their DNA	Setlow et al., 1969

ally be identified in terms of a specific defective enzyme. Others in this group will continue to be identified by abnormal cellular metabolism, but not by defective enzyme; presence of the abnormal cell phenotype may nevertheless continue to be a method of choice for diagnosis. Some metabolic defects will continue to be listed in both A and B sections of Table 4-I because the defective enzyme *and* abnormal cell phenotype will both be useful for diagnosis.

Stains of various types are useful to identify cellular storage diseases in cultured cells, in much the same manner as in tissues taken directly from the affected individual (Table 4-II). Cells in primary culture or in fibroblast-like monolayer culture may be grown directly on coverslips and stained for examination. Cells grown on coverslips are flat and do not need freezing or embedding and sectioning. In the study of human metabolic diseases, cellular metachromasia is proving of value to diagnose the carrier as well as the homozygote defective. In some storage diseases, such as the mucopolysaccharidoses, *in vitro* culture is indicated for diagnosis of cellular metachromasia in the carrier state since direct tissue examination has not proved successful. Toluidine blue stain is used to demonstrate the "pink" metachromasia (Fig. 4-1) found in the diseases listed in Table 4-III except in the sulfatide lipidoses (metachromatic leukodystrophy) when a "brown" metachromasia is found following cresyl-fast violet stain (or toluidine blue).

Lymphocytes in Hurler-Hunter disease (mucopolysacchari-

TABLE 4-II

STAINS USEFUL FOR THE DIAGNOSIS OF STORAGE DISEASES
(Bodian and Lake, 1963)

Stain	Material Demonstrated
Periodic acid schiff reaction (P. A. S.)	Carbohydrates containing a 1:2 glycol group
Sudan black	Lipids
Scharlach (Sudan) red	Lipids
Luxol-fast blue	Phospholipoproteins
Toluidine blue	Metachromasia of a strongly acidic group, most probably sulfate (as in sulfated mucopolysaccharides)
Cresyl-fast violet	"Brown" metachromasia of a strongly acidic group, most probably sulfate (as in sulfated cerebrosides)

TABLE 4-III

EXAMPLES OF METABOLIC DISORDERS OF THE WHOLE INDIVIDUAL
REFLECTED IN SERIAL MONOLAYER CULTURE BY THE
PRESENCE OF CELLUAR METACHROMASIA

Disease State	Comments	Reference
Cystic fibrosis	Useful for carrier detection	Danes and Bearn, 1969
Fabry's lipidosis (Glycolipid lipidosis)	Cultured cells accumulate both a trihexosyl ceramide (GL-3) and an acid mucopolysaccharide material (see Table 4-IB)	Matalon et al., 1969
Ganglioside lipidoses Early onset (Tay-Sachs)	Increased total acid mucopolysaccharide occurs	Matalon and Dorfman, 1969
Juvenile (Spielmeyer-Vogt)	Useful for carrier detection	Danes and Bearn, 1968b
Gaucher's disease (Cerebroside lipidosis)	Useful for carrier detection	Danes and Bearn, 1968a
Krabbe's disease	Increased total acid mucopolysaccharide occurs (see Table 4-IB)	Matalon and Dorfman, 1969
Marfan syndrome	Accumulation of hyaluronic acid occurs (see Table 4-IB)	Matalon and Dorfman, 1969
Mucopolysaccharidoses	Various types of clinical mucopolysaccharide storage diseases were studied. Useful for carrier detection	Danes and Bearn, 1967b
	Variants were also studied	Matalon and Dorfman, 1969
Myotonic muscular dystrophy	These cells are said also to grow in a more disorganized pattern and to a higher cell density than control human diploid monolayer cultures.	Swift and Finegold, 1969
Pseudoxanthoma elasticum	Percentage of metachromatic cells was affected by growth rate and subculturing.	Cartwright et al., 1969
Sulfatide lipidoses (metachromatic leukodystrophy)	Primary cultures from cerebral white matter show brown cellular metachromasia	Cravioto et al., 1967

⟶

Figure 4-1. Fibroblast-like cells from skin biopsy of a patient with mucopolysaccharidosis were grown in monolayer culture on coverslips. Metachromasia could be demonstrated in the cytoplasm of more than 90% of the cells after they were allowed to reach confluency on the coverslip. Many were giant "gargoyl" cells, as shown in this figure, upper left. (Toluidine blue stain, 100X oil emersion objective.)

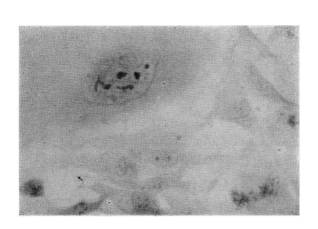

doses) show cytoplasmic metachromatic inclusions on direct examination but after stimulation with phytohemagglutinin these inclusions may be lost during "blastoid" changes (Zelson and Dekaban, 1969) (see Chap. 1, on short-term peripheral blood culture). Therefore, short-term peripheral blood culture may be a less reliable culture method for identifying cellular metachromasia, although its use in both mucopolysaccharidoses and cystic fibrosis has been reported (Foley *et al.*, 1969; Danes and Bearn, 1969).

Changes in cell morphology can now be followed in serial cultures from individuals with storage diseases (Fig. 4-2b) Bartman and Blanc, 1970). The sequential progression of storage at the cellular level is extremely difficult to study in biopsies from humans or in autopsy material. In the past, many observations relating morphology to various stages of disease have been based on assumptions concerning the temporal sequence of changes, rather than on direct observations.

CARRIER DETECTION AND EARLY DIAGNOSIS

The use of monolayer cell culture for carrier detection has already been mentioned for specifically identified enzyme defects and for other types of "inborn" abnormalities in cell structure and function. The need to obtain a tissue biopsy to start off the cell culture may be a disadvantage for mass screening of the general population. Perhaps the most useful role of monolayer cell culture for carrier detection and for early diagnosis of the defective homozygote will be in certain high risk groups, particularly in families with a known affected individual, and for antenatal diagnosis (see Chap. 5). When the purpose of enzyme analysis is carrier detection based on absolute levels of enzyme activity, culture conditions affecting the levels of activity must be considered (see the section later in this chapter on enzyme synthesis in relation to the cell cycle and time of subculture). The problem of multiple mutant alleles with different degrees of defective activity must also be kept in mind.

Short-term peripheral blood culture has been used to detect carriers of mucopolysaccharidoses (Foley *et al.*, 1969), cystic

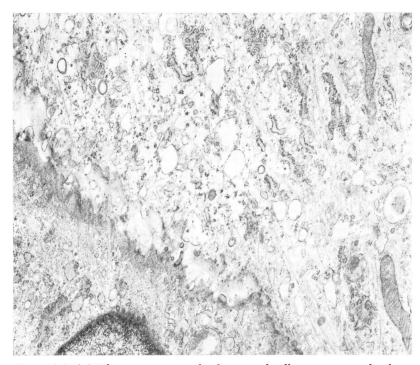

Figure 4-2. (a) Electron micrograph of a control cell grown in serial culture from skin biopsy of a normal male. Cytoplasm occupies the upper and middle portions of the photograph. The nucleus is lower left. The cytoplasm is seen to contain endoplasmic reticulum and ribosomes, mitochondria, some single membrane bound vacuoles and autophagic vacuoles. (b) Electron micrograph of a cell grown in serial culture from skin biopsy of a patient with type II mucopolysaccharidosis. Cytoplasm is to the right, nucleus to the left. Vacuoles are seen to coalesce and occupy most of the cytoplasm. (Fixative: gluteraldehyde and osmium; stain: lead acetate and uranyl acetate; magnification X8,000.) Electron microscopy by Harriet McKelvey.

fibrosis (Danes and Bearn, 1969), glycogenosis type 2 (Hirschhorn *et al.*, 1969), and familial deficiency of lysosomal acid phosphatase (Nadler and Egan, 1970); although the use of phytohemagglutinin stimulated lymphocytes for carrier detection in mucopolysaccharidoses may be unreliable (Zelson and Dekaban, 1969).

In X-linked disorders the heterozygous female may be demon-

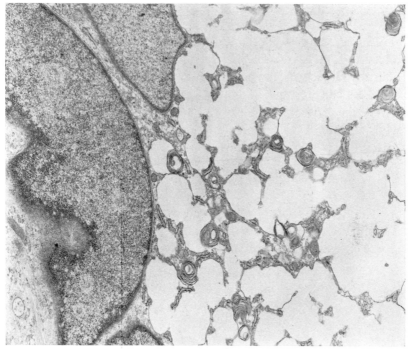

Figure 4-2b.

strated to have two clonal populations in cells cultured from her, both enzyme normal and enzyme defective. The hypothesis of random X-chromosome inactivation at the cellular level would predict two clonal populations in carriers of X-linked disorders, provided a proper test was applied to detect differences between individual cells. The growth of many cultured monolayer cells from a single cell by the process of cloning (see Chap. 2) has furnished an excellent way to study single cells, and two populations in regard to enzyme function have been demonstrated for X-linked hyperuricemia (Migeon *et al.*, 1968) and for glucose-6-phosphate dehydrogenase deficiency (Davidson *et al.*, 1963).

Carrier detection in autosomal disorders may take other pathways besides identification of intermediate levels of enzyme activity or stored metabolite. In the example shown in Fig. 4-3 identification of the heterozygote would rest on the presence of a metabolite not present in either normal or mutant cells. Furthermore, qualitative identification of both normal and mutant isoenzyme patterns may be possible in a carrier.

In one study (Tedesco and Mellman, 1969) carrier detection took the form of comparing the relative activities of two metabolically adjacent enzymes, rather than the absolute values of each. In cultured cells from carriers and patients with galactosemia, the ratio of transferase to galactokinase activity correlated well with the transferase genotypes of the original tissue donors. (Recall that this disease involves mutant genes for transferase activity).

GENETIC HETEROGENEITY

The need to study in detail the patient's own defective metabolic pathway in order to understand and treat his disease ef-

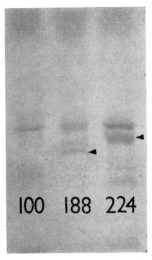

Figure 4-3. The ganglioside patterns in cells cultured from a normal individual (Culture No. 100); a severely affected child with recessively inherited lipomucopolysaccharidosis (mucopolysaccharide-variant storage disease) and accumulation of excess ganglioside in multiple tissues (Culture No. 188); and the mother of the affected child, a presumed carrier (Culture No. 224). The affected child (188) shows a band (arrow) not present in the mother or in the normal. The mother (224) shows increased intensity of yet another band (arrow). Courtesy Dr. Stephen I. Goodman, Dept. of Pediatrics, University of Colorado Medical Center.

fectively, has already been mentioned earlier in this chapter. One review of genetic heterogeneity (Childs and Der Kaloustian, 1968) lists about a dozen enzyme deficiencies in man with clinical disease variations suggesting more than one genotype (Table 4-IV). This number is increasing rapidly as more cases are diagnosed. Of the listed enzyme deficiencies over half have been shown to be carried as genetic "markers" in cultured cells from the affected individual, and thus can be studied in detail without subjecting the patient to repeated tests and therapeutic trials. The variants of acatalasia have already been studied extensively in cultured cells (Krooth *et al.*, 1962).

The distinction may or may not be clear between enzyme variants causing clinical disease and those that do not. Table 4-V lists some *in vivo* enzyme variants not regularly associated with clinical disease and detectable in serial human cell cultures. Study of these variants also increases the understanding of metabolic disease (see section later in this chapter on "Special Uses for Somatic Cell Culture to Study Metabolic Defects"). When they occur commonly these variants are useful to monitor the "purity" of human cell lines (strains) and to check for possible cross-cell contamination with cells of other species during laboratory maintenance (see Chap. 1).

TABLE 4-IV

ENZYME DEFICIENCIES WITH CLINICAL DISEASE VARIATIONS
SUGGESTING MORE THAN ONE GENOTYPE*

> Acatalasia
> Branched chain ketonuria
> Cystathioninuria
> Familial nonhemolytic jaundice
> Galactosemia
> Gaucher's disease
> Glucose-6-phosphate dehydrogenase deficiency
> Hemolytic anemia (pyruvate kinase deficiency)
> Histidinemia
> Hyperuricemia
> Phenylketonuria

*Not all have been studied in cultured cells (see text).

TABLE 4-V

SOME *IN VIVO* ENZYME VARIANTS NOT REGULARLY ASSOCIATED
WITH CLINICAL DISEASE AND DETECTABLE IN SERIAL
HUMAN CELL CULTURES

Phosphoglucomutase (PGM)
6-Phosphogluconic dehydrogenase (6PGD)
Lactic dehydrogenase (LDH)
Adenylic kinase (AK)

THE PROBLEM OF METABOLIC ACTIVITY CONFINED TO SPECIALIZED CELL TYPES

Some well defined enzyme defects such as those in histidinemia and phenylketonuria are not presently carried in the usual types of serial monolayer fibroblast-like culture or short-term peripheral blood culture. The eventual goal in somatic cell genetics is to achieve differentiated cultures that will preserve all the enzyme or metabolic functions needed for study. A step in this direction concerns histidase, the enzyme deficient in histidinemia and studied in skin epidermal homogenates for diagnosis of the disease. Activity of this enzyme is not found in the usual fibroblast-like monolayer cultures from skin of normal individuals, but is preserved in epithelial-like primary culture from skin (Barnhisel *et al.*, 1970) (also see Chap. 1 for a discussion of different types of culture and Chap. 9 on differentiation).

The investigation of some varieties of transport defect is a potential use for cell culture. Examples of human disease probably involving defects in amino acid transport are cystinuria, Hartnup disease and certain forms of hyperglycinuria. It is possible that some of these biochemical lesions are expressed only in certain specialized cell types, such as renal tubular epithelium and intestinal mucosal cells. An alternative hypothesis is that many individual somatic cells are affected, possibly to varying degrees. To test these (and other) hypotheses, a method was developed for kinetic studies of amino acid transport in human monolayer fibroblast-like cells. Differences in transport of L-tryptophane, with and without competing amino acids, were found between different human cultured cell strains, suggesting that the method might be useful for studying human transport defect "markers" *in vitro* (Platter and Martin, 1966).

The level of enzyme activity may vary from one tissue to another. Whereas galactose-1-phosphate uridyl transferase activity in both cultured skin fibroblast-like cells and peripheral blood leukocytes (directly after separation from whole blood) were similar, galactokinase was approximately three times as active in fibroblast-like cells as in leukocytes (Tedesco and Mellman, 1969).

LYSOSOMAL DISEASES

When lysosomes were first recognized as distinct cell organelles, it was clear that they would be of special interest in cellular and subcellular pathology. They contain a variety of enzymes (acid hydrolases) that break down all the major constituents of living organisms (Allison, 1967). Changes in lysosome morphology and behavior are involved in a wide range of normal and abnormal processes; many can be studied at the cellular or subcellular level, utilizing techniques of *in vitro* cell culture (Table 4-VI). Screening of somatic cells for abnormalities of lysosomal enzymes should include analysis for the enzymes listed in Table 4-VII.

One preliminary proposal to sort out the various types of mucopolysaccharidoses and variants thereof, is based on activity of lysosomal hydrolases, as determined by studies of multiple tissues taken directly from involved patients, usually at autopsy (Table 4-VIII; Van Hoof and Hers, 1968). The extension or further confirmation of this classification may rest, in part, on studies of acid hydrolases in cells cultured from normal as well as affected individuals. These cells survive the severely affected patient and can be available for continued study, particularly if organized efforts are made to store cultured cells from patients with various clinical manifestations of the mucopolysaccharidoses. A disease classification based on abnormal metabolite or enzymatic characteristic is essential.

TABLE 4-VI

SOME LYSOSOMAL DISEASES STUDIED IN CELL CULTURE

Disease	Type of Culture Studied	Observations	Reference
Chediak-Higashi syndrome	Long-term peripheral blood suspension culture	Giant cytoplasmic granules (representing abnormal lysosomes) are present in cultures from homozygotes and heterozygotes.	Blume *et al.*, 1969
	Fibroblast-like monolayer culture	Abnormal cytoplasmic inclusions are also present for up to six months in cultures from both homozygotes and heterozygotes.	Danes and Bearn, 1967a
Cystinosis	Fibroblast-like monolayer culture	Cystine is stored in amorphous form in cell organelles resembling lysosomes, by EM.	Hummeler *et al.*, 1970
Ganglioside lipidosis (Tay-Sachs)	Fibroblast-like monolayer culture	Hexosaminidase (component A) is deficient. This is a lysosomally localized enzyme.	Okada and O'Brien, 1969
Generalized gangliosidoses	Fibroblast-like monolayer culture	Decreased activity of beta-galactosidase(s) is present; enzyme(s) lysosomally localized.	Sloan *et al.*, 1969
Lysosomal acid phosphatase deficiency	Fibroblast-like monolayer culture; short-term peripheral blood culture	Lysosomal fraction is deficient in acid phosphatase; carriers can be distinguished from normals in fibroblast-like cells and in PHA stimulated lymphocytes.	Nadler and Egan, 1970

SPECIAL USES FOR SOMATIC CELL CULTURE TO STUDY METABOLIC DEFECTS

Study of Metabolically Adjacent Enzymes

If activity of one sequential enzyme in a metabolic pathway is demonstrated in cultured cells, then activity of the next may normally be expected. If activity of this second enzyme is not found, then the cells may carry an "inborn" defect present in the individual from whom the cells were taken, or special conditions in the culture are interrupting the pathway and merit further study. In either case the investigation is of potential interest.

To look at the problem of metabolically adjacent enzymes

TABLE 4-VII

A PROPOSED LIST OF ENZYMATIC ACTIVITIES TO BE
INCLUDED IN SCREENING OF SOMATIC CELLS
FOR LYSOSOMAL ABNORMALITIES*
(from Van Hoff and Hers, 1968)

alpha-glucosidase
beta-glucuronidase
N-acetyl-beta-glucosaminidase
N-acetyl-beta-galactosaminidase
alpha-mannosidase
alpha-fucosidase
alpha-galactosidase
beta-galactosidase
alpha-arabinosidase
beta-xylosidase
beta-glucosidase
acid phosphatase
cathepsin D

*This list of enzymatic activities is based on studies, primarily on rat liver, that document lysosomal localization of activity for these acid hydrolases.

TABLE 4-VIII

CLASSIFICATION OF MUCOPOLYSACCHARIDOSES BASED ON
ACTIVITY OF LYSOSOMAL HYDROLASES
(from Van Hoof and Hers, 1968)

Present Designation	Proposed Designation Symbol	Stored Material	Main Enzymatic Characteristics
Fucosidosis (Hurler-variant)	F	Fucose containing acid mucopolysaccharides and glycolipids	Generalized absence of alpha-L-fucosidase
Generalized gangliosidosis (Hurler-variant)	Gal	Galactose-rich mucopolysaccharides and G_{M1} ganglioside*	Generalized absence of acid beta-galactosidase*
Hurler or Hurler-variant	Gal −	Acid mucopolysaccharides and glycolipids	Partial deficiency of acid beta-galactosidase in some tissue but not in others.
Hurler-variant	Gal +	?	Large increase of acid beta-galactosidase
Hurler-variant	M	Mannosides	Diminished activity of alpha-mannosidase

*Subcategories are now described (O'Brien, 1969).

from another point of view, if more than one "inborn" enzymatic defect in a sequential metabolic pathway is known to cause different clinical diseases, and one of these defects has already been demonstrated in cultured cells from an affected individual, then it might be predicted that the other defects would also be demonstrable, and should be looked for. As an example, among disorders involving the urea cycle, defective activity of argininosuccinic acid synthetase was demonstrated in cultured cells from the disease citrullinemia (Tedesco and Mellman, 1967). Later, defective activity of the next enzyme in the pathway, argininosuccinase, was demonstrated in cultured cells from the disease argininosuccinic aciduria (Shih *et al.*, 1969).

More than one sequential enzymatic defect in a metabolic pathway may be present in one disease state, as in orotic aciduria when both orotidylic pyrophosphorlase and orotidylic decarboxylase activity are reduced in cells cultured from an affected individual. Studies of such a cell strain showed that these two enzyme activities developed almost normal levels when the cells were grown in 6-azauridine (Pinsky and Krooth, 1967) (see Chap. 14, on control mechanisms in cultured human cells).

Systematic study of sequential enzymes in various metabolic pathways in cultured cells from both normal and abnormal humans will unquestionably continue to contribute a great deal to the understanding of metabolic disease.

Metabolic Defects Affecting Cell Growth in Culture

Rate of cell multiplication, total cell protein, and total DNA are quantitative measures of the growth behavior of a culture. These parameters may be used to follow the effects of metabolic defects on cell growth. It was noted that normal cultured cells utilize galactose, grow, and thrive when galactose was substituted for glucose in the culture medium (Tedesco and Mellman, 1969). However, when glucose was removed from the medium there was little difference in the poor survival of galactosemic cells in the presence or absence of galactose. Thus it is possible that the toxicity in galactosemia may be related to the availability of glucose to the cells, rather than to accumulation of galactose-1-phosphate alone.

Cells from patients with orotic aciduria will grow in culture if uridine is supplied and uridine also causes remission of symptoms in the affected individual (Wuu and Krooth, 1968). Therefore, it is likely that assays of cell multiplication in various human culture strains can be used to test tolerance to various dietary metabolites, provided a direct response of culture growth rate can be achieved.

Measurement of Mutation Rates in Cultured Cells with Metabolic Defects

A high reverse mutation rate of somatic cells *in vivo* would provide a possible correction of metabolic defect. We know already that a minority of individuals with inborn errors of metabolism improve clinically as they grow older. In most cases we do not know why they improve. Estimates of spontaneous mutation rates at specific loci in human somatic cells are generally crude or entirely lacking. Can cultured human cell strains carrying metabolic defects be used to measure the chances of reverse-mutations? Quantitative measurements of spontaneous and chemically induced gene mutations in cultured mammalian cells reveal that mutation rates, both forward and reverse, depend on conditions of the experiment, including cell inoculum size, time allowed for the mutation to be expressed, and conditions used to select for the mutation (Chu and Malling, 1968). Nevertheless, from this type of study reasonable expectations can be derived for a test to measure return of heterozygous levels of activity to enzyme defective human cultured cells; it might be necessary to detect return of heterozygous levels of activity in as few as 2 to 5 cells per 10^7 cells per generation (Chu *et al.*, 1969). Mixing of one normal (enzyme sufficient) cell in 10^3 enzyme deficient cells was the limit of detection of activity for keto acid decarboxylating enzyme, the enzyme defective in cells cultured from patients with branched chain ketonuria (maple syrup urine disease) (Gartler, 1964). Thus the test was not sensitive enough in this particular experiment, but the test model needs further investigation, along with the use of conditions to select for spontaneous reverse-mutations (see examples of selective conditions, Chap. 11, on somatic cell hybridization).

Enzyme Synthesis in Relation to the Cell Cycle and Time of Subculture*

"Most enzymes are synthesized discontinuously at periods in the cell cycle which are characteristic of each enzyme. If the enzyme is stable, this produces a 'step' pattern similar to that for DNA in higher cells. If the enzyme is unstable, a 'peak' pattern is produced " (Mitchison, 1969, p 663). In human cultured cells thymidine kinase, thymidylate kinase, alkaline phosphatase and DNA polymerase were found to show a "peak" (P) pattern (Fig 4-4). However, lactic dehydrogenase and fumarase were found to be synthesized continuously (Bello, 1969). Much more information is needed about patterns of human enzyme synthesis in relation to the cell cycle.

Patterns of enzyme activity in relation to subculture are also characteristic of the enzyme (Table 4-IX). One pattern in human cells is represented by catalase specific activity; in both diploid and nondiploid cells it increases as the culture grows. Although the rise is not large it is exponential with time and repeatable. Following subculture, catalase activity falls again (Pan and Krooth, 1968). For carrier detection and other studies, when the level of activity must be known for diagnosis of enzymatic defect, the pattern of activity in relation to subculture must also be known, for the particular enzyme studied.

In the case of X-linked hyperuricemia (HGPRT deficiency), when normal and abnormal cells were mixed prior to culture, there was progressive increase in enzyme activity with culture time (as measured by incorporation of cellular label following incubation with tritiated hypoxanthine). Reduction of cell density by subculture produced a reversion to original values (Dancis *et al.*, 1969a).

---

*Also see Chapters 2 and 12.

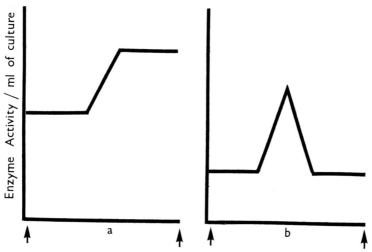

Figure 4-4. Two patterns of enzyme synthesis during one cell life cycle in synchronous culture. Arrows mark cell divisions.

a = step   b = peak

TABLE 4-IX

SPECIFIC ENZYME ACTIVITIES THAT ARE KNOWN TO CHANGE
AS CULTURED HUMAN CELLS GROW
(from Pan and Krooth, 1968)

Alkaline phosphatase
Beta-glucuronidase
Catalase
Galactose-1-phosphate uridyl transferase
Glucose-6-phosphate dehydrogenase
Lactic acid dehydrogenase
Malic acid dehydrogenase
Orotidine-5'-monophosphate decarboxylase
Thymidine-5'-diphosphate phosphatase
Thymidine-5'-monophosphate phosphatase
UDP-galactose-4-epimerase

Enzymes in Human Autosomal Trisomy Syndromes

It would be useful to identify changes in enzymatic activity in trisomy syndromes (also see Chap. 3 on chromosome abnormality syndromes). Thus far increase in activity of an enzyme or, in fact, identification of any consistent change has not been achieved in cultured cells from autosomal trisomy syndromes (Nadler *et al.*, 1967).

Metabolic Cooperation Between Genetically Marked Cultured Cells

Mixing of cells with different metabolic defects (genetic markers) may lead to changes in the cellular manifestations of the defect in culture. The same may be said if metabolically defective and normal cells are mixed. If the defect can be "corrected" *in vitro*, one step is accomplished in studying treatment of disease. The biochemical defect of cultured skin fibroblasts from Type I or Type II mucopolysaccharidosis (resulting in excessive intracellular accumulation of sulfated mucopolysaccharide) may be corrected if cells of these two genotypes are mixed with each other or with normal cells. The effect is mediated by substances released into the medium (Fratantoni *et al.*, 1968).

In the case of X-linked hyperuricemia (HGPRT deficiency) metabolic cooperation between diploid fibroblast-like cells has also been demonstrated. When normal and enzyme defective cells are mixed and incorporation of cellular label analyzed following incubation with tritiated hypoxanthine, defective cells located close to normal cells are seen to increase activity (label) (Friedmann *et al.*, 1968).

REFERENCES
General

Allison, A.: Lysosomes and disease. *Sci Amer, 217:*62, 1967.

Childs, B., and Der Kaloustian, V. M.: Genetic heterogeneity. *New Eng J Med, 279:*1205, 1968.

Gartler, S. M.: Genetic markers as tracers in cell culture. *Nat Cancer Inst Monogr, 26:*167, 1967.

Krooth, R. S.: Genetics of cultured somatic cells. *Med Clin N Amer, 53:* 795, 1969.

Littlefield, J. W.: Control mechanisms in animal cell cultures. *Arch Biochem, 125*:410, 1968.

Priest, J. H.: Human cell culture: An important tool for the diagnosis and understanding of disease. *J Pediat, 72*:415, 1968.

Stanbury, J. B.; Wyngaarden, J. B., and Frederickson, D. S. (Ed.): The *Metabolic Basis of Inherited Disease.* New York, McGraw-Hill, 1966.

Specific

Allison, A.: Lysosomes and disease. *Sci Amer, 217*:62, 1967.

Barnhisel, M. L.; Priest, R. E., and Priest, J. H.: Histidase activity in human epidermal cells. *J Cell Physiol, 76*:7, 1970.

Bartman, J., and Blanc, W. A.: Fibroblast cultures in Hurler's and Hunter's syndromes. *Arch Path (Chicago), 89*:279, 1970.

Bartman, J.; Wiesmann, U., and Blance, W. A.: Ultrastructure of cultivated fibroblasts in cystic fibrosis of the pancreas. *J Pediat, 76*:430, 1970.

Bello, L. J.: Studies on gene activity in synchronized culture of mammalian cells. *Biochim Biophys Acta, 179*:204, 1969.

Blume, R. S.; Glade, P. R.; Gralnick, H. R.; Chessin, L. N.; Haase, A. T., and Wolff, S. M.: The Chediak-Higashi syndrome: Continuous suspension cultures derived from peripheral blood. *Blood, 33*:821, 1969.

Bodian, M., and Lake, B. D.: The rectal approach to neuropathology. *Brit J Surg, 50*:702, 1963.

Cartwright, E.; Danks, D. M., and Jack, I.: Metachromatic fibroblasts in pseudoxanthoma elasticum and Marfan's syndrome. *Lancet, 1*:533, 1969.

Childs, B., and Der Kaloustian, V. M.: Genetic heterogeneity. *New Eng J Med, 279*:1205, 1968.

Chu, E. H. Y.; Brimer P.; Jacobson, K. B., and Merriam, E. V.: Mammalian cell genetics, I. Selection and characterization of mutations auxotrophic for L-glutamine or resistant to 8-azaguanine in Chinese hamster cells *in vitro. Genetics, 62*:359, 1969.

Chu, E. H. Y., and Malling, H. V.: Mammalian cell genetics, II. Chemical induction of specific locus mutations in Chinese hamster cells *in vitro. Proc Nat Acad Sci USA, 61*:1306, 1968.

Cravioto, H.; O'Brien, J.; Lockwood, R.; Kasten, F. H., and Booher, J.: Metachromatic leukodystrophy (sulfatide lipidoses) cultured *in vitro. Science, 156*:243, 1967.

Dancis, J.; Cox, R. P.; Berman, P. H.; Jansen, V., and Balis, M. E.: Cell population density and phenotypic expression of tissue culture fibroblasts heterozygotes of Lesh-Nyhan's disease (inosinate pyrophosphorylase deficiency). *Biochem Genet, 3*:609, 1969a.

Dancis, J.; Hutzler, J., and Cox, R. P.: Enzyme defect in skin fibroblasts in intermittent branched-chain ketonuria and in maple syrup urine disease. *Biochem Med, 2*:407, 1969b.

Dancis, J.; Hutzler, J.; Lynfield, J., and Cox, R. P.: Absence of acid maltase in glycogenesis type 2 (Pompe's disease) in tissue culture. *Amer J Dis Child, 117*:108, 1969c.

Danes, B. S., and Bearn, A. G.: Cell culture and the Chediak-Higashi syndrome. *Lancet, 2*:65, 1967a.

Danes, B. S., and Bearn, A. G.: Cellular metachromasia, a genetic marker for studying the mucopolysaccharidoses. *Lancet, 1*:241, 1967b.

Danes, B. S., and Bearn, A. G.: Gaucher's disease: A genetic disease detected in skin fibroblast cultures. *Science, 161*:1347, 1968a.

Danes, B. S., and Bearn, A. G.: Metachromasia and skin-fibroblast cultures juvenile familial amaurotic idiocy. *Lancet, 2*:855, 1968b.

Danes, B. S., and Bearn, A. G.: Cystic fibrosis: An improved method for studying white blood-cells in culture. *Lancet, 2*:437, 1969.

Davidson, R. G.; Nitowsky, H. M., and Childs, B.: Demonstration of two populations of cells in the human female heterozygous for glucose-6-phosphate dehydrogenase variants. *Proc Nat Acad Sci NSA, 50*:481, 1963.

Foley, K. M.; Danes, B. S., and Bearn, A. G.: White blood cell cultures in genetic studies on the human mucopolysaccharidoses. *Science, 164*:424, 1969.

Fratantoni, J. C.; Hall, C. W., and Neufeld, E. F.: Hurler and Hunter syndromes: Mutual correction of the defect in cultured fibroblasts. *Science, 162*:570, 1968.

Fratantoni, J. C.; Hall, C. W., and Neufeld, E. F.: The defect in Hurler and Hunter syndromes. II. Deficiency of specific factors involved in mucopolysaccharide degradation. *Proc Nat Acad Sci USA, 64*:360, 1969.

Friedmann, T.; Seegmiller, J. E., and Subak-Sharpe, J. H.: Metabolic cooperation between genetically marked human fibroblasts in tissue culture. *Nature (London), 220*:272, 1968.

Gartler, S. M.: Metabolic errors of the whole organism reflected in cell culture. *Retention of Functional Differentiation in Cultured Cells.* Wistar Institute Symposium Monograph No. 1. Philadelphia, Wistar Institute Press, 1964, p. 63.

Henderson, J. F.; Rosenbloom, F. M.; Kelley, W. N., and Seegmiller, J. E.: Variations in purine metabolism of cultured skin fibroblasts from patients with gout. *J Clin Invest, 47*:1511, 1968.

Herndon, J. H.; Steinberg, D.; Uhlendorf, B. W., and Fales, H. M.: Refsum's disease: Characterization of the enzyme defect in cell culture. *J Clin Invest, 48*:1017, 1969.

Hirschhorn, K.; Nadler, H. L., and Waithe, W. I.: Pompe's disease: Detection of heterozygotes by lymphocyte stimulation. *Science, 166*:1632, 1969.

Hummeler, K.; Zajac, B. A.; Genel, M.; Holtzapple, P. G., and Segal, S.: Human cystinosis: Intracellular deposition of cystine. *Science, 168*:859, 1970.

Krooth, R. S.; Howell, R. R., and Hamilton, H. B.: Properties of acatalasic cells growing *in vitro. J. Exp Med, 115*:313, 1962.

Leroy, J. G.; Dumon, J., and Radermecker, J.: Deficiency of arysulphatase A in leucocytes and skin fibroblasts in juvenile metachromatic leucodystrophy. *Nature (London), 226*:553, 1970.

Matalon, R.; Cifonelli, J. A. Zellweger, H., and Dorfman, A.: Lipid abnormalities in a variant of the Hurler-syndrome. *Proc Nat Acad Sci USA, 59*:1097, 1968.

Matalon, R., and Dorfman, A.: Acid mucopolysaccharides in cultured human fibroblasts. *Lancet, 2*:838, 1969.

Matalon, R.; Dorfman, A.; Dawson, G., and Sweeley, C. C.: Glycolipid and mucopolysaccharide abnormality in fibroblasts of Fabry's disease. *Science, 164*:1522, 1969.

Migeon, B. R.; Der Kaloustian, V. M.; Nyhan, W. L.; Young, W. J., and Childs, B.: X-linked hypoxanthine-quanine phosphoribosyl transferase deficiency: Heterozygote has two clonal populations. *Science, 160*:425, 1968.

Mitchison, J. M.: Enzyme synthesis in synchronous cultures. *Science, 165*: 657, 1969.

Morrow, G.; Mellman, W. J.; Barness, L. A., and Dimitrov, N. V.: Proprionate metabolism in cells cultured from a patient with methylmalonic acidemia. *Pediat Res, 3*:217, 1969.

Nadler, H. L., and Egan, T. J.: Deficiency of lysosomal acid phosphatase. *New Eng J Med, 282*:302, 1970.

Nadler, H. L.; Inouye, T., and Hsia, D. Y.: Enzymes in cultivated human fibroblasts derived from patients with autosomal trisomy syndromes. *Amer J Hum Genet, 19*:94, 1967.

Nitowsky, H. M.; Davidson, R. G.; Soderman, D. D., and Childs, B.: Glucose-6-phosphate dehydrogenase activity of skin fibroblast cultures from enzyme-deficient subjects. *Bull Hopkins Hosp, 117*:363, 1965.

O'Brien, J. S.: Five gangliosidoses. *Lancet, 2*:805, 1969.

Okada, S., and O'Brien, J. S.: Tay-Sachs disease: Generalized absence of a beta-D-N-acetylhexosaminidase component. *Science, 165*:698, 1969.

Pan, Y. L., and Krooth, R. S.: The influence of progressive growth on the specific catalase activity of human diploid cell strains. *J Cell Physiol, 71*:151, 1968.

Perona, G. P.; Baccichetti, C., and Tenconi, R.: Acid phosphatase in spleen tissue-culture in Gaucher's disease. *Lancet, 2*:358, 1968.

Pinsky, L., and Krooth, R. S.: Studies on the control of pyrimidine biosynthesis in human diploid cell strains. I. Effect of 6-azauridine on cellular phenotype. *Proc Nat Acad Sci USA, 57*:925, 1967.

Platter, H., and Martin, G. M.: Tryptophane transport in cultures of human fibroblasts. *Proc Soc Exp Biol Med, 123*:140, 1966.

124 *Human Cell Culture in Diagnosis of Disease*

Porter, M. T.; Fluharty, A. L., and Kihara, H.: Metachromatic leukodystrophy: Arylsulfatase-A deficiency in skin fibroblast cultures. *Proc Nat Acad Sci USA*, 62:887, 1969.

Romeo, G., and Migeon, B. R.: Genetic inactivation of the alpha-galactosidase locus in carriers of Fabry's disease. *Science*, 170:180, 1970.

Russell, J. D., and DeMars, R.: UDP-glucose: Alpha-D-galactose-1-phosphate uridylytransferase activity in cultured human fibroblasts. *Biochem Genet*, 1:11, 1967.

Schneider, J. A.; Rosenbloom, F. M.; Bradley, K. H., and Seegmiller, J. E.: Increased free-cystine content of fibroblasts cultured from patients with cystinosis. *Biochem Biophys Res Commun*, 29:527, 1967.

Seegmiller, J. E.; Rosenbloom, F. M., and Kelley, W. H.: Enzyme defect associated with a sex-linked human neurological disorder and excessive purine synthesis. *Science*, 155:1682, 1967.

Setlow, R. B.; Regan, J. D.; German, J., and Carrier, W. L.: Evidence that xeroderma pigmentosum cells do not perform the first step in the repair of ultraviolet damage to their DNA. *Proc Nat Acad Sci USA*, 64:1035, 1969.

Shih, V. E.; Littlefield, J. W., and Moser, H. W.: Argininosuccinase deficiency in fibroblasts cultured from patients with argininosuccinic aciduria. *Biochem Genet*, 3:81, 1969.

Sloan, H. R.; Uhlendorf, B. W.; Jacobson, C. B., and Fredrickson, D. S.: Beta-galactosidase in tissue culture derived from human skin and bone marrow: Enzyme defect in G_{M1} gangliosidosis. *Pediat Res*, 3:532, 1969.

Swift, M. R., and Finegold, M. J.: Myotonic muscular dystrophy: Abnormalities in fibroblast culture. *Science*, 165:294, 1969.

Tedesco, T. A., and Mellman, W. J. Argininosuccinate synthetase activity and citrulline metabolism in cells cultured from a citrullinemic subject. *Proc Nat Acad Sci USA*, 57:829, 1967.

Tedesco, T. A., and Mellman, W. J.: Galactose-1-phosphate uridyltransferase and galactokinase activity in cultured human diploid fibroblasts and peripheral blood leukocytes. I. Analysis of transferase genotypes by the ratio of the activities of the two enzymes. *J Clin Invest*, 48:2390, 1969.

Uhlendorf, B. W., and Mudd, S. H.: Cystathionine synthase in tissue culture derived from human skin: Enzyme defect in homocystinuria. *Science*, 160:1007, 1968.

Van Hoof, F., and Hers, H. G.: The abnormalities of lysosomal enzymes in mucopolysaccharidoses. *Europ J Biochem*, 7:34, 1968.

Wuu, K., and Krooth, R. S.: Dihydroorotic acid dehydrogenase activity of human diploid cell strains. *Science*, 160:539, 1968.

Zelson, J., and Dekaban, A. S.: Biological behavior of lymphocytes in Hunter-Hurler's disease. *Arch Neurol (Chicago)*, 20:358, 1969.

Chapter Five

ANTENATAL DIAGNOSIS

S everal types of diagnosis may now be made on the unborn living child, for the purpose of detecting abnormal genotypes. Sex, chromosome constitution, and certain facts about the metabolic status of the fetus can be established prior to birth. Many of these tests involve culture of cells from the amniotic fluid, although sex chromatin analysis is usually performed on the cells without culture (Tables 5-I and 5-II). Amniocentesis is an invaluable diagnostic tool; in the hands of the experienced the complication rate is small but must always be taken into consideration (Creasman *et al.*, 1968).

TABLE 5-I

TESTS THAT HAVE BEEN PERFORMED FOR
ANTENATAL DIAGNOSIS

Material Analyzed	Diagnosis Looked for or Made	Reference*
Cells cultured from fetal ascitic fluid taken during intrauterine blood transfusion for erythroblastosis	Chromosome analysis revealed normal male karyotype	Chang and Bowman, 1968
Transabdominal placental biopsy	Morphologic examination; diagnosis of fetal hydrops and hydatidiform mole	Alvarez, 1966
Amniotic fluid	Adrenogenital syndrome diagnosed by measuring levels of 17-ketosteroids and pregnanetriol	Merkatz *et al.*, 1969
	Chemical composition of amniotic fluid to detect fetal distress and fetal maturity in high risk pregnancies	Horger and Hutchinson, 1969
	Erythroblastosis fetalis: diagnosis and management	Horger and Hutchinson, 1969
	Mucopolysaccharidoses	Matalon *et al.*, 1970

125

TABLE 5-I (Continued)

Material Analyzed	Diagnosis Looked for or Made	Reference*
	Deficiency of alpha-1, 4-glucosidase (Pompe's disease)	Nadler and Messina, 1969b
	Deficiency of hexosaminidase-A (Tay-Sachs disease)	Schneck et al., 1970
Fetal cells taken directly from amniotic fluid	Sex chromatin analysis for the management of X-linked disorders such as hemophilia and muscular dystrophy	Riis and Ruchs, 1966
	ABO blood grouping and other immunogenetic markers	Fuchs et al., 1956
	Fetal age—by staining characteristics of cells	Gordon and Brosens, 1967
	Biochemical analysis	Dancis, 1968 Nadler and Messina, 1969b Berman et al., 1969
Fetal cells cultured *in vitro* from amniotic fluid	Chromosomal and biochemical characteristics	See Table 5-II

*The references cited are not necessarily the first description in the literature.

TABLE 5-II

VARIOUS TYPES OF DIAGNOSIS ON FETAL CELLS
CULTIVATED *IN VITRO* FROM AMNIOTIC FLUID

Chromosomal Constitution	Reference
D/D translocation carrier was diagnosed at the 17th week of pregnancy in a known D/D translocation carrier mother. Postnatal studies confirmed the intrauterine studies.	Jacobson and Barter, 1967
Normal female karyotype was diagnosed at the 26th week of pregnancy in a woman who had previously delivered an infant with trisomic Down's syndrome. The diagnosis was confirmed with the birth of a normal female.	Jacobson and Barter, 1967
A normal female karyotype was found at the 16th week of pregnancy in a known D/G translocation carrier mother. The baby delivered at term had a normal female karyotype.	Nadler, 1968b
D/G translocation Down's syndrome was diagnosed at the 20th week of pregnancy in a known D/G translocation carrier mother. Clinical Down's syndrome was confirmed in the fetus after therapeutic abortion.	Valenti et al., 1968

TABLE 5-II (Continued)

Chromosomal Constitution	*Reference*
Among 82 amniocenteses performed because maternal age was greater than 40 years, 2 cases of Down's syndrome were diagnosed and treated by therapeutic abortion, while 80 were chromosomally normal.	Nadler and Gerbie, 1970

Biochemical Characteristics

Prior to elective cesarean section, a sample of amniotic fluid was cultured from a woman who had previously delivered an infant with *galactosemia*. Cord blood at the time of delivery had no detectable galactose-1-uridyl transferase activity. After 6 weeks of cultivation the amniotic fluid cells also contained no detectable enzyme activity. Both parents had intermediate levels in blood and were considered to be heterozygotes.	Nadler, 1968b
Large cells containing metachromatic granules (toluidine blue stain) were found in culture of amniotic fluid taken for diagnosis of Rh incompatibility at the 28th week of pregnancy. The newborn infant appeared normal but fibroblast-like cultures derived from skin also showed metachromatic cells and by 5 months of age clinical evidence of *mucopolysaccharidosis* had developed.	Nadler, 1968b
Metachromatic staining with toluidine blue and a distinctive kinetic pattern of radioactive sulfate incorporation into mucopolysaccharide were found in cultures of amniotic fluid from two women who had previously borne children affected with *type 1 and type 2 mucopolysaccharidosis*, respectively. The diagnosis of type 1 (autosomal recessive) was confirmed in the subsequent clinical development of the child after delivery. The diagnosis of type 2 (X-linked) was not confirmed after delivery because fetal karyotype analysis revealed XY male chromosomes and the patient elected to have a therapeutic abortion on the basis of a 50% risk for mucopolysaccharidosis.	Fratantoni *et al.*, 1969
Cells were cultured from amniotic fluid of a 17-week fetus in a heterozygote for X-linked hyperuricemia (*hypoxanthine-guanine phosphoribosyl transferase deficiency*). There were colonies of cells that did incorporate H_3-hypoxanthine and colonies that did not. These two populations of cells made the diagnosis of carrier of an X-linked disease.	Fujimoto *et al.*, 1968
Cells cultured from amniotic fluid of a 22-week fetus in a heterozygote for X-linked hyperuricemia (*hypoxanthine-quanine phosphoribosyl transferase deficiency*), lacked sex chromatin and were unable to incorporate hypoxanthine. Diagnosis of a defective male was confirmed at birth of enzyme-deficient, hyperuricemic twin boys whose amniotic membrane cells failed to incorporate hypoxanthine.	DeMars *et al.*, 1969
Amniotic fluid cells obtained from a known carrier of *branched chain ketonuria* at 17 weeks of fetal gestation contained normal levels of alpha-keto-isocaproate decarboxylase. A healthy female infant was delivered at term; at age 2½ months she had developed normally, with no detectable amino-aciduria.	Nadler, 1969a

TABLE 5-II (Continued)

Biochemical Characteristics	Reference
Cultivated amniotic fluid cells from 8 pregnancies of women who had previously delivered children with *type 2 glycogen storage disease*, revealed deficient activity of alpha-1, 4-glucosidase activity in one fetus. This pregnancy was terminated and examination of the fetus revealed deficient enzyme activity in all organs and cultivated fibroblast-like cells, confirming the in-utero diagnosis.	Nadler and Messina, 1969b
Aryl sulfatase A activity was deficient in cultivated amniotic fluid cells obtained from a woman who had previously delivered a child with metachromatic leukodystrophy. The pregnancy was terminated by hysterotomy and aryl sulfatase A activity in the liver of the fetus was deficient.	Nadler and Gerbie, 1970
Lysosomal acid phosphatase was deficient in amniotic fluid cultured cells and in the fetus after therapeutic abortion.	Nadler and Egan, 1970
Heterozygous genotype was diagnosed in a fetus at 27 weeks gestation of a woman who had previously delivered two children with *cystinosis*.	Schulman *et al.*, 1970

CULTURE OF AMNIOTIC FLUID CELLS

Steel and Breg (1966) showed that amniotic fluid contained viable cells as measured by exclusion of the vital dye trypan-blue. Between 4,300 and 30,000 cells per ml of amniotic fluid were non-staining (viable) as long as seventy-two hours after amniocentesis, when stored at 2.5°C. These cells could be grown in culture using standard techniques for monolayer cells. Short-term peripheral blood culture technique, however, was not successful (see Chap. 1 on culture techniques). Two basic cell types were noted in the amniotic fluid; the predominant type was a large cell with irregular borders and a small nucleus, resembling a squamous epithelial cell. The other less frequent type was round-to-oval, with smooth borders and small nucleus, resembling a renal epithelial cell. In culture, the growing cells were epithelial-like or fibroblast-like in appearance, the latter eventually predominating (Figure 5-1).

Nadler (1969a) feels that the optimum time for amniocentesis to be performed for detection of hereditary disorders is at about the sixteenth week of pregnancy when ease and safety of the procedure are maximal. This time allows for processing of the sample to be completed by the end of the nineteenth week of

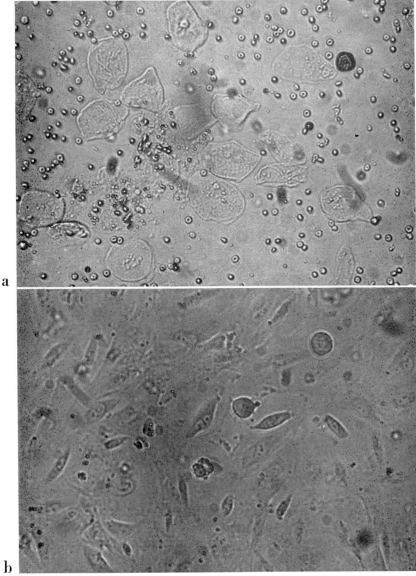

Figure 5-1. Appearance of amniotic fluid cells in culture at (a) 0 days, (b) 10 days, and (c) 28 days. Mixed cell morphology is present initially and many cells do not attach to the surface of the culture container. As the culture grows, the fibroblast-like cells predominate and reach confluency. Courtesy Dr. Henry L. Nadler: Prenatal detection of genetic defects. *J Pediat,* 74:132, 1969.

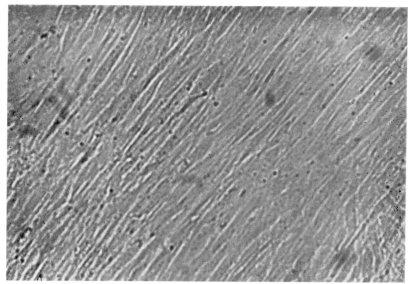

Figure 5-1c.

pregnancy, and for a second attempt (if necessary) to be completed before the twenty-fourth week. Usually 5 to 10 ml of fluid were collected for culture, in a study of thirty-seven amniocenteses performed at various times during pregnancy (Nadler, 1968b; Table 5-III). First subculture was usually performed eighteen to twenty-five days after the culture was initiated; after three to five days the cells were subcultured a second time and could then be used for cytogenetic and biochemical analysis. When the culture failed it was often associated with conditions in the amniotic fluid likely to decrease cell viability, such as the presence of numerous red cells, high levels of bilirubin or prolonged storage of the sample.

Each laboratory culturing amniotic cells has initiated modifications of procedure to increase the percentage of successful cultures and to speed up the growth rate (Lisgar *et al.*, 1970). It is generally agreed that the type of serum enrichment in the defined medium is extremely important to a successful outcome. Usually at least 20 to 25 percent fetal calf serum is used. Cells are removed from the amniotic fluid by gentle centrifugation, resuspended in culture medium and inoculated into small culture containers

TABLE 5-III

RESULTS OF 37 AMNIOCENTESES PERFORMED AT
SPECIFIC TIMES DURING PREGNANCY
(Nadler, 1968b)

Culture of Amniotic Fluid Cells

Gestational Weeks	Attempted	Successful*
10	5	4
16	4	3
20	3	3
24	6	4
28	9	7
32	8	4
36	2	2
Total	37	27

*Successful cultivation of amniotic fluid cells was defined as the ability to maintain the culture after two subcultures.

(petri dishes, Leighton tubes). Medium is added or changed as needed. The shortest reported time for growth of enough cells for chromosome analysis is about one to two weeks (Gregson, 1970; Santesson *et al.*, 1969); in this situation the analysis is performed on cells trypsinized from primary culture or grown on coverslips.

CHROMOSOMAL AND BIOCHEMICAL STUDIES ON CULTIVATED AMNIOTIC FLUID CELLS

Chromosome analysis on amniotic fluid cells has proved useful to diagnose Down's syndrome when parents are carriers or previous children have been involved (Table 5-II). However, chromosomal studies provide no information concerning metabolic disease, except indirectly to identify sex in X-linked recessive disorders.

A first step toward evaluating diagnosis of enzymatic defects in amniotic fluid cells was to find out if enzymes with general tissue distribution were indeed found in amniotic cells. Five enzymes were selected for assay, those associated with branched chain ketonuria, galactosemia, hypervalinemia, isovaleric acidemia and X-linked hyperuricemia (Dancis, 1968). Except for suggestive evidence of minimal amounts of valine transaminase, no enzyme activity could be detected in amniotic cells analyzed directly from taps performed during the last trimester of pregnancy. The next step was to study enzymatic activity in cultured cells, under conditions suitable for increase in cell numbers as well as maintenance of cellular metabolic processes. Activity of the enzymes listed in Table 5-IV has been demonstrated in cultivated amniotic fluid cells obtained as early as ten weeks of fetal gestation (Nadler, 1969a). This list is increasing rapidly and with time and need (or opportunity); the diseases diagnosed in cultures of amniotic fluid cells should correspond in number and kind to those diagnosed in other serial cell cultures (see Table 4-I, Chap. 4).

At the present stage of techniques to diagnose metabolic defects antenatally, success rates are far from established. In many situations confirmation of the diagnosis is not possible. When it is, the number of cases in any one category is still too small for statistical evaluation.

Much more must be known about the production of enzymes by fetal cells at different times during gestation and during

TABLE 5-IV

ENZYMATIC ACTIVITY DETECTED IN CULTIVATED
AMNIOTIC FLUID CELLS
(after Nadler)

Acid phosphatase*
Alkaline phosphatase
Alpha-glucosidase*
Alpha-keto-isocaproate decarboxylase
Beta-glucuronidase*
Cystathionine synthase
Galactose-1-phosphate uridyl transferase
Glucocerebrosidase
Glucose-6-phosphate dehydrogenase*
Hypoxanthine-guanine phosphoribosyl transferase
Lactic dehydrogenase*
Lysosomal acid phosphatase
Phytanic acid alpha-hydroxylase
6-phosphogluconic dehydrogenase
Sphingomyelinase(s)
Valine transaminase

*Intracellular distributions of these enzymes in cultivated amniotic fluid cells at various stages of fetal gestation have been shown to be similar to their distribution in fibroblast-like cells derived from skin biopsies of children and adults.

different individual "normal" or "abnormal" pregnancies. Quantitative differences in glucose-6-phosphate dehydrogenase activity at different stages of fetal gestation have been reported; increased activity associated with a decreased percentage of sex chromatin positive cells were found in cells cultured from two ten-week fetuses but after six weeks the cultures contained normal levels of activity and normal numbers of sex chromatin positive cells (Nadler, 1968a). Utilizing starch-gel electrophoresis he also showed qualitative differences of glucose-6-phosphate dehydrogenase and lactate dehydrogenase associated with gestational time, but failed to demonstrate such differences for acid phosphatase, alkaline phosphatase and 6-phosphogluconic dehydrogenase.

When glucose-6-phosphate dehydrogenase was studied, a more rapidly migrating band was demonstrated in cells derived from two female fetuses at ten weeks of gestation. One possible explanation for this extra band is that it represents an embryonic form of glucose-6-phosphate dehydrogenase. Qualitative changes of lactate dehydrogenase (LDH) in cultivated amniotic fluid cells, consisting of a relative increase of LDH_5 associated with increased migration toward the cathode, have been found to vary directly with the duration of fetal gestation. Wiggert and Villee (1964) have shown that multiple molecular forms of lactic dehydrogenase are present during fetal development and are affected by tissue distribution and age of the fetus. . . . Future work must carefully define the "normal characteristics" of cultivated amniotic fluid cells. The presence or absence of embryonic or fetal enzymes, as well as the quantitative and the qualitative changes of enzymes at different stages of fetal gestation, must be determined if this material is to be correctly interpreted (Nadler, 1969a, pp. 138-140).

CELL CULTURE AND ABORTIONS*

Diagnoses from cell culture of stillborns or aborted fetuses concern, for the most part, identification of chromosome constitution (Geneva Conference, 1966). The incidence of chromosome abnormalities in spontaneous abortions is high, about 25 percent in one study (Carr, 1965). In a selected study of thirteen abortuses showing cystic degeneration of the majority of their chorionic villi, ten had chromosome anomaly, nine being triploid

---

*Also see Chapter 3.

(69 chromosomes) and one, tetraploid (92 chromosomes) (Carr, 1969).

When cell cultures are established, care must be taken to avoid any possibility of culturing maternal tissue. Tissue for explanting is usually selected according to its availability and includes amnion, chorion, umbilical cord, and parts of embryos.

In some instances diagnosis of metabolic defect from cell culture of a stillborn infant or aborted fetus would be indicated to make predictions for further pregnancies or to diagnose the reason for loss of the pregnancy; possibly to confirm earlier findings in amniotic fluid culture.

POTENTIAL USES OF AMNIOTIC FLUID CELL CULTURES

The value of certain types of diagnosis on amniotic fluid cells is still to be proved. These include cytogenetic analysis for the evaluation of chromosome breaking agents. In addition, the relationship between Down's syndrome and neonatal leukemia could be investigated by comparing *in vitro* responses to oncogenic stimuli (such as simian virus 40) using amniotic cell cultures of various types, including those from fetuses with Down's syndrome. Morphologic differentiation and primary cloning of amniotic fluid cells could be evaluated, as well as the relation of this differentiation to production of specialized products such as enzymes not found in the usual monolayer serial cultures of amniotic cells. If embryonic and fetal enzymes are identified, they could be studied further in culture, particularly the responses to environmental changes (see Chap. 14 on control mechanisms). The problem of X-chromosome inactivation (facultative heterochromatization, Chap. 13) during early development could be studied further in relation to production of enzymes by X-linked genes in fetal cells. Any one type of study just mentioned might not justify transabdominal amniocentesis, but several in combination might do so, depending to some extent on circumstances of the individual pregnancies and need for other amniotic fluid studies of proved value. Amniotic fluid can also be obtained at the time of uterine surgery for other reasons.

REFERENCES

General

Horger, E. O., and Hutchinson, D. L.: Diagnostic use of amniotic fluid. *J Pediat*, 75:503, 1969.

Nadler, H. L.: Prenatal detection of genetic defects. *J Pediat*, 74:132, 1969.

Nelson, M. M., and Emery, A. E. H.: Amniotic fluid cells; prenatal sex prediction and culture. *Brit Med J*, 1:523, 1970.

Specific

Alvarez, H.: Diagnosis of hydatidiform mole by transabdominal placental biopsy. *Amer J Obstet Gynec*, 95:538, 1966.

Berman, P. H.; Balis, M. E., and Dancis, J.: A method for the prenatal diagnosis of congenital hyperuricemia. *J Pediat*, 75:488, 1969.

Carr, D. H.: Chromosome studies in spontaneous abortions. *Obstet Gynec*, 26:308, 1965.

Carr, D. H.: Cytogenetics and the pathology of hydatidiform degeneration. *Obstet Gynec*, 33:333, 1969.

Chang, T. D., and Bowman, J. M.: Chromosomes from foetal ascitic fluid. *Lancet*, 1:1431, 1968.

Creasman, W. T.; Lawrence, R. A., and Thiede, H. A.: Fetal complications of amniocentesis, *JAMA*, 204:949, 1968.

Dancis, J.: The antepartum diagnosis of genetic diseases. *J Pediat*, 72:301, 1968.

DeMars, R.; Sarto, G.; Felix, J. S., and Benke, P.: Lesch-Nyhan mutation: Prenatal detection with amniotic fluid. *Science*, 164:1303, 1969.

Fratantoni, J. C.; Neufeld, E. F.; Uhlendorf, B. W., and Jacobson, C. B.: Intrauterine diagnosis of the Hurler and Hunter syndromes. *New Eng J Med*, 280:686, 1969.

Fuchs, F.; Freiesleben, E.; Knudsen, E. E., and Riis, P.: Determination of foetal bloodgroup. *Lancet*, 1:996, 1956.

Fujimoto, W. Y.; Seegmiller, J. E.; Uhlendorf, B. W., and Jacobson, C. B.: Biochemical diagnosis of an X-linked disease in utero. *Lancet*, 2:511, 1968.

Geneva Conference: Standardization of procedures for chromosome studies in abortion. *Cytogenetics (Basel)*, 5:361, 1966.

Gordon, H., and Brosens, I.: Cytology of amniotic fluid: A new test for fetal maturity. *Obstet Gynec*, 30:652, 1967.

Gregson, N. M.: A technique for culturing cells for amniotic fluid. *Lancet*, 1:84, 1970.

Horger, E. O., and Hutchinson, D. L.: Diagnostic use of amniotic fluid. *J Pediat*, 75:503, 1969.

Jacobson, C. B., and Barter, R. H.: Intrauterine diagnosis and management of genetic defects. *Amer J Obstet Gynec,* 99²:796, 1967.

Lisgar, F.; Gertner, M.; Cherry, S.; Hsu, L., and Hirschhorn, K.: Prenatal chromosome analysis. *Nature (London),* 225:280, 1970.

Matalon, R.; Dorfman, A.; Nadler, H. L., and Jacobson, C. B.: A chemical method for the antenatal diagnosis of mucopolysaccharidoses. *Lancet,* 1:83, 1970.

Merkatz, I. R.; New, M. I.; Peterson, R. E., and Seaman, M. P.: Prenatal diagnosis of adrenogenital syndrome by amniocentesis. *J Pediat,* 75:977, 1969.

Nadler, H. L.: Patterns of enzyme development utilizing cultivated human fetal cells derived from amniotic fluid. *Biochem Genet,* 2:119, 1968a.

Nadler, H. L.: Antenatal detection of hereditary disorders. *Pediatrics,* 42:912, 1968b.

Nadler, H. L.: Prenatal detection of genetic defects. *J Pediat,* 74:132, 1969a.

Nadler, H. L., and Egan, T. J.: Deficiency of lysosomal acid phosphatase: A new familial metabolic disorder. *New Eng J Med,* 282:302, 1970.

Nadler, H. L., and Gerbie, A. B.: Role of amniocentesis in the intrauterine detection of genetic disorders. *New Eng J Med,* 282:596, 1970.

Nadlar, H. L., and Messina, A. M.: In-utero detection of type-II glycogenosis (Pompe's disease). *Lancet,* 2:1277, 1969b.

Riis, P., and Fuchs, F.: Sex chromatin antenatal sex diagnosis. In Moore, K. L. (Ed.): *The Sex Chromatin.* Philadelphia, Saunders, 1966, Chap. 13.

Santesson, B.; Akesson, H. O.; Book, J. A., and Brosset, A.: Karyotyping human amniotic-fluid cells. *Lancet,* 2:1067, 1969.

Schneck, L.; Valenti, C.; Amsterdam, D.; Friedland, J.; Adachi, M., and Volk, B. W.: Prenatal diagnosis of Tay-Sachs disease. *Lancet,* 1:582, 1970.

Schulman, J. D.; Fujimoto, W. Y., Bradley, K. H., and Seegmiller, J. E.: Identification of heterozygous genotype for cystinosis in utero by a new pulse-labeling technique: Preliminary report. *J Pediat,* 77:468, 1970.

Steele, M. W., and Breg, W. R.: Chromosome analysis of human amniotic-fluid cells. *Lancet,* 1:383, 1966.

Valenti, C.; Schutta, E. J., and Kehaty, T.: Prenatal diagnosis of Down's syndrome. *Lancet,* 2:220, 1968.

Wiggert, B. O., and Villee, C. A.: Multiple molecular forms of malic and lactic dehydrogenase during development. *J Biol Chem,* 239:444, 1964.

Chapter Six

DIAGNOSIS OF IMMUNE RESPONSES

TESTS OF LYMPHOCYTE RESPONSE IN SHORT-TERM PERIPHERAL BLOOD CULTURE

Tests of lymphocyte function involving *in vitro* response to allogenic (mixed) cells, mitogens and antigens depend on short-term culture of peripheral blood (Tables 6-I and 6-II; also see Chap. 1 on various types of human cell culture).

The mixed leukocyte culture test (Bach and Hirschhorn, 1964) measures the combined response of leukocytes of each of two test subjects to the stimulus provided by the other's cells. This test represents either an immunologic response of the small lymphocyte or a more subtle cell-cell interaction. One population of cells is able to recognize an immunologic or cell-surface difference in the second population of cells. However *no previous sensitization of the donors to the cells of the other is required*

TABLE 6-I

TESTS OF LYMPHOCYTE FUNCTION

Response to Allogenic Cells
    Mixed leukocyte culture test—two-way stimulation
    Mixed leukocyte culture test—one-way stimulation

Response to Plant Mitogens
    Phytohemagglutinin (PHA)—from Phaseolus vulgaris (red kidney bean)
    Pokeweed mitogen (PWM)—from Phytolacca americana
    Wax-bean glycoprotein

Response to "Specific" or "Nonspecific" Antigens or Stimulating Substances
    Antibiotics
    Hemophilus pertussis antigen
    Kveim antigen
    Leukocyte antiserum
    Pollen extract
    Purified protein derivative (PPD)
    Staphylococcal filtrate
    Toxoids—tetanus, diphtheria
    Vaccines—vaccinia
    Various cell or tissue extracts

TABLE 6-II

CHARACTERISTICS OF THE LYMPHOCYTE RESPONSE[*]
(BLASTOID REACTION)

1. Mitotic index (number of mitoses) increases (see Fig. 1-3, Chap. 1).
2. The small lymphocyte changes morphologically to a large blastoid cell (see Fig. 1-4, Chap. 1); dense chromatin becomes less dense; nucleoli appear; cytoplasm acquires pyroninophilia and basophilia.
3. Lymphocytes incorporate DNA precursors (H_3-TdR).
4. Synthesis of RNA and specific protein is stimulated.

[*]The term lymphocyte transformation should be avoided whenever possible in this context, since a different meaning is assigned to the process of transformation (see Chap. 8).

and it is not certain that enhanced reactivity is obtained when one donor has been immunized with the cells of the other (Hardy and Ling, 1969, p. 545). Furthermore, an irreversible process leading to blastoid cell change develops in leukocyte cultures from single subjects after contact for sixty minutes, or sometimes only for ten minutes, with cell-free medium derived from mixed leukocyte cultures (Kasakura and Lowenstein, 1968).

Modifications of the mixed leukocyte test make possible the assay of one-way stimulation (Elves, 1969). Treatment with mitomycin C or X-irradiation of the population of cells intended to stimulate, prevents the treated cells from responding but does not affect their ability to stimulate. Freezing and thawing the stimulating cells will also render them unresponsive but such disrupted cells may cause very weak reactions. Stimulating populations of macrophages can be produced from blood leukocytes by a short period of culture before mixing with the allogenic "responder" cells; this last method is more time consuming than the other methods.

The lymphocyte response can also be produced by treatment of short-term peripheral blood cultures or more purified lymphocyte cultures with various plant mitogens (Tables 6-I and 6-II). The mechanisms of action are not proved to be purely antigenic and will be discussed later in this chapter under a consideration of phytohemagglutinin (PHA), the most studied member of this group of stimulating agents (also see Chap. 1). Another member is pokeweed mitogen (PWM) (Reisfeld *et al.*, 1967). In these situations human peripheral blood lymphocytes may nevertheless be said to provide an *in vitro* system for the study of immune capabilities of the cell donor (see the section later in this Chap. on host defense failure syndromes).

A large range of substances, some more purified than others, are loosely referred to as "specific" or "nonspecific" antigens and will produce the lymphocyte response (Tables 6-I and 6-II). In these situations human peripheral blood lymphocytes may also be said to provide an *in vitro* system for the study of immune capabilities of the cell donor. In addition, the cultured lymphocytes can be tested for response to antigens to which the lymphocyte donor had been specifically sensitized (see the section later in this chapter on disease states involving hypersensitivity).

PREDICTION OF HISTOCOMPATIBILITY

In the mixed leukocyte culture test reported by Bach and Hirschhorn (1964) lymphocytes from two unrelated individuals, cultured together in the same tube, changed morphologically to large (blastoid) cells and also divided. There was a direct correlation between the degree of this response and the degree of crossreactivity of grafts from the two individuals, placed on a third unrelated recipient. In another study that involved mixing of leukocytes from pairs of human subjects (Bain and Lowenstein, 1964) the reaction was measured quantitatively by uptake of H_3-thymidine into cells in short-term culture. In experiments with fifteen sibling pairs, the leukocytes of most individuals reacted less strongly with those of their siblings than with those of an unrelated subject. Thus if lymphocyte response is related to the ability of one population of cells to recognize an immunogenetic difference in another population of cells, the mixed leukocyte culture should be useful as one test to predict survival for organ transplants. Lymphocytes from proposed organ donor and organ recipient are mixed. A low degree of lymphocyte response suggests that the proposed transplant is likely to "take"; a marked lymphocyte response suggests that the proposed transplant would not succeed. Kidney allograft survival in the dog has already been predicted by mixed leukocyte tests prior to transplantation (Kisken and Malek, 1969).

In human recipients of organ transplants (renal and cardiac) short *in vitro* exposure of their lymphocytes to tritiated thymidine has been used as a test to predict rejection of the transplant (Hersh *et al.*, 1970). A rise in the percent of cells incorporating tritiated thymidine was correlated with graft rejection and usually preceded clinical evidence of graft rejection.

HOST DEFENSE FAILURE SYNDROMES

The tests of lymphocyte function involving *in vitro* response to allogenic cells (mixed leukocyte test), mitogens and antigens are one way to diagnose cellular defects in the host defense failure syndromes (Douglas and Fudenberg, 1969; Table 6-III). The lymphocytes from patients with immunological deficiency states, such as chronic lymphatic leukemia, Hodgkin's disease, and the agammaglobulinemias usually respond much less to these various stimuli (allogenic lymphocytes, mitogens and antigens), except that cells from some agammaglobulinemics (both X-linked and acquired) may show normal cellular enlargement and division after stimulation with PHA (Lieber *et al.*, 1969). A sex difference was also noted in this study, female cells responding to a greater extent than male cells.

TABLE 6-III

CLINICAL AND LABORATORY STUDIES TO DIAGNOSE
HOST DEFENSE FAILURE SYNDROMES
(from Douglas and Fudenberg, 1969)

Cellular Defects
    Number of plasma cells and circulating lymphocytes
    Granulocyte function—bactericidal capacity
    Monocyte function—monocyte receptor sites
    Lymphocyte function—response to allogenic cells, mitogens and antigens
    Histopathology by light microscopy of thymus and lymphoid tissues including
        lymph nodes, spleen, tonsils, Peyer's patches, ileum and appendix
    Morphologic abnormalities—electron microscopy, cytochemistry

Immunologic Defects
    Immunoglobulin levels
        Serum: IgG, IgA, IgM, IgD, IgE
        Secretory immunoglobulins
    Humoral antibody response—response to different types of antigens
    Cell mediated response—delayed sensitivity

DISEASE STATES INVOLVING HYPERSENSITIVITY

The response of lymphocytes in culture may be used to evaluate hypersensitivity in the lymphocyte donor (Table 6-IV). There is evidence that the large number of blastoid cells found after six days in antigen-stimulated human peripheral blood cultures could arise from a small number of cells that undergo repeated cell division to form clones (Marshall *et al.*, 1969). The recruitment of lymphocytes not themselves initially sensitive to antigen may serve as an additional mechanism to enlarge the hypersensitivity response of lymphocytes; tuberculin-sensitive human lymphocytes cultured for thirty-six hours with tuberculin elaborate a soluble material which causes nonsensitive lymphocytes to respond *in vitro* by transformation and proliferation (Valentine and Lawrence, 1969).

TABLE 6-IV

EVALUATION OF HYPERSENSITIVITY BY MEANS OF
THE LYMPHOCYTE RESPONSE

"Sensitized" State	*Diagnostic Findings*	*Reference*
Autoimmune diseases (multiple sclerosis, post-rabies and post-measles encephalopathy, Guillain-Barre, infantile eczema, chronic thyroiditis, discoid lupus erythematosus, rheumatoid arthritis)	In contrast to the normal subject, many but not all of the patients with possible autoimmune diseases gave positive *in vitro* lymphocyte reactions to extracts of their own lymphocytes.	Hashem and Carr, 1963
Sarcoidosis	Increased response of cultured lymphocytes (more mitoses and blastoid cells) occurs after *in vitro* treatment with Kveim antigen.	Hirschhorn *et al.*, 1964
Acute idiopathic polyneuritis (Guillain-Barre syndrome)	Lymphocytes from affected individuals were stimulated when cultured with peripheral nerve antigen (a basic protein from sciatic nerve) while lymphocytes from patients with other types of peripheral neuropathy showed no response.	Knowles *et al.*, 1969
Antibiotic sensitivity	Increased lymphocyte response to ampicillin and tetracycline in culture was directly correlated with clinical allergy and positive skin tests to these antibiotics.	Reichenberger and Heitmann, 1969

TABLE 6-IV (Continued)

"Sensitized" State	Diagnostic Findings	Reference
Down's syndrome	Lymphocytes in mixed leukocyte cultures of Down's syndrome (DS) with normal person (NP) or in DS/DS mixtures showed more blastoid response with a higher mitotic index than in NP/NP mixtures or unmixed cultures.	Sasaki and Obara, 1969
Tuberculin sensitivity	Tuberculin-sensitive lymphocytes in culture respond to tuberculin in culture; they transform into blastoid cells, synthesize DNA and divide.	Valentine and Lawrence, 1969

CONSIDERATION OF PHYTOHEMAGGLUTININ (PHA) ACTION

Many responses of the human lymphocyte to PHA have been reported. Some of these responses are summarized in Table 6-V. They have also been discussed in Chapter 1 under a consideration of the short-term peripheral blood culture, since PHA is routinely used to initiate this type of culture, for a variety of purposes. The mechanism of PHA action is not understood at present.

TABLE 6-V

RESPONSES OF THE HUMAN PERIPHERAL BLOOD LYMPHOCYTE
TO PHYTOHEMAGGLUTININ

Cell Characteristics

PHA-induced blastoid cells, stained with May Grunwald-Giemsa and examined by light microscopy, show: (a) granular, basophilic cytoplasm; (b) cytoplasmic vacuoles as large as 3 microns in diameter, as many as 100 per cell; (c) a crescentic clear area next to the nucleus; (d) prominent nucleoli; (e) open-meshed appearance of nucleus. Electron microscopy reveals: (a) cytoplasmic vacuoles 1 to 3 microns in diameter, membrane bound, some containing mitochondrial cristae, some containing amorphous material of low density; (b) denser cytoplasmic bodies; (c) absence of normal mitochondria; (d) dispersed chromatin in nucleus; (e) evidence of active pinocytosis.	Marshall and Roberts, 1963 Stockert and Macario, 1968
PHA-stimulated lymphocytes increase their cell mass 2 to 3 times before they start to synthesize DNA and 5 to 6 times before they divide.	Steffen and Soren, 1968

TABLE 6-V (Continued)

Culture Characteristics

Phytohemagglutinin induces an increase in the level of DNA synthesis and mitosis in peripheral blood cultures. The first wave of mitosis starts at about 40 hours and every mitosis is preceded by *in vitro* DNA duplication. Although individual cells undergo at least 4 mitoses, the cultures have a lifespan limited to about two weeks.

Bender and Prescott, 1962

"Nonspecific" stimulants such as PHA produce a response in most of the cultured lymphocytes, while "specific" agents such as various protein and nonprotein allergens stimulate only a minority of the lymphocytes.

Hirschhorn *et al.*, 1963

The human thymus contains a population of small cells (lymphocytes) that can be stimulated to incorporate tritiated thymidine and enlarge, when PHA is administered *in vitro*.

Claman, 1966

PHA concentration required for optimal lymphocyte response is linearly related to the serum concentration. This observation is in keeping with reports of precipitation of PHA with serum-factors.

Forsdyke, 1966

PHA can induce the *in vitro* change of small lymphocyte to large blast-like cell, and back to small lymphocyte.

Caron, 1968

Molecular and Biochemical Changes

PHA causes a rapid increase in rate of incorporation of precursors into the lipid fraction of lymphocytes; this increase is independent of the effects of PHA on RNA and protein synthesis.

Kay, 1968

Human lymphocytes cultured with PHA show marked stimulation of DNA polymerase activity.

Loeb *et al.*, 1968

Human lymphotoxin (HLT) is a cytotoxic factor released by human lymphocytes *in vitro* after stimulation with PHA. This factor has properties characteristic of a protein with molecular weight of approximately 85,000.

Kolb and Granger, 1968

Stimulation of human lymphocytes with PHA *in vitro* induces marked changes in the properties of the nuclear DNA-protein complexes. These changes include an increased capacity to bind acridine orange and acetylation of histones. An altered affinity for actinomycin D can be observed before RNA synthesis is initiated.

Darzynkiewicz *et al.*, 1969

DNA and RNA synthesis-stimulating activity of PHA can be separated from erythroagglutinins, leukoagglutinins and cytotoxic factors in PHA. Substances stimulating the synthesis of DNA and RNA are probably *not* proteins, nucleic acids or carbohydrates.

Goldberg *et al.*, 1969

TABLE 6-V (Continued)

Nuclei isolated from human peripheral blood lymphocytes stimulated by PHA have a greater capacity to prime for nucleotide incorporation into RNA in the presence of exogenous bacterial RNA polymerase than nuclei from unstimulated lymphocytes.	Hirschhorn *et al.,* 1969
Certain enzymes acting on cell membrane, such as trypsin and neuraminidase, will make the lymphocytes temporarily refractory to PHA. (Cells treated with trypsin are refractory to PHA but not to simulation by allogenic cells, termed mixed lymphocyte reaction.)	Lindahl-Kiessling and Peterson, 1969
Increase in acridine orange (AO) binding sites in the DNA-protein complex (DNP) occurs in human leukocytes during the first 60 min. after PHA stimulation. It is theorized that the binding between DNA and surrounding proteins in DNP is altered by the action of PHA and thereby increasing numbers of DNA phosphate groups become uncovered, followed by RNA synthesis.	Rigler and Killander, 1969
Both ribosomal and 4S RNA are synthesized as a response to PHA stimulation. A decreased acetylation of histones is found to accompany RNA synthesis. Increased methylation is observed but found to be puromycin-sensitive and therefore associated with *de novo* protein synthesis as opposed to labeling of pre-existing histones as would be expected in a regulatory mechanism.	Monjardion and MacGillivray, 1970

Modification by Other Agents

Addition of PHA appears to protect lymphocytes against the cytotoxic effects of X-irradiation. Radioprotection was observed whether the PHA was added at any time from 4 days before to 2 days after irradiation.	Schrek and Stefani, 1964
Lymphocyte response stimulated by PHA is suppressed by prednisolone and chloroquine. (Both of these substances stabilize the lysosomal membrane and protect it from agents causing enzyme release.)	Hirschhorn and Hirschhorn, 1965
Mycoplasma species that utilize arginine for energy, also inhibit PHA stimulation in cultured lymphocytes. This effect of Mycoplasma is presumably due to depletion of available arginine; thus the lymphocytes are deprived of an essential amino-acid.	Barile and Leventhal, 1968
The blastoid response to PHA is markedly decreased in cultures of lymphocytes that have been separated from those leukocytes that adhere to nylon fiber and glass. The response of these "purified" lymphocyte cultures can be restored by adding either autologous, or homologous, glass-adherent, phagocytic leukocytes. The responding cells in these reconstituted cultures are derived from the "purified" lymphocytes.	Levis and Robbins, 1970

TABLE 6-V (Continued)

Colchicine at concentrations of 5 microg/ml to 15 microg/ml given for 1 hr. to 6 hrs. causes significant depressions of DNA synthesis and of the mitotic index in PHA-stimulated human lymphocytes. Colchicine appears both to prevent cells from beginning DNA synthesis and to reduce the rate of synthesis of cells already in S. There is also evidence that the progress of cells through G2 is slowed.	Fitzgerald and Brehaut, 1970

In Vivo Effects

Remission of some cases of aplastic anemia has been achieved by *in vivo* administration of PHA.	Humble, 1964

ANTIGENIC RESPONSES OF CELLS IN LONG-TERM CULTURE

Immunofluorescence has become an important method for the determination of species of origin of cell cultures (Larkin, 1965). Specific antisera are prepared from laboratory animals injected with specific antigens (trypsinized organs and embryos; cells from primary and established cell lines). Immune serum globulins thus obtained are conjugated with fluorescein compounds such as fluorescein isothiocyanate. Cell cultures to be identified may be grown on coverslips, rinsed in phosphate-buffered saline and stained with fluorescent conjugate. By this method, only live cells are studied and only surface fluorescence is utilized to determine the species of cells. It is obvious that methods of immunofluorescence would not work if cells in long-term culture did not retain specific antigenic properties present in the original cells. The preservation, modification or loss of antigens in many types of cultured cells, including both diploid and nondiploid established human cultures, is a matter of intensive investigation.

Immunofluorescence has been used to follow the fate of different types of human cells mixed in culture (Holmgren and Merchant, 1968). Two established human cell lines known to differ in their surface antigenic pattern were studied, a line derived from amnion cells and one derived from carcinoma of the larynx (HEp-2). After *in vitro* mixing, inhibition or reproductive death of the amnion cells occurred, while the HEp-2 cells were relatively unaffected or markedly stimulated. Partial protection of the amnion cells was afforded by exposure to antibody before growth in mixed culture.

> The application of cell culture techniques to human genetic analysis depends on the availability of means to isolate variants *in vitro* . . . . Variant human fibroblast substrains, resistant to a cytotoxic human isoantiserum, were isolated from sensitive strains by repeated exposure to isoantiserum and rabbit complement. The resistant phenotype was stable, apparently occurred at low frequency, and was associated with loss of surface isoantigens (Adman and Pious, 1970, p. 370).

USE OF CELL CULTURE TO STUDY ANTIGENICITY OF NEOPLASMS

Studies have shown both cellular and humoral immunity to neuroblastomas and a variety of other human solid tumors, reflected as a decrease in the efficiency of tumor cell plating in culture after exposure of the tumor cells to the patient's own blood lymphocytes or plasma (Hellstrom *et al.*, 1968).

In mixed leukocyte test of human cells, lymphocytes from remission period leukemia were cultivated in the presence of mitomycin C-treated autologous leukemic leukoblasts from acute phase leukemia. An increase in thymidine incorporation *in vitro* into lymphocytes from the remission period was observed (Fridman and Kourilsky, 1969). Thus remission lymphocytes were stimulated by autologous leukoblasts from the acute phase.

Studies of established human leukemic peripheral blood cultures show that leukemic cell antigenicity detectable when cells are first taken from the blood, can still be detected after several months in culture. Furthermore the antigenicity can be increased by *in vitro* culture (Belpomme *et al.*, 1969). These experiments point out the possibility of studying tumor antigens in long-term culture.

REFERENCES

General

Douglas, S. D., and Fudenberg, H. H.: Genetically determined defects in host resistance to infection. Cellular immunologic aspects. *Med Clin N Amer*, 53:903, 1969.

Nossal, G. J. V.: How cells make antibodies. *Sci Amer, 211*:106, 1964.
Robbins, J. H.: Tissue culture studies of the human lymphocyte, *Science, 146*:1648, 1964.

Specific

Adman, R., and Pious, D. A.: Isoantigenic variants: Isolation from human diploid cells in culture. *Science, 168*:370, 1970.
Bach, F., and Hirschhorn, K.: Lymphocyte interaction: A potential histocompatibility test *in vitro*. *Science, 143*:813, 1964.
Bain, B., and Lowenstein, L.: Genetic studies on the mixed leukocyte reaction. *Science, 145*:1315, 1964.
Barile, M. F., and Leventhal, B. G.: Possible mechanism for Mycoplasma inhibition of lymphocyte transformation induced by phytohaemagglutinin. *Nature (London), 219*:751, 1968.
Belpomme, D.; Lee Borgne de Kaouel, C.; Ajuria, E.; Jasmin, C., and Dore, J. F.: Increase in antigenicity of permanent tissue culture lines ICI 101, ICI 104, ICI 202. *Nature (London), 222*:890, 1969.
Bender, M. A., and Prescott, D. M.: DNA synthesis and mitosis in cultures of human peripheral leukocytes. *Exp Cell Res, 27*:221, 1962.
Caron, G. A.: Fate of transformed human lymphocytes induced by phytohaemagglutinin and antigens *in vitro*. *Nature (London), 218*:1053, 1968.
Claman, H. N.: Human thymus cell cultures—evidence for two functional populations. *Proc Soc Exp Biol Med, 121*:236, 1966.
Darzynkiewicz, A.; Bolund, L., and Ringertz, N. E.: Nucleoprotein changes and initiation of RNA synthesis in PHA stimulated lymphocytes. *Exp Cell Res, 56*:418, 1969.
Douglas, S. D., and Fudenberg, H. H.: Genetically determined defects in host resistance to infection: Cellular immunologic aspects. *Med Clin N Amer, 53*:903, 1969.
Elves, M. W.: Comparison of mitomycin C and X-rays for the production of one-way stimulation in mixed leucocyte cultures. *Nature (London), 223*:90, 1969.
Fitzgerald, P. H., and Brehaut, L. A.: Depression of DNA synthesis and mitotic index by colchicine in cultured human lymphocytes. *Exp Cell Res, 59*:27, 1970.
Forsdyke, D.: Response to phytohaemagglutinin. *Lancet, 1*:713, 1966.
Fridman, W. H., and Kourilsky, F. M.: Stimulation of lymphocytes by autologous leukaemic cells in acute leukaemia. *Nature (London), 224*: 277, 1969.
Goldberg, M. L.; Rosenau, W., and Burke, G. C.: Fractionation of phytohemagglutinin. I. Purification of the RNA and DNA synthesis-stimulating substances and evidence that they are not proteins. *Proc Nat Acad Sci USA, 64*:283, 1969.

Hardy, D. A., and Ling, N. R.: Effects of some cellular antigens on lymphocytes and the nature of the mixed lymphocyte reaction. *Nature (London),* 221:545, 1969.

Hashem, N., and Carr, D. H.: Mitogenic stimulation of peripheral lymphocyte cultures by autologous lymphocyte extracts in autoimmune diseases. *Lancet,* 2:1030, 1963.

Hellstrom, I.; Hellstrom, K. E.; Pierce, G. E., and Yang, J. P. S.: Cellular and humoral immunity to different types of human neoplasms. *Nature (London),* 220:1352, 1968.

Hersh, E. M.; Butler, W. T.; Rossen, R. D., and Morgen, R. O.: Lymphocyte activation: A rapid rest to predict allograft rejection. *Nature (London),* 226:757, 1970.

Hirschhorn, K.; Back, F.; Kolodny, R.; Firchein, I. L., and Hashem, N.: Immune response and mitosis of human peripheral blood lymphocytes *in vitro. Science,* 142:1185, 1963.

Hirschhorn, K., and Hirschhorn, R.: Role of lysosomes in the lymphocyte response. *Lancet,* 1:1046, 1965.

Hirschhorn, K.; Schreibman, R. R.; Bach, F. H., and Siltzbach, L. E.: *In vitro* studies of lymphocytes from patients with sarcoidosis and lymphoproliferative diseases. *Lancet,* 2:842, 1964.

Hirschhorn, R.; Troll, W.; Brittinger, G., and Weissmann, G.: Template activity of nuclei from stimulated lymphocytes. *Nature (London),* 222:1247, 1969.

Holmgren, N. G., and Merchant, D. J.: Allogenic inhibition between two human cell lines. *J Nat Cancer Inst,* 40:561, 1968.

Humble, J. G.: The treatment of aplastic anaemia with phytohaemagglutinin. *Lancet,* 1:1345, 1964.

Kasakura, S., and Lowenstein, L.: Effect of length of exposure to cell-free medium from mixed leucocyte cultures on blastogenesis in leucocyte cultures from single subjects. *Nature (London),* 219:652, 1968.

Kay, J. E.: Phytohaemagglutinin: An early effect on lymphocyte lipid metabolism. *Nature (London),* 219:172, 1968.

Kisken, W. A., and Malek, G. H.: Kidney allograft survival in the dog predicted by mixed leucocyte culture tests. *Nature (London),* 224:1110, 1969.

Knowles, M.; Currie, S.; Saunders, M.; Walton, J. N., and Field, E. J.: Lymphocyte transformation in the Guillain-Barre syndrome. *Lancet,* 2:1168, 1969.

Kolb, W. P., and Granger, G. A.: Lymphocyte *in vitro* cytotoxicity: Characterization of human lymphotoxin. *Proc Nat Acad Sci USA,* 61:1250, 1968.

Larkin, E. P.: A simple method for species differentiation of cell cultures by immunofluorescence. *Growth,* 29:201, 1965.

Levis, W. R., and Robbins, J. H.: Effect of glass-adherent cells on the blastogenic response of "purified" lymphocytes to phytohemagglutinin. *Exp Cell Res*, *61*:153, 1970.

Lieber, E.; Hirschhorn, K., and Fudenberg, H. H.: Response of agammaglobulinaemic lymphocytes in mixed lymphocyte culture. *Clin Exp Immunol*, *4*:83, 1969.

Lindahl-Kiessling, K., and Peterson, R. D. A.: The mechanism of phytohemagglutinin (PHA) action. II. The effect of certain enzymes and sugars. *Exp Cell Res*, *55*:81, 1969.

Loeb, L. A.; Agarwal, S. S., and Woodside, A. M.: Introduction of DNA polymerase in human lymphocytes by phytohemagglutinin. *Proc Nat Acad Sci USA*, *61*:827, 1968.

Marshall, W. H., and Roberts, K. B.: The growth and mitosis of human small lymphocytes after incubation with a phytohaemagglutinin. *Quart J Exp Physiol*, *48*:146, 1963.

Marshall, W. H.; Valentine, F. T., and Lawrence, H. S.: Cellular immunity *in vitro*. Clonal proliferation of antigen-stimulated lymphocytes. *J Exp Med*, *130*:327, 1969.

Monjardino, J. P. P. V., and MacGillivray, A. J.: RNA and histone metabolism in small lymphocytes stimulated by phytohaemagglutinin. *Exp Cell Res*, *60*:1, 1970.

Reichenberger, M., and Heitmann, H. P.: Lymphocyte transformation in patients allergic to ampicillin and tetracycline. *Lancet*, *2*:491, 1969.

Reisfeld, R. A.; Borjeson, J.; Chessin, L. N., and Small, P. A.: Isolation and characterization of a mitogen from pokeweed (Phytolacca americana). *Proc Nat Acad Sci USA*, *58*:2020, 1967.

Rigler, R., and Killander, D.: Activation of deoxyribonucleoprotein in human leucocytes stimulated by phytohemagglutinin. II. Structural changes of deoxyribonucleoprotein and synthesis of RNA. *Exp Cell Res*, *54*:171, 1969.

Sasaki, M., and Obara, Y.: Hypersensitivity of lymphocytes in Down's syndrome shown by mixed leukocyte culture experiments. *Nature (London)*, *222*:596, 1969.

Schrek, R., and Stefani, S.: Radioresistance of phytohemagglutinin-treated normal and leukemic lymphocytes. *J Nat Cancer Inst*, *32*:507, 1964.

Steffen, J., and Soren, L.: Changes in dry mass of PHA stimulated human lymphocytes during blast transformation. *Exp Cell Res*, *53*:652, 1968.

Stockert, J. C., and Macario, A. J. L.: Composition of vacuoles in PHA-stimulated blasts. *Lancet*, *2*:685, 1968.

Valentine, F. T., and Lawrence, H. S.: Lymphocyte stimulation: Transfer of cellular hypersensitivity to antigen *in vitro*. *Science*, *165*:1014, 1969.

SECTION III
ANALYSIS OF PRINCIPLES OF DISEASE

Chapter Seven

AGING

THE CELLULAR MODEL FOR AGING

Human diploid fibroblast-like cells in monolayer culture have a finite life expectancy of about fifty population doublings (Hayflick, 1965). At the end of this time cell division gradually stops and subculture is impossible. If cells of different ages in culture are mixed the culture doubling potential is that of the younger cells. Furthermore cells from adult primary explants have a significantly shorter culture lifetime than do cells from fetal primary explants. Thus senescence at the cellular level is a phenomenon related to both the length of time in culture and the age of the original primary explant. It has been noted that cells from individuals with the premature aging syndromes, Progeria (Goldstein, 1969) and Werner's syndrome (Martin *et al.*, 1965), show considerably decreased life expectancy in culture (Table 7-I). The relation of aging of the entire individual to aging of this cellular model is an interesting, unsolved problem.

TABLE 7-I

KARYOTYPE STABILITY AND LIFE EXPECTANCY OF SOME
FIBROBLAST-LIKE MAMMALIAN CELLS IN
MONOLAYER CULTURE

Cell Type	Diploid Life in Culture Length (Population Doublings)	Karyotype Stability	Nondiploid Life in Culture Length (Population Doublings)	Karyotype Stability
Human embryonic	50 ± 10	Yes	0	
Human adult	40 ± 10	Yes	0	
Human trisomy	0		$40\text{-}50 \pm 10$	Yes

TABLE 7-I (Continued)

Humans with aging syndromes (Progeria and Werner's syndrome)	Usually not more than 20	Yes	0	
Rat	250 ± 50	Yes	Infinite, following prolonged diploid stage	Yes
Mouse	Very short	No	Infinite	No
Chinese hamster	Very short	No	Infinite	No
Some mammalian tumors	0		Infinite	No
Human cell, transformed by virus or chemical	Variable, not exceeding 50 ± 10 before transformation	Yes, before transformation	Infinite	No

CELL LIFE EXPECTANCY IN CULTURE

Figure 7-1 summarizes observations concerning the life expectancy of human diploid monolayer cells in culture. A period of slower initial growth is termed phase I, rapid proliferation phase II, and cessation of growth phase III. A human cell culture may start to multiply indefinitely but it is then no longer diploid. Usually virus or chemical transformation is required. This concept of infinite life in culture may be called a cellular model for neoplasia and is considered further in Chapter 8. The characterization of culture age in terms of population doublings is explained in the figure legend for Figure 7-1 and also in Table 7-II.

The karyotype stability and life expectancy of human monolayer cells in culture may be compared to the same characteristics of other mammalian fibroblast-like monolayer cells (Table 7-I). Some cells do not demonstrate a diploid phase II, while for others it may be relatively prolonged. For certain genetic studies, particularly those involving "inborn" metabolic defects in cell culture (Chap. 4), there are distinct advantages to the genetically stable diploid lifetime of human cells. The finite lifetime may present problems if biochemical assays require cloned cells (cultured cells

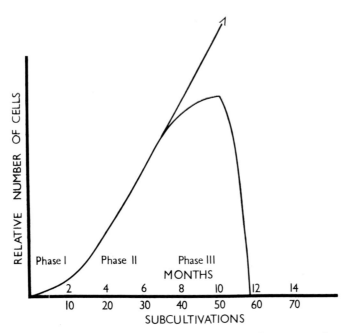

Figure 7-1. The lifetime of human diploid cells may be expressed in terms of months in culture but more exactly in terms of subcultivations or passages from one culture container into two other containers. By this manner of subculture (at a 1:2 split ratio) each population of cells within a container is allowed to multiply until cell number has doubled. Therefore subcultivation number is the same as population doubling number. Phase I refers to an initial period of slow growth and phase II refers to rapid multiplication. During phase III there is increased generation time, gradual cessation of mitotic activity, accumulation of cellular debris and total degeneration of the culture. Human cultured cells can multiply indefinitely, as shown by the arrow, but they are no longer diploid.

derived from a single cell). A minimum of twenty population doublings are usually required before human diploid cells reach the stage of first subculture, and for each subsequent cloning. Thus the culture may be already entering senescence before it can be used for assay. Special cloning procedures may avoid these difficulties (see Chap. 2 on cloning). Storage of early phase II cells in liquid nitrogen allows retrieval of ample numbers of diploid cells for most biochemical procedures. Some assays do not require diploid cells; the importance of established nondiploid

TABLE 7-II

CHARACTERIZATION OF CULTURE AGE IN TERMS OF
POPULATION DOUBLINGS

Subcultivation Split Ratio°	Subcultivation Number at a 1:2 Split Ratio	Number of Population Doublings
1:1		0
1:2	1	1
1:4	2	2
1:8	3	3
1:16	4	4
1:32	5	5
1:64	6	6

°Human diploid monolayer cells are usually subcultured at 1:2, 1:4 or 1:8 split ratios. Higher ratios are seldom performed because the subcultured cells may not recover logarithmic increase in cell number, or may remain in lag growth phase (poor increase in cell number) for a prolonged period of time. Needless to say, higher split ratios usually involve discarding a certain portion of the cells. If, for some reason, a large number of cells is desired for study, larger culture containers are usually employed rather than large numbers of smaller containers. The split ratio chosen for subculture may be smaller when cells are moved from small to large containers and the time between subculturing may increase, but the relationship between split ratio and population doubling number always remains as described here, and is an exponential function. Total time in culture, total number of subcultures, or time between subculturing are never exact measures of culture age unless the split ratio is also described.

cell lines such as HeLa cell should not be underestimated.

Progression of phases in human diploid monolayer cell cultures, as described in Figure 7-1, may be altered by certain types of environmental manipulations, not involving transformation or demonstrable change in the chromosomes. For instance, two lines of human amnion cells were treated with hydrocortisone to the culture medium, serial subcultivation was stopped, and a prolonged stationary stage was induced resembling advanced phase III. A spontaneous recovery stage then followed and was characterized by the criteria for phase II cells, including diploid chromosome complement (Sonnenschein and Chang, 1969).

Where human leukocyte cell lines fit into the scheme of culture life expectancy is not settled. There is evidence that a leukocyte cell line from peripheral blood of a healthy individual may have indefinite life expectancy, a high degree of diploidy, and no evidence of neoplasia as tested by implantation into hamster

cheek pouch (Christofinis, 1969) (also see Chap. 8, on characteristics of transformed or neoplastic cells in culture).

CHARACTERISTICS OF "YOUNG" AND "OLD" CELLS IN CULTURE

It is reasonable to study the senescence of human diploid cells
in culture by detailed observations of cellular characteristics in
the various culture phases. It is known that cells of fetal lung
origin, after the fortieth population doubling grow very hetero-
geneous regarding lengths of the cell cycle; the fraction of cells
involved with DNA synthesis after a short pulse of tritiated
thymidine is smaller; the mean cell cycle time is prolonged; there
is retardation in G1; and the rate of RNA synthesis decreases,
although active RNA synthesis can occur in all phase III cells
(Macieira-Coelho *et al.*, 1966). Some degree of aneuploidy may
also be present in phase III cells, after the fortieth population
doubling (Saksela and Moorhead, 1963).

More recent comparisons between cells in culture from human
fetal and from human adult sources confirm the original observations by Hayflick (1965) that adult cells are already aged as
compared to embryonic cells (Table 7-III) (Macieria-Coelho
and Ponten, 1969). However between the two types of cells
there appear to be no differences in time spent in S-phase of the

TABLE 7-III

PHASE II CULTURES FROM HUMAN ADULTS MAY PRESENT SOME
GROWTH PATTERNS FOUND ONLY IN PHASE III CULTURES
FROM HUMAN EMBRYOS

1. Wide fluctuation in the number of cells synthesizing DNA during a 24 hour
   period; decreased number of cells synthesizing DNA during a 24 hour period.

2. Decreased number of "growing" cells entering the cell cycle between subcultivation and saturation density when the culture container holds no more
   cells.

3. Lower saturation density.

4. Longer G2 period.

5. The most common D/G translocation chromosome associated with Down's

6. Increase in cell size.

cell cycle (period of DNA synthesis) or in mitosis. The authors propose that mechanisms involved in the slow-down of cell division associated with aging *in vitro* may be located in the preparation for DNA synthesis and mitosis. Proof for this hypothesis must await further experimental data. If cell aging and subsequent reproductive death represent irreversible G1 arrest (see Chap. 12 on the significance of cell cycle events) then proof of this fact is yet to come.

Late-passage cultured cells ("old") are more susceptible to transformation by simian virus 40 than early-passage cells ("young"). This change in susceptibility occurs between the twentieth and thirtieth population doubling, before any increase in chromosome abnormalities occurs. Cells from elderly individuals (over age 70) also show a higher susceptibility to transformation than their embryonic and newborn counterparts, all being tested at the same time (early) in their culture lives (Todaro, 1968) (also see Chap. 8 on cell transformation).

The specific activity of a mitochondrial enzyme, cytochrome oxidase, was determined in a normal human fibroblast-like strain from shortly after its *in vitro* cultivation to the cessation of division in phase III (Hakami and Pious, 1968). No age-dependent reduction in cytochrome oxidase activity was found in "old" cells; this observation argues against changes in mitochondrial content as the basis for the limited *in vitro* lifespan of normal human fibroblast-like cells. Nevertheless the search for enzymatic differences must continue.

USES OF THE CELLULAR MODEL FOR AGING

An interesting use of human diploid cellular aging concerns the growth capacity of cultured human fibroblast-like cells from individuals who do not show overt diabetes mellitus but carry a high genetic risk to do so (Goldstein *et al.*, 1969). High-risk subjects in this study were the offspring of two clinically overt diabetics. Normal controls were matched for age but had negative family histories for diabetes and no clinically overt disease as defined in the study. The culture lifespans of control and "high-risk" cells were statistically indistinguishable; however there was a significant difference in plating efficiency between the two groups of cells, "high-risk" cells being lower. Recall that the plating efficiency test (Chap. 2) measures the ability of a standard number of individual cells to produce clones (colonies). This difference in plating efficiency between control and "high-risk" cells was evident earlier in the culture lifetimes (at 20, 30 and 40 generations) but not late, after fifty generations. The authors propose that the cell culture system studied "should be useful in studying the inheritance of the diabetic gene(s), the pathogenesis of the diabetic state, and the relationship between aging and diabetes, both of which decrease plating efficiency."

REFERENCES

General

Hayflick, L.: Human cells and aging. *Sci Amer, 218:*32, 1968.

Specific

Christofinis, G. J.: Chromosome and transplantation results of a human leukocyte cell line derived from a healthy individual. *Cancer, 24:*649, 1969.

Goldstein, S.: Lifespan of cultured cells in progeria. *Lancet, 1:*424, 1969.

Goldstein, S.; Littlefield, J. W., and Soeldner, J. S.: Diabetes mellitus and aging: Diminished plating efficiency of cultured human fibroblasts. *Proc Nat Acad Sci USA, 64:*155, 1969.

Hakami, N., and Pious, D. A.: Mitochondrial enzyme activity in "senescent" and virus-transformed human fibroblasts. *Exp Cell Res, 53:*135, 1968.

Hayflick, L.: The limited *in vitro* lifetime of human diploid cell strains. *Exp Cell Res, 37:*614, 1965.

Macieira-Coelho, A., and Ponten, J.: Analogy in growth between late passage human embryonic and early passage human adult fibroblasts. *J Cell Biol, 43:*374, 1969.

Macieira-Coelho, A.; Ponten, J., and Philipson, L.: The division cycle and RNA synthesis in diploid human cells at different passage levels *in vitro. Exp Cell Res, 42:*673, 1966.

Martin, G. M.; Gartler, S. M.; Epstein, C. J., and Motulsky, A. G.: Diminished lifespan of cultured cells in Werner's syndrome. *Fed Proc, 24:*678, 1965.

Saksela, E., and Moorhead, P. S.: Aneuploidy in the degenerative phase of serial cultivation of human cell strains. *Proc Nat Acad Sci USA, 50:*390, 1963.

Sonnenschein, C., and Chang, R. S.: Karyotypic analysis of normal human amnion cells in the recovery phase. *Exp Cell Res,* 57:328, 1969.

Todaro, G. J.: Variable susceptibility of human cell strains to SV40 transformation. *Nat Cancer Inst Monogr* 29:271, 1968.

Chapter Eight

NEOPLASIA AND TRANSFORMATION

THE CELLULAR MODEL FOR NEOPLASIA

When human diploid monolayer cell cultures are exposed to an oncogenic or tumor-producing virus such as simian virus 40 (SV40), interesting changes occur in the growth characteristics of the cells, resembling many of the changes associated with neoplasia and malignancy. The cell growth rate increases, the culture life becomes immortal, the cells have a greater tendency to overgrow each other, and chromosome constitution changes from diploid to nondiploid. In one study viral-transformed cells of human embryonic origin were found to stop dividing at twice the cell density in a confluent culture, when compared to nontransformed cultured diploid cells from the same source (Macieira-Coelho, 1967). This cultural model of neoplasia raises many questions and provides an opportunity for study of basic mechanisms in malignancy (also see Chap. 7 on the cellular model for aging). The process just described, involving permanent change in cell culture characteristics, is called transformation; the term "cell transformation" should be reserved for heritable changes. Viruses are only one category of agents known to induce transformation (Table 8-I). Other inducers include various drugs and chemicals (Fig. 8-1), and the process of somatic cell hybridization (Chap. 11). In many instances the transforming agent is not identified with certainty. In such cases, the question always arises: Is there such a thing as "spontaneous" transformation?

Neoplasia in this chapter is defined as the capacity of cells to multiply and invade in situations where normal cells are restricted from multiplication and invasiveness (Prescott, in press).

161

TABLE 8-I

EXAMPLES OF SOME AGENTS KNOWN TO TRANSFORM
HUMAN CELLS IN CULTURE

A. *Viruses*

Simian virus 40 (SV40)	Shein and Enders, 1962
Adeno 7-SV40 hybrid virus	Black and Todaro, 1965
Adenovirus 12	Sultanian and Freeman, 1966
Schmidt-Ruppin strain of Rous sarcoma virus (RSV)	Macieira-Coelho, 1967
Chicken-embryo-lethal-orphan virus (CELO)	Anderson *et al.*, 1969

B. *Chemicals*

Benzpyrene	Hirschhorn and Bloch-Shtacher, 1970

C. *Somatic cell hybridization* (see Chap. 11)

Human diploid (fibroblast-like cell) and mouse nondiploid (L-cell) cross, producing *human-mouse* transformed cells by the use of selective media.	Weiss and Green, 1967
Human diploid (fibroblast-like cell) and human nondiploid (HeLa cell) cross, producing *human-human* transformed cells by use of selective media.	Matsuya and Green, 1969
Human diploid (peripheral blood leukocyte) and mouse nondiploid (L-cell) cross, producing *human-mouse* transformed cells by fusion, using Sendai virus.	Nabholz *et al.*, 1969

CHARACTERISTICS OF TRANSFORMED OR NEOPLASTIC CELLS IN CULTURE

"The time-honored criteria of the histopathologist do not necessarily distinguish between non-neoplastic and neoplastic cells in culture" (Foley, 1968, p. 218). A series of observed characteristics may help to make the distinction (Table 8-II; Fig. 8-1); at present cultured cells must also be tested for tumorigenicity in intact animals, if neoplasia is defined as the capacity of cells to multiply *and* invade in situations where normal cells are restricted. Unfortunately, failure of transplanted cells to grow in a laboratory animal under certain test situations may not rule out their ability to multiply and invade in another test animal. Ultimately, and as more is known about tissue and organ culture,

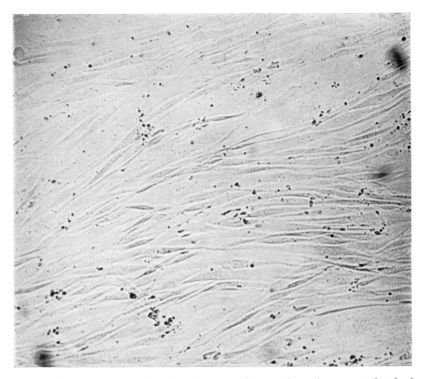

Figure 8-1. (a) Cells in fibroblast-like monolayer culture from an individual with Fanconi anemia. The diploid cells at confluency show an organized and parallel arrangement. (b) The disorganized growth pattern seen in the same cell line transformed in this case by a chemical (benzpyrene). Bright field photography. Courtesy Dr. K. Hirschhorn. In Genetic Concepts and Neoplasia, *Proc 23rd Ann Symposium Fundamental Concepts of Cancer,* Houston, Texas, 1969.

there will be strict *in vitro* or cultural characteristics of cell invasiveness.

With the present limitations in knowledge about invasiveness of cultured cells, it should be emphasized that the terms "transformation" and "neoplasia" do not have the same definitions, but are commonly (and carelessly) used synonymously. *Usually* the same culture characteristics apply to both transformed and neoplastic cells but by strict definition "transformed" applies to persistence of these characteristics (Table 8-II) through many

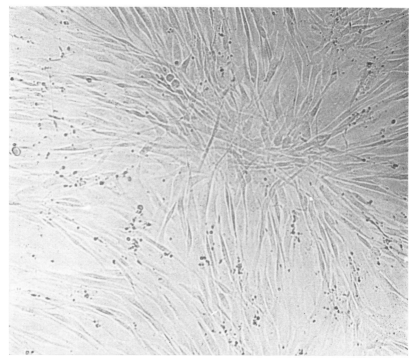

Figure 8-1b.
TABLE 8-II

SOME COMMONLY REPORTED CHARACTERISTICS
OF CULTURED HUMAN CELLS*
(from Foley, 1968)

Characteristics	Non-neoplastic	Neoplastic
Cellular morphology	Not reliably distinguishing	
Morphology of growth in monolayer	Orderly	May be less orderly; more tendency for cells to overgrow each other.
Chromosomes— karyotype†	Normal; may be altered	Altered; may be normal or near-normal
Maximum population density in monolayer	Lower	Higher
Growth in suspension culture	No	Yes, sometimes
Plating efficiency	Lower	Higher

TABLE 8-II (Continued)

Characteristics	Non-neoplastic	Neoplastic
Life expectancy†	Finite for diploid culture	Infinite for nondiploid culture
Tumorigenicity in test animals	Not present	Present, usually
Biochemical	Not reliably distinguishing at present	
Immunological	Not reliably distinguishing at present	
Cells may be said to be transformed	No, usually	Yes, usually

°In this table generalized characteristics are described that may not apply to *all* cultures.

†For human cells infinite culture life expectancy is associated with nondiploid chromosome morphology; finite life in culture is associated with diploid morphology. However, aneuploidy in the degenerative phase III of serial culture of human diploid cells is described (Saksela and Moorhead, 1963; see Chap. 7). Furthermore neoplasia and nondiploid chromosome constitution cannot be strictly equated.

cells divisions in culture and "neoplastic" applies also to ability of the cells to divide and invade in intact animal hosts. As an example, chicken-embryo lethal-orphan virus (CELO) transforms human amnion cells, with the production of continuous (established) cell lines containing CELO-specific "T" antigen (Anderson *et al.*, 1969). Other characteristics of transformed cultured cells were present, but proof that the cells were neoplastic rested on production of rapidly growing fibrosarcomas on inoculation into hamster cheek pouch.

Many other characteristics of cultured human cells, besides those listed in Table 8-II, are reported less frequently or occur with less regularity; these findings may nevertheless be useful to characterize transformed or neoplastic cells in culture (Table 8-III).

Established human monolayer cell lines have demonstrated the potential to be subcultured indefinitely *in vitro* and also have many characteristics of both transformed and neoplastic cells (see Table 8-II and also Chap. 1). However there is evidence that a leukocyte cell line from peripheral blood of a healthy individual may have indefinite life expectancy, a high degree of

TABLE 8-III

SOME CHARACTERISTICS OF CULTURED HUMAN CELLS, REPORTED
LESS FREQUENTLY OR OCCURRING WITH LESS REGULARITY,
BUT ASSOCIATED WITH NEOPLASIA AND TRANSFORMATION

Reference

Simian virus 40 induces reproducible *epithelioid change* in primary cultures of human renal tissue. The change is characterized by abnormal growth pattern, greatly accelerated growth rate and chromosomal aberrations.	Shein and Enders, 1962
Nucleoli were examined in many diploid, near-diploid and nondiploid or transformed human cultures. In all cultures multiple, small spherules (termed nucleolini) were noted as subnucleolar structures. In the diploid and early passage cultures the nucleolini were almost invariably the same size and were evenly distributed (*isonucleolinosis*). In all the other cultures the nucleolini varied markedly in size in the same nucleolus or in different nucleoli in the same nucleus (*anisonucleolinosis*).	Love, 1965
The karyology of a permanent human cell line, which retains a viral induced complement-fixing antigen as a result of its original transformation with simian virus 40 is described. This line (W-18VA2), is primarily *subdiploid* and exhibits *high variability of chromosome number.*	Weinstein and Moorhead, 1965
Human diploid cells derived from embryonic lung tissue (strain LEP 13) have a significantly lower *primary resistance to cold exposure* (4°C) than human cells of a nondiploid line (HeLa).	Michl *et al.*, 1966
Fibroblast-like cells from human embryonic lung were infected with adenovirus type 12, with characteristics of cultural transformation. *Giant and syncytial cells* became commonplace. An induced *new cell antigen* persisted for at least 20 culture passages.	Sultanian and Freeman, 1966
Study of *environmental processes that may affect transformation* by SV40 revealed: (a) X-irradiation blocks cell transformation but not virus synthesis; (b) hydrocortisone delays appearance of transformed foci; (c) some older cultures are more easily transformed than some younger cultures; overcrowding in a culture may delay the appearance of transformed foci.	Chang and Sinskey, 1968
Cell lines grown from brain tissue obtained during diagnostic biopsies of two patients with subacute sclerosing panencephalitis (SSPE) *stopped dividing* after 12 to 14 passages. The cultures were *maintained in stationary phase* by refeeding with fresh medium at weekly intervals. After 5-7 weeks, cultures of *surviving cells exhibited luxuriant growth, nuclear pleomorphism, and aneuploid karyotypes.*	Katz *et al.*, 1969

diploidy, and no evidence of neoplasia as tested by implantation into hamster cheek pouch (Christofinis, 1969).

The Relation of Viruses to Transformation and Neoplasia

The reproducible production of transformed cultures following controlled introduction of certain viruses into diploid cultures is convincing evidence relating certain viruses to human cell transformation (Table 8-I, A). A large amount of less direct evidence is accumulating to suggest that (a) other viruses may also be transforming and (b) the appearance of transformed human cultures may also be related to "uncontrolled" exposure of the cells to virus at some time in their lifetime, either prior to or during the culture period (Table 8-IV).

TABLE 8-IV

VARIOUS TYPES OF INDIRECT EVIDENCE SUGGESTING RELATION
BETWEEN VIRUSES AND TRANSFORMATION IN CULTURED CELLS

	Reference
The occurrence of *H.L.V.* (*herpes-like virus*) antigen and herpes-like particles in long-term peripheral blood cultures derived from patients with a variety of lymphoproliferative disorders and from healthy individuals suggests that this agent is common in nature. H.L.V. may be responsible for the long-term *in vitro* proliferative potential of peripheral blood cells. It is equally possible that the viral genome of H.L.V. is present in the host cell but the stimulus for cell proliferation is caused by another agent.	Glade *et al.*, 1968
Cell lines grown from brain tissue obtained during diagnostic biopsies of two patients with subacute sclerosing panencephalitis (SSPE) stopped dividing after 12 to 14 passages. The cultures were, however, maintained in stationary phase by refeeding with fresh medium at weekly intervals. After 5-7 weeks, cultures of surviving cells exhibited luxuriant growth, nuclear pleomorphism, and aneuploid karyotypes. Isoenzyme patterns and mixed agglutination confirmed human origin of the cells. No evidence of infection with SV40, or viruses other than the *measles-like agent* previously reported in such cells in SSPE, was detected.	Katz *et al.*, 1969
Cultures were initiated from a malignant pleural effusion of a patient with liposarcoma. (Liposarcoma cells were present on direct cytological examination of the pleural fluid.) Foci of cells appeared in the cultures and had the characteristics of transformed cells as well as cytological appearance of the	Morton *et al.*, 1969

TABLE 8-IV (Continued)

original liposarcoma. These foci contained *viral particles by EM morphologically similar to the sarcoma viruses of the avian and murine species.*

A systematic attempt was made to find viruses in human cell strains derived from a wide variety of normal and neoplastic tissue. A sucrose gradient method was used to search for occult, noncytopathic viruses; to screen large numbers of cells the method had advantages over electron microscopy, and serological testing for specific known viruses. *Three of 22 strains from tumor patients were virus-positive while none of the cultures derived from 34 nontumor patients showed evidence of virus.* The virus was covert but persistent in the positive lines and could be transmitted only with low efficiency to other human cells; these were considered properties to be expected of tumor viruses. The virus in one tumor cell line (from human breast carcinoma) was possibly related to the B-type particles associated with mouse mammary tumors. In any case, each of the three virus-containing cell lines grows readily in culture, and therefore the viruses they produce can be studied further. These studies may resolve whether the viruses are etiologically involved in human cancer or are merely "passenger" viruses.

Todaro *et al.*,
1970

The DNA isolated from simian virus 40 (SV40) is now shown to transform human fibroblast-like cells in culture (Aaronson and Todaro, 1969). Clonal lines of DNA-transformed human cells were obtained that showed properties characteristic of cells transformed by whole virus. DNA-transformed cells contained SV40 T-antigen and infectious virus was recovered. Thus purified viral DNA is shown to produce permanent genetic change (transformation) in human cells.

The role of viruses in the permanent establishment of leukocyte cell lines is still uncertain. In one report (Gerber *et al.*, 1969), three separate attempts to establish long-term leukocyte cultures from peripheral blood of a healthy adult were consistently unsuccessful. On the other hand, *in vitro* infection of buffy-coat of this donor with Epstein-Barr virus resulted in blastoid change of the lymphocytes and long-term growth potential. These changes were also accompanied by major chromosome changes.

The Relation of Chromosome Changes to Transformation

Chromosome changes may be followed sequentially during experimental transformation of cultured human diploid cells. Introduction of SV40 into human diploid monolayer cells has been studied extensively in this regard (Table 8-V). The time between introduction of SV40 and appearance of morphological changes of transformation and abnormal karyotype may vary with culture age. That both chromosomal and transformational changes occur following virus infection is undisputed. Usually the two changes occur at about the same time.

TABLE 8-V

SOME STUDIES OF CHROMOSOME CHANGES FOLLOWING SV40
TRANSFORMATION OF HUMAN DIPLOID MONOLAYER CELLS

Reference

Karyotype changes consisted of monosomy, trisomy, abnormal "marker" chromosomes, and chromosomal breakage. There was evidence that chromosome aberrations reflected changes in the cell genome caused by cell-virus interaction at the time of transformation. During subcultivation after transformation, environmental factors may have selected certain of the observed chromosome abnormalities.

Yerganian *et al.*, 1962

In the degenerating growth-phase of human diploid monolayer fibroblasts, tetraploid and nondiploid cells began to appear. SV40 infection of these cultured fibroblast-like cells in the declining growth phase resulted in rapid and extensive chromosome alterations in the first few days following infection. These additional changes included sharp increase in tetraploid metaphases, breaks, dicentric chromosomes, pronounced secondary constrictions, chromosome loss, and telomeric associations. "Rapid" transformation appeared to be correlated with infection of older cultures.

Wolman *et al.*, 1964

In order to determine the order of appearance of the various types of chromosomal aberrations, the transformation process in SV40-infected human diploid cultures was sampled at close intervals before, during and after the observed morphological changes. An increase in single chromatid breakage usually coincided with the first observable signs of morphological transformation. Following this wave of "breaks" there was a progression of increased tetraploidy, dicentric formation and general heteroploidy. This simple relation in time of appearance of primary and derived types of chromosome changes does not differ from chromosome changes induced in plant and other materials with either mutagenic chemicals

Moorhead and Saksela, 1965

TABLE 8-V (Continued)

Reference

or radiation. The "silent" period after SV40 infection (prior to morphological transformation and increase in chromatid breaks) varied in the studies reported here.

Loss of contact regulation of cell division (one feature of transformation) occurred prior to alteration of chromosome morphology. The chromosomal changes represented the first cytological alteration detectable.   Weinstein and Moorhead, 1967

Leukocyte cell lines may have both indefinite life expectancy and a high degree of diploidy (Christofinis, 1969). However, in another report (Gerber *et al.*, 1969) introduction of virus was accompanied by both major chromosome change and long-term growth potential. Since chromosome studies in established leukocyte cell lines are presently under investigation, general conclusions are tenative.

The Problem of "Spontaneous" Transformation

The problem of whether or not "spontaneous" transformation occurs in human cultured cells may be purely semantic. On the other hand it is valuable to consider this question from the point of view that it is always important to identify transforming agents. If one cannot be identified, it is perhaps best to consider that the cause of changes in cultured cell characteristics is unsolved rather than spontaneous, if one defines "spontaneous" as: "arising without external constraint or stimulus."

The Problem of Biochemical Differences between Transformed and Nontransformed Cultured Cells

The distinguishing property of the cancer cell is its capacity to multiply and invade in situations where normal cells are restricted from multiplication and invasiveness. The extraordinary research effort of the last decades to translate this primary difference between cancer and normal cells into unique and specific biochemical differences is based on the very reasonable premise that the discovery of a unique biochemical property for all cancer cells is virtually an essential step in the eventual design of completely and absolutely specific anticancer chemotherapeutic agents. Unfortunately the efforts to achieve such translation have so far largely failed, but in the course of this "failure" an enormous amount has been learned about cell chemistry, physiology, and reproduction (Prescott, in press).

Although there is no generally accepted, coherent hypothesis to explain neoplasia in biochemical terms, specific differences between transformed (neoplastic) and nontransformed cultured human cells are reported from many laboratories (Table 8-VI). In many reports, no differences are noted (Castor and Naylor, 1969).

TABLE 8-VI

EXAMPLES OF REPORTED BIOCHEMICAL DIFFERENCES
BETWEEN "TRANSFORMED" AND "NONTRANSFORMED"
HUMAN CULTURED CELLS

Type of "Non-transformed" Cell Studied	Type of "Transformed" Cell Studied	Conclusions	Reference
Parathyroid adenoma cells in monolayer culture	Parathyroid adenoma cells in monolayer culture, transformed with SV40.	*Production of parathyroid hormone* by parathyroid cells growns as monolayer cultures has not been reported. However, transformation by SV40 results in continued hormone production.	Deftos *et al.*, 1968
WI-38, embryo lung SRO, adult skin	HeLa-S3, cervical carcinoma WISH, amnion WI-38, SV40 transformed, embryo lung	*Specific enzyme activity* (cytidine aminohydrolase which converts cytidine to uridine) not present in diploid cells, may be present in transformed cells.	Ellem, 1968
WI-38 and WI-120 embryo lung, diploid JMC1 and JMC2 embryo muscle, diploid	HeLa-wild, HeLa-S3, FL amnion; all nondiploid	The nondiploid cells showed greater capacity to proliferate when rate of ribosomal RNA synthesis was depressed, possibly because DNA synthesis was freed from some of the controls present in diploid cells.	Studzinski and Ellem, 1968

TABLE 8-VI (Continued)

Type of "Non-transformed" Cell Studied	Type of "Transformed" Cell Studied	Conclusions	Reference
Leukocytes from normal individuals	Leukemic lymphocytes	Differences in *tRNA species* are noted between peripheral blood leukocytes in culture from normal individuals and from patients with acute and chronic lymphatic leukemia.	Gallo, 1969
WI-38, embryo lung	WI-38, RSV (Rous sarcoma virus transformed, embryo lung)	Treatment of resting state diploid cultures with RSV suspensions stimulates their *DNA synthesis* during the following 24 hrs.	Macieira-Coelho *et al.*, 1969
	HeLa Ch (cloned HeLa constitutive for high levels of alkaline phosphatase)	A *fetal-like alkaline phosphatase* is produced. The stimulus may be derepression of the genome in the HeLa cell, in other words, renewed expression of genes normally acting early but not later in development.	Elson and Cox, 1969

HUMAN DISEASES ASSOCIATED WITH CELL TRANSFORMATION IN CULTURE

An assay system has been developed to measure the fraction of cells in a given culture population that become transformed after the addition of a transforming agent, SV40 and adeno 7-SV40 "hybrid" virus (Todaro, 1968) or human adenovirus type 12 (Todaro and Aaronson, 1968). Cells derived from various human sources have been studied in regard to their susceptibility to transformation (Table 8-VII). The most susceptible cells were derived from patients with Fanconi anemia, a rare autosomal recessive disorder associated with a high risk of tumor formation. Cell strains from these individuals also show a high level of chromosome breakage, but do not evolve into permanent cell lines, unless a transforming agent is introduced (Fig. 8-1) (also see Chap. 3, single gene defects associated with chromosome abnormalities). Late passage ("old") diploid cultures are also more easily transformed than early passage ("young") cultures; this age-related susceptibility occurs before any increase in chromosome abnormalities can be detected in the cultures. Furthermore, cells from individuals over seventy years are more susceptible than cells from embryos or newborns. "Finally, if one wished to look for oncogenic agents for human cells, the highly susceptible cells such as those derived from patients with Fanconi's anemia appear to offer the most sensitive *in vitro* test system" (Todaro, 1968, p. 273).

TESTS OF ANTITUMOR AND TUMOR-PRODUCING AGENTS

The original goal of tumor chemotherapy was to find chemical substances more toxic to neoplastic cells than to normal cells. Although this goal has not been achieved so simply, tests have been devised to determine the toxicity of candidate antitumor compounds on various mammalian cells in culture, including human cells. When cell protein formation was the parameter mea-

TABLE 8-VII

TRANSFORMATION SUSCEPTIBILITY OF DIPLOID
HUMAN CELL LINES
(from Todaro, 1968; transforming agents SV40 and
adeno 7-SV40 "hybrid" virus)

Source	Number of Cultures Tested	Number of Cultures with Increased Susceptibility
Embryo lung	12	0
Newborn foreskin	8	0
Adult skin	17	1*
Aged adult skin	4	1
Down's syndrome	5	5
Fanconi anemia		
Homozygous	4	4
Heterozygous	5	5
"Sarcoma-prone" family†	5	3
"Transformation-prone" family	3	3*

*Since the index case was found to produce cells susceptible to transformation, other family members were checked; two siblings and his father also produced susceptible cells, making a total of 4 susceptible individuals in a "transformation-prone" family.

†Several cases of sarcoma occurred in the family.

sured, a similarity in the response of various cultured cells to a given inhibitor was evident, irrespective of cell source; in many cases there was correlation between inhibitory activity on protein synthesis of cultured cells (or inhibition of cell numbers) and antitumor activity in an animal host (Perlman, 1968; Table 8-VIII). Unfortunately cytotoxicity in culture was not always correlated with toxicity to the whole animal and *in vivo* tissue specificity was not always predictable.

It might be possible to improve the correlation between test assay results and *in vivo* effect if other cellular functions or specific cell components were used as markers for cytotoxicity assays in culture. On the other hand, some of the lack of positive correlation might be due to simple failure of agents to reach cells

TABLE 8-VIII

SENSITIVITY OF SOME EXPERIMENTAL ANIMAL TUMORS
AND OF KB (HUMAN NONDIPLOID) CULTURES,
TO ANTITUMOR COMPOUNDS
(from Perlman, 1968)

Compound	*Inhibition of Tumors*[*] (No. of Animals With Tumors Inhibited/ No. of Animals With Tumors Tested)	*Cell Culture Toxicity*[†] (ID_{50} micrograms/ml)
Diethylstilbestrol	0/8	>10.0
Urethan	0/8	>10.0
Potassium arsenite	1/8	0.1
Myleran	1/8	1.0
Hydrocortisone	1/8	7.0
6-Mercaptopurine	2/8	0.07
Vinblastine	2/8	0.1
Methotrexate	3/8	.01
Dactinomycin	3/8	.004
5-Fluorouracil	3/8	0.8
N-Deacetylthiocolchicine	2/8	.001
2'-Deoxy-5-fluorouridine	5/8	.008
Mitomycin C	5/8	.025
Cyclophosphamide	8/8	.01

[*]Tumors used included melanoma B16, carcinoma C1025, adenocarcinoma E0771, Ridgeway osteogenic sarcoma, sarcoma T241, Walker carcinosarcoma 256, Ehrlich ascites tumor, and Mecca lymphosarcoma.

[†]Measured in ID_{50} microg/ml = amount of antitumor compound needed to reduce growth of KB cell cultures to approximately half that observed in untreated control.

in the whole animal, or failure to reach them in proper concentration. As mentioned in Chapter 2 (assays of the effects of environmental agents on cultured cells), correlation between dose directly to individual cells and dose to an intact individual is never easy to determine.

Established cell lines derived from the buffy coat of normal humans and patients with neoplastic diseases have been studied regarding cell sensitivity to various antimetabolites (Aoki and Moore, 1969). Cell lines were found to differ significantly from one another in sensitivity to 5-fluorouracil, Methotrexate®, and cystosine arabinoside. The different levels of sensitivity did not lie in a continuous spectrum, but could be grouped into discrete classes. The authors suggested that these sensitivity classes might be related to actual genetic differences between the cell lines.

Chemical transformation of human cell cultures has already been mentioned earlier in this chapter. Assays of the ability of a compound to transform and also its toxicity to cultured cells are used to test carcinogenicity of the compound (Table IX).

> Cell cultures have certain limitations as test systems for the carcinogenicity of chemicals. For example, noncarcinogenic chemicals that *in vivo* are metabolized to derivatives with carcinogenic activity may be missed in a cell-culture system. Conversely, carcinogens that are rapidly inactivated *in vivo* may be "false positives" in a cell-culture system. . . . Transformation phenomenon in cell cultures exhibit a considerable variability with respect both to the percentage of transformed cells and to the time lag between treatment with the carcinogen and the appearance of transformed cells. These parameters are apparently dependent on the carcinogen studied as well as on the cell type and the culture conditions used. . . . The number of chemicals tested for their ability to induce cellular transformation in culture is quite limited (Table IX). In particular weak carcinogens have so far not been included in significant numbers in these tests. Cell cultures have in fact been used more as model systems to study the mechanisms of action of highly active carcinogens than as screening systems to detect carcinogen activity (Schindler, 1969, p. 235-236).

CULTURES FROM TUMORS

Many cell cultures have been started from benign and malignant human neoplasms (Tables 8-X and 8-XI). Some of these

TABLE 8-IX

COMPOUNDS TESTED FOR "CARCINOGENICITY" IN CELL CULTURE
(from Schindler, 1969)

Tested for Ability to Transform
benzo(a)pyrene
3-methylcholanthrene
7,12-dimethylbenz(a)anthracene
7-methylbenz(a)anthracene
dimethylnitrosamine
N-nitrosomethylurea
4-nitroquinoline-1-oxide
6-chloro-4-nitroquinoline-1-oxide
4-hydroxyaminoquinoline-1-oxide
urethane
4-dimethylaminoazobenzene
3'-methyl-4-dimethylaminoazobenzene

Tested for Cell Toxicity
3-methylocholanthrene
benzo(a)pyrene
7,12-dimethylbenz(a)anthracene
N-nitrosomethylurea
croton oil

cultures have been used for assay of antitumor agents. Others have contributed useful information about the behavior of tumor cells in culture. Some reflect selected cell types with questionable relation to the original neoplastic cells.

THE FUTURE OF CELL CULTURE AND THE STUDY OF NEOPLASIA

Knowledge of whether a tumor is unicellular or multicellular in origin may provide important insight into its pathogenesis. Information relevant to this point can be obtained by studying cells cloned from neoplasms arising in individuals with two or more genetically different cell populations (see Chap. 2, on cloning). At present, both unicellular and multicellular origins have been suggested from studies of different types of neoplasms (Fialkow *et al.*, 1967).

Looking toward treatment of malignancy, cells hybridized by the viral fusion technique (see Chap. 11 on somatic cell hybridization) can be used to immunize a host animal against challenge with his own tumor cells (Watkins and Chen, 1969). Hybrid cells

TABLE 8-X

EXAMPLES OF ESTABLISHED HUMAN CELL LINES DERIVED
FROM NEOPLASMS AND AVAILABLE FROM THE
AMERICAN TYPE CUTURE COLLECTION*

Name of Cell Line	Origin	Cell Repository Number
HeLa	Carcinoma, cervix	CCL 2
HeLa 229	Carcinoma, cervix	CCL 2.1
KB	Carcinoma, oral	CCL 17
Hep-2	Carcinoma, larynx	CCL 23
J-111	Monocytic leukemia	CCL 24
RPMI 2650	Quasidiploid tumor	CCL 30
Tu Wi	Wilms' tumor	CCL 31
EB-3	Burkitt lymphoma	CCL 85
RAJI	Burkitt lymphoma	CCL 86
Jijoye	Burkitt lymphoma, clone P-2003	CCL 87
CCRF-CEM	Peripheral blood, acute lymphoblastic leukemia	CCL 119
CCRF-SB	Peripheral blood, acute lymphoblastic leukemia	CCL 120
CCRF-HBS-2	Human tumors in hamsters; source: peripheral blood, acute lymphoblastic leukemia	CCL 120.1

*American Type Culture Collection Cell Repository
12301 Parklawn Drive
Rockville, Maryland 20852

are formed between tumor cells with weak transplantation antigens and cultured cells with transplantation antigens that are
very strong in the tumor host animal, because of species difference. These hybrids of tumor cells and of cells of another
species may be regarded as an "attenuated" tumor for the host
with the original tumor. It is possible that "attenuated" tumor
cells could be used to immunize humans against their own
malignancies (also see Chap. 6, on use of cell culture to study
antigenicity in neoplasms).

Although the etiology of neoplasia is far from solved, conclusions and techniques derived thus far from studies of cultured
cells will contribute to the overall solution or to the direction of
investigations. Firstly,

both transformation of cultures *in vitro* and malignant transformation represent the induction of heritable mutations usually involving

TABLE 8-XI

EXAMPLES OF USES OF CULTURES FROM HUMAN TUMORS

Problem to be Solved	Methodology	Solution	Reference
Does cell selection occur during culture of tumor cells to obtain enough mitotic figures for chromosome analysis?	Minced tumor tissue was converted to a suspension of cells by shaking. Karyotypes were prepared: (a) directly; (b) after culture for 1-4 days. Karyotypes were also prepared from 1-3 day cultures of minced tumor tissue.	Cell line selection was not demonstrated during the short-term culture techniques used.	Kolter and Lubs, 1967
What is the relation of differentiated function to neoplasia? Does neoplasia necessarily represent loss of differentiation?	Cells from a human parathyroid adenoma were infected with simian virus 40 and maintained in serial monolayer culture.	These transformed cells continued to produce parathyroid hormone.	Deftos et al., 1968
	Line BeWo derived from human gestational choriocarcinoma has been permanently established.	A high degree of synthesis of functional human chorionic gonadotropin has been maintained for 18 months in culture.	Pattillo et al., 1968
	Two cell lines were derived from an embryonal rhabdomyosarcoma. Cells of both lines grew as monolayers in liquid medium and formed colonies in agar medium.	Each line consisted of 2 cytologic types resembling those of the original tumor spindle cells and large multinucleated cells. Cells of both lines contained myosin-ATPase and cells of one line contained myoglobin.	McAllister et al., 1969
What is the role of viruses in cultures from various human tumors?	Susceptibility was determined of Burkitt's lymphoma cell lines to reovirus (type 3) infection and to	Reovirus carrier state could be established in Burkitt's lymphoma cultures, without enhancement of herpes	Levy et al., 1968

TABLE 8-XI (Continued)

Problem to be Solved	Methodology	Solution	Reference
	reovirus plus herpes group virus infection.	group virus carrier state. These viruses may not have an etiologic role in the tumor.	
	After 15 months of *in vitro* cultivation and after "spontaneous" transformation from fibroblast-like to epithelial-like morphology, a human Wilms' tumor culture was shown to contain a small virus.	Morphologically the virus resembled papova viruses. Attempts are continuing to establish a biological assay for the virus and to recover similar agents from other Wilms' tumors.	Smith *et al.*, 1969
	Cultures were initiated from a malignant pleural effusion of a patient with liposarcoma. (Liposarcoma cells were present on direct cytological exam of the pleural fluid.)	Foci of cells appeared in the cultures and had the characteristics of transformed cells as well as the cytological appearance of liposarcoma. These foci contained viral particles by EM, similar to sarcoma viruses of avian and murine species.	Morton *et al.*, 1969
Can the agar culture method be used to differentiate neoplastic from hyperplastic cells?	Explants and trypsin-dispersed cells from solid tumors, leukemic bone marrow, normal fetal tissues, and hyperplastic human tissues were cultured in soft agar.	Solid tumor cells formed colonies with histologic characteristics of the original tumor. Leukemic bone marrow did not form colonies; cells from normal fetal tissues did not form colonies; cells from hyperplastic tissues did form colonies. Thus, agar culture growth does not distinguish neoplastic, hyperplastic, and normal growth.	McAllister and Reed, 1968

TABLE 8-XI (Continued)

Problem to be Solved	Methodology	Solution	Reference
Can cell lines from particular human malignant neoplasms be used to test specific antitumor agents?	The cytopathic effect of three chemotherapeutic agents on breast carcinoma cells in culture was observed.	The results were found to parallel those observed clinically.	Martorelli et al., 1969
If gonadal tumors arise from a germ cell line that has undergone meiosis, are cultured tumor cells missing one gene from each heterozygous pair present in somatic cells of the person who has the tumor?	Three independently segregating allelic isozymes in 11 benign cystic teratomas of the human ovary were compared with normal tissue of the same case. (Glucose-6-phosphate dehydrogenase and two phosphoglucomutases were studied.)	Some but not all of the tumors from heterozygous persons were homozygous for a particular isozyme. Therefore these tumors probably arose from a germ cell that had undergone meiosis with varying degrees of crossing-over.	Linder, 1969
Can tumor cells be selected from a population of normal cells by in vitro culture techniques?	Cell cultures from human sarcomas differed from those derived from normal adult tissue in that in some cases the sarcoma cells formed colonies when inoculated as single cells onto monolayers of contact-inhibited cells.	This system provided a method of selecting cells that have decreased contact inhibition and may be used to select tumor cells from a population containing a large excess of normal cells.	Aaronson et al., 1970

mitotic instability and potentials for progressive evolution as a cell population. . . . Genetic damage is the common denominator of the known classes of carcinogenic agents: irradiation, chemicals and viruses (Moorhead and Saksela, 1965, p. 282).

Secondly,

in basic research in cell biology, the study of the loss of regulation of cell reproduction logically proceeds from a prior understanding of the molecular basis for the intact regulatory mechanism in normal tissues. This latter understanding is in turn dependent upon a firm and detailed knowledge of the processes that constitute cell growth and cell division (Prescott, in press) (also see Chap. 12 on cell cycle events).

Thirdly,

Although the length of the cell cycle varies in different kinds of cells, it is shorter in certain cells of the adult animal than in some of the fastest growing tumors. Tumor growth, therefore, must involve other kinetic parameters besides speed of cell proliferation. Since these parameters are related to control of cell division and since a cell in DNA synthesis is generally a cell that has already taken the decision to divide, the various factors involved in initiation of DNA biosynthesis are of particular interest in any attempt to explain the mechanism of tumor growth (Baserga, 1965, p. 581).

REFERENCES
General

Dulbecco, R.: The induction of cancer by viruses. *Sci Amer, 216*:28, 1967.

Foley, G. E.: Methods for determining neoplastic properties. *Nat Cancer Inst Monogr, 29*:217, 1968.

Hayflick, L.: Oncogenesis *in vitro. Nat Cancer Inst Monogr, 26*:355, 1967.

Hayflick, L., and Moorhead, P. S.: The limited *in vitro* lifetime of human diploid cell strains. In Harris, R. J. C. (Ed.): *Cytogenetics of Cells in Culture. Symposia of the International Society for Cell Biology 3.* New York, Academic Press, 1964, pp. 155-173.

Prescott, D. M.: Biology of cancer and the cancer cell: Normal and abnormal regulation of cell reproduction. *Proceedings of the 6th National Cancer Congress,* in press.

Specific

Aaronson, S. A., and Todaro, G. J.: Human diploid cell transformation by DNA extracted from the tumor virus SV40. *Science, 166*:390, 1969.

Aaronson, S. A.; Todaro, G. J., and Freeman, A. E.: Human sarcoma cells in culture. *Exp Cell Res, 61*:1, 1970.

Anderson, J.; Yates, V. J.; Jasty, V., and Mancini, L. O.: The *in vitro* transformation by an avian adenovirus (CELO). III. Human amnion cultures. *J Nat Cancer Inst, 43*:575, 1969.

Aoki, Y., and Moore, G. E.: Comparative sensitivity to various antimetabolites of several established cell lines derived from the buffy coat of normal humans and patients with neoplastic diseases. *Cancer Res,* 29:1307, 1969.

Baserga, R.: The relationship of the cell cycle to tumor growth and control of cell division: A review. *Cancer Res,* 25:581, 1965.

Black, P. H., and Todaro, G. J.: *In vitro* transformation of hamster and human cells with the adeno 7-SV 40 hybrid virus. *Proc Nat Acad Sci USA,* 54:374, 1965.

Castor, C. W., and Naylor, B.: Characteristics of normal and malignant human mesothelial cells studied *in vitro. Lab Invest,* 20:437, 1969.

Chang, R. S., and Sinskey, T. J.: Observations on the transformation of human amnion cell cultures by simian virus 40. *J Nat Cancer Inst,* 40:505, 1968.

Christofinis, G. J.: Chromosome and transplantation results of a human leukocyte cell line derived from a healthy individual. *Cancer,* 24:649, 1969.

Deftos, L. J.; Rabson, A. S.; Buckle, R. M.; Aurbach, G. D., and Potts, J. T.: Parathyroid hormone production *in vitro* by human parathyroid cells transformed by simian virus 40. *Science,* 159:435, 1968.

Ellem, K. A. O.: Cystidine aminohydrolase activity in intact cultured transformed cells. *J Cell Physiol,* 71:17, 1968.

Elson, N. A., and Cox, R. P.: Production of fetal-like alkaline phosphatase by HeLa cells. *Biochem Genet,* 3:549, 1969.

Fialkow, P. J.; Gartler, S. M., and Yoshida, A.: Clonal origin of chronic myelocytic leukemia in man. *Proc Nat Acad Sci USA,* 58:1468, 1967.

Foley, G. E.: Methods for determining neoplastic properties. *Nat Cancer Inst Monogr,* 29:217, 1968.

Gallo, R. C.: Transfer RNA's in human leukemia. *J Cell Physiol,* 74 (Suppl.)1:149, 1969.

Gerber, P.; Whang-Peng, J., and Monroe, J. H.: Transformation and chromosome changes induced by Epstein-Barr virus in normal human leukocyte cultures. *Proc Nat Acad Sci USA,* 63:740, 1969.

Glade, P. R.; Hirshaut, Y.; Douglas, S. D., and Hirschhorn, K.: Lymphoid suspension cultures from patients with viral hepatitis. *Lancet,* 2:1273, 1968.

Hirschhorn, K., and Bloch-Shtacher, N.: Transformation of genetically abnormal cells. In *Genetic Concepts and Neoplasia.* Proc 23rd Ann Symposium Fundamental Concepts of Cancer. Baltimore, Williams and Wilkins 1970.

Katz, M.; Koprowski, H., and Moorhead, P.: Transformation of cells cultured from human brain tissue. *Exp Cell Res,* 57:149, 1969.

Kotler, S., and Lubs, H. A.: Comparison of direct and short-term tissue culture techniques in determining solid tumor karyotypes. *Cancer Res,* 27:1861, 1967.

Levy, J. A.; Henle, G.; Henle, W., and Zajac, B. A.: Effect of reovirus type 3 on cultured Burkitt's tumour cells. *Nature (London),* 220:607, 1968.

Linder, D.: Gene loss in human teratomas. *Proc Nat Acad Sci USA,* 63:699, 1969.

Love, R.: Differences in the internal structure of nucleoli of diploid and non-diploid transformed or neoplastic cells *in vitro. Exp Cell Res,* 40:188, 1965.

McAllister, R. M.; Melnyk, J.; Finklestein, J. Z.; Adams, E. C., and Gardner, M. B.: Cultivation *in vitro* of cells derived from a human rhabdomyosarcoma. *Cancer,* 24:520, 1969.

McAllister, R. M., and Reed, G.: Colonial growth in agar of cells derived from neoplastic and non-neoplastic tissues of children. *Pediat Res,* 2:356 1968.

Macieira-Coelho, A.: Dissociation between inhibition of movement and inhibition of division in RSV transformed human fibroblasts. *Exp Cell Res,* 47:193, 1967.

Macieira-Coelho, A.; Hiu, I. J., and Garcia-Giralt, E.: Stimulation of DNA synthesis in resting stage human fibroblasts after infection with Rous sarcoma virus. *Nature (London),* 222:1172, 1969.

Martorelli, B.; Parshley, M. S., and Moore, J. G.: Effects of chemotherapeutic agents on two lines of human breast carcinomas in tissue culture. *Surg Gynec Obstet,* 1282:1001, 1969.

Matsuya, Y., and Green, H.: Somatic cell hybrid between the established human line D98 (presumptive HeLa) and 3T3. *Science,* 163:697, 1969.

Michl, J.; Rezacoba, D., and Holeckova, E.: Adaptation of mammalian cells to cold. IV. Diploid cells. *Exp Cell Res,* 44:680, 1966.

Moorhead, P. S., and Saksela, E.: The sequence of chromosome aberrations during SV40 transformation of a human diploid cell strain. *Hereditas (Lund),* 52:271, 1965.

Morton, D. L.; Hall, W. T., and Malmgren, R. A.: Human liposarcomas: Tissue cultures containing foci of transformed cells with viral particles. *Science,* 165:813, 1969.

Nabholz, M.; Miggiano, V., and Bodmer, W.: Genetic analysis with human-mouse somatic cell hybrids. *Nature (London),* 223:358, 1969.

Pattilo, R. A.; Gey, G. O.; Delfs, E., and Mattingly, R. F.: Human hormone porduction *in vitro. Science,* 159:1467, 1968.

Perlman, D.: Value of mammalian cell culture as a biochemical tool. *Science,* 160:42, 1968.

Prescott, D. M.: Biology of cancer and the cancer cell: Normal and abnormal regulation of cell reproduction. *Proceedings of the 6th National Cancer Congress,* in press.

Saksela, E., and Moorhead, P. S.: Aneuploidy in the degenerative phase of serial cultivation of human cell strains. *Proc Nat Acad Sci USA,* 50:390, 1963.

Schindler, R.: Suitability of cell cultures for carcinogenicity tests. *Food Cosmet Toxic,* 7:233, 1969.

Shein, H. M., and Enders, J. F.: Transformation induced by simian virus 40 in human renal cell cultures. I. Morphology and growth characteristics. *Proc Nat Acad Sci USA,* 48:1164, 1962.

Smith, J. W.; Pinkel, D., and Dabrowski, S.: Detection of a small virus in a cultivated human Wilms' tumor. *Cancer,* 24:527, 1969.

Studzinski, G. P., and Ellem, K. A. O.: Differences between diploid and heteroploid cultured mammalian cells in their response to puromycin aminonucleoside. *Cancer Res,* 28:1773, 1968.

Sultanian, I. V., and Freeman, G.: Enhanced growth of human embryonic cells infected with adenovirus 12. *Science,* 154:665, 1966.

Todaro, G. J.: Variable susceptibility of human cell strains to SV40 transformation. *Nat Cancer Inst Monogr,* 29:271, 1968.

Todaro, G. J., and Aaronson, S. A.: Human cell strains susceptible to focus formation by human adenovirus type 12. *Proc Nat Acad Sci USA,* 61:1278, 1968.

Todaro, G. J.; Zeve, V., and Aaronson, S. A.: Virus in cell culture derived from human tumor patients. *Nature (London)* 226:1047, 1970.

Watkins, J. F., and Chen, L.: Immunization of mice against Ehrlich ascites tumour using a hamster/Ehrlich ascites tumour hybrid cell line. *Nature (London),* 223:1018, 1969.

Weinstein, D., and Moorhead, P. S.: Karyology of permanent human cell line, W-18VA2, originated by SV40 transformation. *J Cell Comp Physiol,* 65:85, 1965.

Weinstein, D., and Moorhead, P. S.: The relation of karyotypic change to loss of contact inhibition of division in human diploid cells after SV40 infection. *J Cell Physiol,* 69:367, 1967.

Weiss, M. C., and Green, H.: Human-mouse hybrid cell lines containing partial complements of human chromosomes and functioning human genes. *Proc Nat Acad Sci USA,* 58:1104, 1967.

Wolman, S. R.; Hirschhorn, K., and Todaro, G. J.: Early chromosomal changes in SV40-infected human fibroblast cultures. *Cytogenetics (Basel),* 3:45, 1964.

Yerganian, G.; Shein, H. M., and Enders, J. F.: Chromosomal disturbances observed in human fetal renal cells transformed *in vitro* by simian virus 40 and carried in culture. *Cytogenetics (Basel),* 1:314, 1962.

Chapter Nine

DIFFERENTIATION

Interesting differentiated functions preserved in serial culture of human cells have already been considered in Chapter 4, metabolic defects in somatic cells. Table 9-I gives examples of additional differentiated functions retained in serial culture and their cells of origin, in order to illustrate the variety of mammalian cell models available for study. The environmental control of these functions is less difficult to study in culture than in the intact individual, and precise knowledge of environmental controls is essential to both therapy and prevention of disease. Morphologically differentiated cells can be grown with the use of specialized cultural conditions (see Chap. 1).

TABLE 9-I

EXAMPLES OF SERIALLY CULTURED MAMMALIAN CELLS
THAT RETAIN ORGAN AND TISSUE-SPECIFIC FUNCTIONS

Differentiated Function or Product	Mammalian Cell Origin
Adrenocorticotropic hormone and growth hormone	Pituitary tumor
Collagen	Fibroblasts
Corticosteroids	Adrenal tumor, Leydig cell tumor
Histamine	Mast cell tumor
Melanin	Iris and retina, melanoma
Mucopolysaccharides	Fibroblast-like cells
Myofibril formation	Myoblasts
Nerve growth factor	Neuroblastoma
Serotonin	Mast cell tumor
Spermatogenesis	Testicular culture

185

PRIMARY CULTURES

Primary cultures (Chap. 1) may preserve differentiation no longer present after the first, or a series of subcultures. A clear example of this point concerns the growth of epidermal tissue. When cultures are established from explants of human skin, the initial epithelial-like primary outgrowth does not persist in the usual type of serial culture but the fibroblast-like cells do persist after subculture. If epidermis is removed from the initial skin explant prior to culture, leaving dermis alone, only fibroblast-like cells grow when the culture is started. Primary epithelial-like (epidermal) outgrowth maintains morphological and biochemical differentiation no longer present later in the serial culture. Cells in the epidermal outgrowth are polygonal, grow as tightly adherent sheets, and show characteristic desmosomes and tonofilaments by light and electron microscopy (Karasek, 1966). Furthermore, human histidase usually isolated from homogenates of stratum corneum (epidermis) of skin, is also present in the primary epidermal outgrowth but is not maintained in serial fibroblast-like culture (Barnhisel *et al.*, 1970).

Dissociated epidermis from human foreskin has been grown in primary culture in chambers designed to allow study by time lapse photography (Cohen and Szabo, 1968). The cultures were followed for up to seven weeks. Different morphological types of cells were observed, including melanocytes and melanoblasts. Epidermal cells divided as frequently as every 12 to 16 hours, formed sheets and seemed to keratinize, though abnormally. Melanocytes also divided, established normal relationship with malpighian cells and pigment donation was observed. Unpigmented cells, often not dendritic in form, became pigment-producing and dendritic.

Placental tissue in primary monolayer culture gives rise to a mixed population of cells; existing methods for cell identification *in vitro* include cytology, enzyme histochemistry and the demonstration of chorionic gonadotrophin production. (a) Three morphologic cell types may be distinguished in cultures of chorionic villi: fibroblast-like, epithelial-like and giant multinucleated cells. It has been suggested that these types originate from mesenchyme, cytotrophoblast and syncytio-trophoblast respectively, but morphological identification alone may be unreliable. (b) Further evidence was provided by histochemical localization of alkaline phosphatase in epithelial-like and multinucleated cells, suggesting origin from trophoblast, in view of the distribution of this enzyme in direct studies of placenta. (c) Gonadotrophic activity of the culture medium was found to decline along with the disappearance of giant multinucleated cells, again suggesting that these might be trophoblastic in origin. In addition, specific fluorescence was shown by the large syncytial masses, in the presence of antitrophoblast serum produced in mice and a fluorescent-labeled antimouse serum (Rigby and Curzen, 1969). These studies of differentiation in placental culture again illustrate the need to correlate morphological, histochemical and biochemical studies both *in vivo* and in subsequent culture.

Cells from amniotic fluid in primary monolayer culture give rise to a mixed population of cells (see Chap. 5). Further study is required to identify the origin and fate of these different cell types in order to increase the diagnostic potential of amniotic fluid cell culture.

The primary outgrowth from explants of tissues that are ciliated *in vivo* may be observed to contain cells with beating cilia. Care must be taken to preserve appropriate culture conditions during observation, particularly in regard to temperature and pH. This preservation of functional cilia permits controlled studies of cilia formation and function, particularly with regard to the influence of environmental factors. Ciliated cultures of trachea from fresh human embryos were also found to be a superior type of culture for isolation of certain human respiratory viruses (Harnette and Hooper, 1968).

Antigenic changes in primary cultures of human colon epithelium have been studied by immunofluorescence using heterologous gastrointestinal-specific antiserum and a serum containing autoantibody to intestine from a patient with ulcerative colitis (Ghose *et al.*, 1968). The number of antigen positive cells and the amount of antigen in individual cells both decreased, but antigen could still be detected in the cultures as long as they survived, about twenty days in these experiments.

SPECIALIZED CELL STRUCTURE AND FUNCTION

Differentiation may be maintained in primary cultures, as just discussed, or after subculture, either with or without special environmental manipulations (Table 9-II).

TABLE 9-II

EXAMPLES OF MAINTENANCE OF SPECIALIZED CELL
STRUCTURE AND FUNCTION IN CULTURE

	Reference
Human fibroblast-like cells in monolayer culture produce *collagen* under the usual conditions of serial culture.	Davies *et al.*, 1967
The Edmonston strain of measles virus was applied to a near-triploid human cell line originally derived from male embryonic lung. *Syncytia formation* was induced by the virus; giant cells contained varying numbers of nuclei from a few to more than 100. Complete or partial synchronization of division between nuclei sharing the same cytoplasm was of frequent occurrence. These nuclei also had points of contact or fusion.	Heneen *et al.*, 1967
Cells from a human parathyroid adenoma were infected with simian virus 40 and maintained in serial monolayer culture. These transformed cells continued to produce *parathyroid hormone.*	Deftos *et al.*, 1968
A malignant tumor of the placenta, chorioepithelioma, is characterized by *production of human chorionic gonadotropin* (HCG). An established cell line (BeWO) derived from this tumor has been in continuous culture through more than 50 passages and produces HCG (about 10^{-5} IU of gonadotropin per cultured cell per 24 hrs.). The BeWO line has maintained the *cellular characteristics of the cytotrophoblast of the patient's original tumor.* The establishment of this cell line required serial passage of the original human tumor in animals (hamster cheek pouch) prior to serial passage in culture containers (see text).	Pattillo *et al.*, 1968
In human synovial cell cultures extensive *pericellular zones* appeared as irregular gel-like structures whose integrity depended on the presence of hyaluronic acid. Such a zone was thought to be potentially significant as a protective barrier.	Clarris and Fraser, 1968
A significant number of cells that morphologically resemble *plasma cells* are present in 7-10 day cultures of lymphocytes stimulated with pokeweed mitogen (PWM). Cells of this type are not observed with phytohemagglutinin or wax bean glycoprotein stimulation (See Chap. 6 and Table 6-I).	Douglas and Fudenberg, 1969

TABLE 9-II (Continued)

Human bone marrow cells cultivated in a chemically defined system incorporate histidine, phenylalanine, or leucine *in vitro*, as demonstrated by autoradiographic studies. *Megakaryocytes* show intense labeling; *platelet formation* occurs; of the immature members of the granulocytic series, *promyelocytes* show greatest amino acid incorporation, *mature neutrophils* and *eosinophils* show the least; *erythroblasts* and *reticulocytes* also show significant amino acid incorporation. The presence of prednisolone in the medium is associated with increased incorporation of precursor as compared to that of cells cultured in hormone-free medium.

Farnes and Barker, 1969

Clonal lines of neuroblastoma cells were found to *extend or retract axons* depending on the concentration of serum in the culture medium. Neurite extension was not inhibited by cyclohexamide but was sensitive to colchicine or vinblastine, suggesting that neurite formation is dependent on the assembly of microtubules or neurofilaments from preformed protein subunits.

Seeds *et al.*, 1970

A successful technique to establish hormone-producing cultures has been to start with hormone-producing tumor cells and adapt them to serial passage between culture containers and animal hosts (Sato and Yasumura, 1966). An example of the use of this technique on a human tumor (chorioepithelioma) is listed in Table 9-II (Pattillo *et al.*, 1968). Once established, this tumor produced human chorionic gonadotropin (HCG) in serial *in vitro* culture. Continued parathyroid hormone production in serial culture has been obtained after viral transformation of hormone-producing tumor cells (human parathyroid adenoma) (Deftos *et al.*, 1968).

The problem of epithelio-mesenchymal interaction has been investigated for a number of years (Grobstein, 1964). Mesodermal tissue is used to "induce" growth and differentiation of epithelium in culture. Human epithelial-like cells established from skin primary explants will grow on a millipore filter when human fibroblast-like cells are placed on the other side of the filter, in a double chamber (personal observations). On the other hand, these two types of cells will also grow together in primary culture without special techniques. The epithelial-like diploid cells cannot as yet be carried in serial culture by the usual dispersion techniques used for monolayer fibroblast-like cells.

CULTURES WITH PRESERVATION OF TISSUE AND ORGAN MORPHOLOGY

Table 9-III lists some human tissues and organs that have been cultured to maintain *in vivo* architecture (also see Chap. 1, on organ culture and morphologically differentiated tissue culture). Contrary to the usual statement that loss of differentiated function is characteristic of neoplasia, cultures from tumors may facilitate preservation of specialized tissue morphology in culture. Selective overgrowth can still be an obstacle to the culture of morphologically differentiated tumors since fibroblast-like cells may also overgrow cultures started from tumors.

Many interesting investigations during the past decade have developed methods to grow embryonic mammalian tissue for the purpose of studying differentiation under controlled conditions. More recently human embryonic tissues have been included in these studies.

How does a single cell—the fertilized egg—give rise to the many different cell types of a multicellular organism?. . . . The process of functional and structural specialization of cells is called differentiation, and the mechanisms controlling differentiation remain major mysteries of biology. . . . What happens within cells during devel-

TABLE 9-III

A LIST OF SOME HUMAN TISSUES AND ORGANS THAT
MAINTAIN *IN VIVO* ARCHITECTURE IN CULTURE

	Reference
Aorta	Eilberg and Mori, 1969
Brain	Ponten and Macintyre, 1968
Embryonic tissues and organs of various types	Friedenstein *et al.*, 1968 (Also see text)
Intestinal mucosa	Bernik *et al.*, 1968
Nasal and tracheal ciliated epithelium	Harnett and Hooper, 1968
Pulp tissue of teeth	DeVincenzo, 1968
Skin	Prose *et al.*, 1967
Tumors of various types	Pattillo *et al.*, 1968 (Also see Chap. 8, on cultures from tumors)

opment to make one cell type different from another?. . . . What controls these qualitative differences? (Wessells and Rutter, 1969, p. 39).

REFERENCES

General

Eagle, H.: Metabolic controls in cultured mammalian cells. *Science, 148*:42, 1965.

Gartler, S. M.: Genetic markers as tracers in cell culture. *Nat Cancer Inst Monogr, 26*:167, 1967.

Wessells, N. K., and Rutter, W. J.: Phases in cell differentiation. *Sci Amer, 220*:36, 1969.

Specific

Barnhisel, M. L.; Priest, R. E., and Priest, J. H.: Histidase activity in human epidermal culture. *J Cell Physiol, 76*:7, 1970.

Bernik, M. B.; Donnellan, W. L., and Hirsch, B.: Tissue culture of the colonic mucosa with observations in ulcerative colitis. *Gastroenterology, 54*:588, 1968.

Clarris, B. J., and Fraser, J. R. E.: On the pericellular zone of some mammalian cells *in vitro. Exp Cell Res, 49*:181, 1968.

Cohen, J., and Szabo, G.: Study of pigment donation *in vitro. Exp Cell Res, 50*:418, 1968.

Davies, L. M.; Priest, J. H., and Priest, R. E.: Collagen synthesis by cells synchronously replicating DNA. *Science, 159*:91, 1968.

Deftos, L. J.; Rabson, A. S.; Buckle, R. M.; Aurbach, G. D., and Potts, J. T.: Parathyroid hormone production *in vitro* by human parathyroid cells transformed by simian virus 40. *Science, 159*:435, 1968.

DeVincenzo, J. P.: An organ culture technique for maintaining the pulp tissue of intact human teeth. *Exp Cell Res, 50*:541, 1968.

Douglas, S. D., and Fudenberg, H. H.: *In vitro* development of plasma cells from lymphocytes following pokeweed mitogen stimulation: A fine structural study. *Exp Cell Res, 54*:277, 1969.

Eilberg, R., and Mori, K.: Early stages of *in vitro* calcification of human aortic tissue. *Nature (London), 223*:518, 1969.

Farnes, P., and Barker, B. E.: Tissue culture studies of human bone marrow. II. Protein synthesis in haemic cells. *Exp Cell Res, 54*:53, 1969.

Friedenstein, A. Y.; Rapoport, R. I., and Luria, E. A.: Histotypical structures arising in diploid human strains in organ cultures. *Exp Cell Res, 49*:488, 1968.

Ghose, T.; Nairn, R. C., and Cerini, M.: Persistence of gastrointestinal specific antigens in primary culture of human colon epithelium. *Exp Cell Res, 49*:513, 1968.

Grobstein, C.: Cytodifferentiation and its controls. *Science, 143*:643, 1964.

Harnett, G. B., and Hooper, W. L.: Test-tube organ cultures of ciliated epithelium for the isolation of respiratory viruses. *Lancet, 1*:339, 1968.

Heneen, W. K.; Nichols, W. W.; Levan, A., and Norrby, E.: Studies on syncytia formation in a cell line (LU 106) of human origin after treatment with measles virus. *Hereditas (Lund), 57*:369, 1967.

Karasek, M. A.: *In vitro* culture of human skin epithelial cells. *Invest Derm, 47*:533, 1966.

Pattillo, R. A.; Gey, G. O.; Delfs, E., and Mattingly, R. F.: Human hormone production *in vitro*. *Science, 159*:1467, 1968.

Ponten, J., and Macintyre, E. H.: Long term culture of normal and neoplastic human glia. *Acta Path Microbiol Scand, 74*:465, 1968.

Prose, P. H.; Friedman-Kien, A. E., and Neistein, S.: Ultrastructural studies of organ cultures of adult human skin. *In vitro* growth and keratinization of epidermal cells. *Lab Invest, 17*:693, 1967.

Rigby, P., and Curzen, P.: Identification of human trophoblast *in vitro*. *Nature (London), 222*:1062, 1969.

Sato, G. H., and Yasumura, Y.: Retention of differentiated function in dispersed cell culture. *Trans NY Acad Sci, 28*:1063, 1966.

Seeds, N. W.; Gilman, A. G.; Amano, T., and Nirenberg, M. W.: Regulation of axon formation by clonal lines of a neural tumor. *Proc Nat Acad Sci USA, 66*:160, 1970.

Wessells, N. K., and Rutter, W. J.: Phases in cell differentiation. *Sci Amer, 220*:36, 1969.

Chapter Ten
CELL INTERACTIONS AND GROWTH

Many assays of the effects of environmental agents on cultured cells involve measurements of cell growth. Furthermore investigations of biological principles involved in cell interactions have been, and will continue to be, intimately associated with cell and tissue culture techniques.

CELL MOVEMENT; CONTACT REGULATION

Populations of cells in tissue culture, dissociated from their original tissue structure either artificially or through their own locomotory activities, also show orientation of their movements, and as a result they too take up characteristic spatial patterns. They do not necessarily do the same things they do *in vivo*. They may sort themselves out according to tissue type in mixed reaggregates, or take up a circular colony form when emigrating from a tissue fragment on a substrate, which are things they may never be called on to do in the organism. But the underlying mechanisms of their directed displacements in culture are open to analysis with a facility that is altogether lacking for the analogous displacements in the organism. A picture that is beginning to have some coherence is building up of the control mechanisms of locomotion in tissue culture environments. We can be confident that the tissue culture environments do not yet comprehend enough of the relevant variables to allow one to treat what happens in the organism as a predictable outcome of a general theory of cell movement, but this of course is the goal. . . . Four main control mechanisms of cell movement appear to be at work *in vitro*. They are contact guidance, chemotaxis, contact inhibition, and associated movement (Abercrombie, 1967, pp. 249-250) (Table 10-I).

The observed events of contact inhibition can be described when diploid fibroblast-like cells growing on a glass surface touch. The normal active ruffling movements of a peripheral cellular membrane are inhibited at the point of contact. The result is eventual formation of a cell monolayer (see Chap. 1, on mono-

TABLE 10-I

DEFINITIONS CONCERNED WITH *IN VITRO* STUDY
OF CELL MOVEMENT
(from Abercrombie, 1967)

Definition	*Further Comment*
Contact Guidance	
The orientation of cell movement according to the oriented structure of the substrate	Is the substrate structure some way imprinted on the cell?
Chemotaxis	
Orientation or movement in relation to chemical agents	"Gradient" chemotaxis requires a cell to respond to a gradient of concentration rather than an absolute value; "boundry" chemotaxis requires response to an absolute value.
Contact Inhibition	
An inhibition of the locomotion of a cell in a direction that would take it across the surface of another cell, the inhibition occurring when contact is made between the two cells	This behavioral reaction is easily seen in cultures of many vertebrate cell types made with a plane surface as substrate. Control of solid-substrate locomotion is involved.
Associative Movement	
A form of behavior such that when cells make contact they form adhesions by means of which the cells draw closer together and maintain themselves in close contact	This movement draws the cell toward what it is adhering to. Movement is oriented by the position of the relevant adhesion.

TABLE 10-II

EVENTS OCCURRING DURING CONTACT INHIBITION
(modified from Abercrombie, 1967)

1. The normal active ruffling movements of peripheral cellular membranes are inhibited when contact is made between two cells.

2. A place of contact between cells quickly becomes an adhesion, which takes some force to break and which may persist for many hours. The cell itself can break the adhesion.

3. The inhibition of locomotion is a local one and does not prevent the cell from setting up a new direction of locomotion, led by a newly ruffled membrane, freeing the cell from its adhesion.

4. As initially discrete cells multiply, and as an increasing proportion of the cell surface is in contact with other cells, there is marked decrease in rate of protein, RNA and DNA synthesis and in rate of cellular growth. Free cyto-

TABLE 10-II (Continued)

plasmic polyribosomes present in growing cells are no longer demonstrable. These effects are reversed after the cultures are subdivided (Levine *et al.*, 1965). When these events are demonstrated, the terms contact regulation of cell growth may be used.

5. Contact inhibition does not always follow a collision between cells. Sometimes a fibroblast-like cell will proceed across the exposed surface of another, as if it was part of the substrate. To compare the amount of contact inhibition in different conditions or between different cell types, the number of overlaps of cell-on-cell (nucleus-on-nucleus) may be scored at a given moment in a short-term culture where cells are exposed to mutual collision.

layer cultures). Other events occur as summarized in Table 10-II. The terms contact regulation of cell division or cell growth may also be used *if* these events are demonstrated as outlined in Table 10-II, 4. It is clear that the incidence of contact inhibitions varies considerably with cell type and culture conditions but certain generalizations may be made about this variation. In regard to cell type, those cells which *in vivo* are able to infiltrate into heterologous cell populations show a relatively small degree of contact inhibition to similar heterologous cells *in vitro*. This principle may eventually allow a satisfactory definition of cell invasiveness in culture, without the need for transplanting cells to animal hosts (see Chap. 8, on characteristics of transformed or neoplastic cells in culture). In regard to variation in contact inhibition caused by environmental influences, both culture media and substrate are important, as well as population density (also see later in this chapter).

The term "contact inhibition" should be applied strictly to events as defined by Abercrombie (1967) (Tables 10-I and 10-II), or else should not be used at all. There has been confusion over other uses. In case of doubt, use "contact regulation" and then describe what is regulated, or if contact is not involved, do not use the term.

NUTRITIONAL CONTROLS

The simplest method for controlling the growth and metabolism of cultured cells is to limit the supply of some essential nutrient in the defined media.

Only 28 growth factors have been shown to be required for the sustained growth of mammalian cells *in vitro,* and through control of the input of one or more of these, the average generation time can be varied from 16 hours to 7 days. Thus, if the intracellular pool of a single amino acid falls below a critical concentration of 0.01 to 0.04 mM, there is no demonstrable protein synthesis or cellular growth. . . . (Eagle, 1965, p. 42) (Table 10-III).

"Minimal" defined medium (with supplemented serum) is satisfactory for most studies of human nondiploid cells. Growth rate, plating efficiency, and other cultural characteristics of human diploid cells can usually be studied best with the use of a more complex defined medium. Ham's F-12 medium, for instance, contains forty-six ingredients (Ham, 1965).

A major advance in cell culture methodology has been the development of defined culture media. However, most mam-

TABLE 10-III

COMPOSITION OF MINIMUM ESSENTIAL MEDIUM (EAGLE)

Amino Acids	L-arginine HCl
	L-cystine
	L-glutamine
	L-histidine HCl
	L-isoleucine
	L-leucine
	L-lysine HCl
	L-methionine
	L-phenylalanine
	L-threonine
	L-tryptophan
	L-tyrosine
	L-valine
Vitamins	D-calcium pantothenate
	choline chloride
	i-inositol
	nicotinamide
	pyridoxal HCl
	thiamin HCl
	folic acid
	riboflavin
Inorganic Salts and Other Components	$CaCl_2$
	dextrose
	KCl
	$MgSO_4$
	NaCl
	$NaHCO_3$
	NaH_2PO_4

malian cells including human diploid cells still require undefined serum factor(s) to be presented in the culture media, for cell growth (multiplication) to occur. It has been shown that exhaustion of essential growth factor(s) present in the serum in the medium is responsible for cessation of growth as the cells become crowded (Holley and Kiernan, 1968). Attempts to isolate growth factor(s) and to define them have met with some success. An alpha-globulin whose major component is a glycoprotein of MW 45,000 has been separated from fetal calf serum (Puck *et al.*, 1968). It promotes colony growth of single HeLa cells when added to completely defined medium (Ham's F-12), although this medium may also support slow growth of some cell strains without any protein supplement. Other laboratories have confirmed the presence of a growth-stimulating, alpha-globulin serum component.

> The divergences of interpretation which have arisen are due to a variety of causes, including . . . the lack of reliable, quantitative tests for titration of the biological activity of this growth-promoting factor; and the fact that various investigators have used different cells, media, and methodologies for assessment of the biological activities of their fractions (Puck *et al.*, 1968, p. 192).

Cell growth requirements are also population-dependent, as demonstrated clearly by human diploid cells.

> A number of compounds that are synthesized by cells must nevertheless be provided in the medium to assure survival and growth. In their absence the cells die because the specific metabolite (or an intermediate in its synthesis) is lost to the medium in amounts which exceed the biosynthetic capacity of the cell. When there are enough cells, however, the medium can be "conditioned"—that is, the concentration in the medium and within the cell can be brought up to metabolically effective levels before the cells die. These paradoxical growth requirements are therefore population-dependent, disappearing at sufficiently high population densities (Eagle, 1965, p. 44).

It is not surprising that the plating efficiency of cells freshly isolated from tissue may be low (see Chap. 2, on primary cloning), and that many cell types have not yet been cultured at low population densities.

GROWTH-INHIBITORY FACTORS

Although growth-inhibitory factors may develop in cell cultures, and although growth-inhibitory effects are sometimes observed when different cells are grown parabiotically, we know nothing about the nature of the compounds involved, the mechanism of their action, or their relevance to growth control *in vivo* (Eagle, 1965, p. 42).

Since this summary, additional studies of human cells confirm Eagle's statements but do not clarify the mechanisms. DNA synthesis is inhibited in sparse cultures of human amnion (no contact between cells) to which medium from crowded cell cultures is added (Kohn, 1968). Both human established cell lines and diploid cell strains are inhibited by crude extract isolated from human tissues including liver, kidney and spleen (Nilsson and Philipson, 1968). Inhibitory factor is membrane-associated, macromolecular in nature, thermolabile and active within a narrow pH-range. RNA and protein synthesis of cultured cells are suppressed before inhibition of DNA synthesis, The correlation between this inhibitor isolated directly from the membrane fraction of human tissue and the growth-inhibitory factors that develop in cell cultures as they grow cannot be assessed at present, but the two types of inhibition show several similarities.

When two established human cell lines are mixed in culture (HEp-2, from carcinoma of the larynx and RP AM1, amnion-derived cells), unilateral inhibition and reproductive death occur (Holmgren and Merchant, 1968). In these studies a specific antiserum containing antibodies for antigen on amnion cells but no antibodies for antigens on HEp-2 cells made it possible to follow the fate of each cell type, by indirect immunofluorescence. Inhibition or reproductive death of the amnion cells occurred and the degree appeared to depend on factors influencing cell contact (also see Chap. 6, on antigenic responses of cells in long-term culture). It may be postulated that *in vivo* this type of cell-cell interaction may function as a surveillance mechanism, capable of eliminating cellular variants differing structurally or antigenically from the general pattern within a given tissue.

If human diploid cells are mixed in culture with mammalian diploid cells of a widely different species (rat) unilateral inhibition and reproductive death of the human cells occur, at a ratio as high as one human cell to ten thousand rat cells (Priest, 1968, unpublished).

GROWTH "REPAIR" PROCESSES IN CULTURE; GROWTH STIMULATION

Various types of normal and neoplastic human cells in culture react to the mechanical removal of a part of the culture. These reactions have been termed "wound healing" in cell culture. Human diploid fibroblast-like cells from skin of embryos (termed normal cells) and a human diploid strain transformed by SV40 (termed neoplastic cells) were studied after removal of part of the culture (Vasiliev *et al.*, 1969). Normal cells actively migrated from the edge of the wound onto cell-free glass. Usually this migration was limited; most migrating cells remained within a certain zone near the edge of the removed portion of the culture. Most cells migrating into the wound were induced to begin DNA synthesis after a latent period of about twelve to eighteen hours. This activation of DNA synthesis was local and the cells in other parts of operated cultures were not activated. Migration of neoplastic cells into the wound was very slow as compared with that of the normal cells, and was not followed by activation of DNA synthesis.

Growth stimulation may be induced by various culture additives. One example involves a study of the effect of 5-hydroxy-tryptamine (serotonin); micromolar amounts (10^{-6}M) increased the growth of fibroblast-like cells from human embryo lung but did not influence growth of HeLa cells (derived from human cervical carcinoma) and KB cells (derived from human oral carcinoma) (Boucek and Alvarez, 1970). The growth-promoting effect was less when serotonin was added longer than two days after subculture of the monolayer fibroblast-like cells. Larger amounts of serotonin were, however, toxic to fibroblast-like cells.

THE ROLES OF HEREDITY VERSUS ENVIRONMENT IN CELL INTERACTIONS

Five cloned strains differing in cell and colony morphology, and isolated from a HeLa-S3 culture, were plated at intervals during their propagation (Jahiel, 1969). Morphological variation was associated with both the strain and the stage of development of the colony. Certain differences in cell shape and cell-cell contact among strains were expressed as early as the one- and two-celled colony stages; other differences among strains appeared at various times during colonial growth. The pattern and timing of some of these changes appeared to be heritable attributes of the strains.

There is evidence that an interaction between neighboring sister cells serves to synchronize (partially) their progression through the cell life cycle as compared to sister cells that do not remain in proximity through their life cycle (Froese, 1967) (see Chap. 12, on cell cycle events).

There have been many attempts to explain the parallel orientation displayed by cultured cells, particularly exemplified by diploid human fibroblast-like cells. Most investigators have been reluctant to explain this orientation simply on the basis of contact inhibition (see earlier, this chapter). However, the parallel arrangement may result from operation of an aligning mechanism which is an inherent population property, and also the result of contact mediated cellular interactions. In the case of some virus transformed fibroblast-like cells, whose pattern of growth is chaotic (see Chap. 8, on characteristics of transformed cells), it is to be assumed that this aligning mechanism is not operating to restrain the cells. One study of the nature of this aligning mechanism suggests that parallel arrangement allows the maximum exercise of cell motility in dense cultures (Elsdale, 1968).

Two mouse established cell lines were hybridized (see Chap. 11 on somatic cell hybridization), one highly sensitive to contact regulation of division, and the other not sensitive (Weiss *et al.*, 1969). A number of hybrid clones isolated were found to be quite sensitive, indicating that behavior of the cell line highly sensitive to contact regulation was more fully expressed in the hybrid. However, on serial subculture, the hybrid lines gave rise to variants less sensitive to contact regulation.

The kinetics of cell division and movement in four epithelial-like established cell lines (including HeLa cell, from cervical carcinoma) were studied by time-lapse cinematography (Castor, 1970). Cells from the line that exhibited early contact regulation of cell division, as they crowded together, also showed a steady decrease in average surface area per cell. In the other three lines, mitosis was not controlled as a function of population density until the cells became much more crowded; these cells had little mutual adhesion and either continuously changed their shapes (2 of the lines) or remained rounded (1 line) such that there was no consistent change in cell membrane surface area to bring about contact regulation of cell division. Thus the hypothesis that rate of division depends on cell surface area was supported.

From the examples just given, it would appear that both hereditary (inherent cell characteristics) and environment play important, and sometimes indistinguishable roles in influencing cell interactions.

REFERENCES

General

Abercrombie, M.: Contact inhibition: The phenomenon and its biological implications. *Nat Cancer Inst Monogr, 26*:249, 1967.

Eagle, H. Metabolic controls in cultured mammalian cells. *Science, 148*:42, 1965.

Specific

Abercrombie, M.: Contact inhibition: The phenomenon and its biological implications. *Nat Cancer Inst Monogr, 26*:249, 1967.

Boucek, R. J., and Alvarez, T. R., 5-hydroxytryptamine: A cytospecific growth stimulator of cultured fibroblasts. *Science 167*:898, 1970.

Castor, L. N.: Flattening, movement and control of division of epithelial-like cells. *J Cell Comp Physiol, 75*:57, 1970.

Eagle, H.: Metabolic controls in cultured mammalian cells. *Science, 148*: 42, 1965.

Elsdale, T. R.: Parallel orientation of fibroblasts *in vitro. Exp Cell Res, 51*:439, 1968.

Froese, G.: An interaction between neighboring cells. *Exp Cell Res, 47*: 285, 1967.

Ham, R. G.: Clonal growth of mammalian cells in a chemically defined, synthetic medium. *Proc Nat Acad Sci USA, 53*:288, 1965.

Holley, R. W., and Kiernan, J. A.: "Contact inhibition" of cell division in

3T3 cells. *Proc Nat Acad Sci USA,* 60:300, 1968.

Holmgren, N. B., and Merchant, D. J.: Allogenic inhibition between two human cell lines. *J Nat Cancer Inst,* 40:561, 1968.

Jahiel, R. I.: Quantitative morphologic studies during colonial growth of heteroploid cell strains differing in cell contact, shape and orientation. *Exp Cell Res,* 56:347, 1969.

Kohn, A.: Thymidine metabolism and DNA synthesis in crowded mono-layers of animal cells. *Exp Cell Res,* 52:161, 1968.

Levine, E. M.; Becker, Y.; Boone, C. W., and Eagle, H.: Contact inhibition, macromolecular synthesis, and polyribosomes in cultured human dip-loid fibroblasts. *Proc Nat Acad Sci USA,* 53:350, 1965.

Nilsson, G., and Philipson, L.: Cell growth inhibition of human cell lines by human tissue extracts. *Exp Cell Res,* 51:275, 1968.

Puck, T. T.; Waldren, C. A., and Jones, C.: Mammalian cell growth pro-teins. I. Growth stimulation by fetuin. *Proc Nat Acad Sci USA,* 59:192, 1968.

Vasiliev, J. M.; Gelfand, I. M.; Domnina, L. V., and Rapoport, R. I.: Wound healing processes in cell cultures. *Exp Cell Res,* 54:83, 1969.

Weiss, M. C.; Todaro, G. J., and Green, H.: Properties of a hybrid be-tween lines sensitive and insensitive to contact inhibition of cell di-vision. *J Cell Physiol,* 71:105, 1968.

Chapter Eleven
SOMATIC CELL HYBRIDIZATION

Intentional mixing of mammalian somatic cells in culture has resulted in new combinations of chromosome material. Initially crosses were made between nondiploid mouse cells (Barski *et al.*, 1960). Subsequently the field of mammalian somatic cell hybridization has expanded to include many types of cells and many eminent investigators. As is invariably the case with development of a special field, nomenclature needs to be specified (Table 11-I). It is wise from the onset to have the purposes of specialized studies clearly defined (Table 11-II) (Ephrussi and Weiss, 1969b). Methodology is also important but

TABLE 11-I

DEFINITIONS RELATED TO SOMATIC CELL HYBRIDIZATION

Term	Definition
Hybrid somatic cell	A somatic cell composed of two or more genetically different cells; often used to mean a somatic cell known to contain two or more genetically different nuclei.
Nucleocytoplasmic hybrid somatic cell	A somatic cell known to contain both nuclear and cytoplasmic components of genetically different cells.
Heterokaryon	A hybrid cell with two or more nuclei of different genetic origin.
Homokaryon	A hybrid cell with two or more nuclei of the same genetic origin.
Heterospecific heterokaryon	A hybrid cell including nuclei from different species.
Homospecific heterokaryon	A hybrid cell including nuclei from genetically different cells of the same species.
Monokaryon	Containing one nucleus.
Dikaryon	Containing two nuclei.

203

would be expected to evolve as studies progress and such is certainly the case with mammalian cell hybridization (Table 11-III).

TABLE 11-II

PURPOSES OF MAMMALIAN SOMATIC CELL HYBRIDIZATION

Somatic cell crosses are an alternative to sexual breeding, for genetic analysis of higher animals, including man.

Hybrid cells may be shown to exhibit the hereditary characteristics of the parents, for further study.

As hybrids multiply they lose some of their chromosomes and this process can be used to produce cells with different combinations of parental genes and chromosomes.

Localization of specific genes to specific chromosomes is possible.

It is possible to apply genetic analysis to specific types of differentiation in cells.

TABLE 11-III

EXAMPLES OF METHODOLOGY IN THE FIELD OF
MAMMALIAN CELL HYBRIDIZATION

Cells may be maintained by standard procedures for serial culture (see Chap. 1) or they may be removed directly from an intact animal.

Experiments in hybridization begin with a mixed culture of two or more parent cells or cell lines, each characterized by the presence of marker chromosomes, enzymes or other differentiated function. Morphology may also be a marker. Cell fusion is accomplished in various ways and the hybrids isolated.

Methods	*Examples*	*References*
1. After cell mixing the hybrids have a natural selective advantage over the parents and overgrow the culture.	Mouse nondiploid X mouse nondiploid	Barski *et al.*, 1960
	Mink diploid X cattle diploid. Cells are cold-shocked immediately after mixing.	Teplitz *et al.*, 1968
2. Double selective medium is used to prevent reproduction of two parents. Each parent has a different nutritional dependency marker; thus the hybrids can grow.	Mouse nondiploid X mouse nondiploid. One parent: thymidine kinase deficient; the other parent: guanylic acid-inosinic acid pyrophosphorylase deficient. Hybrid has both enzymes and can grow in the presence of hypoxanthine,	Littlefield, 1964

TABLE 11-III (Continued)

Methods	Examples	References
	amethopterine and thymidine (HAT medium), while parents cannot.	
	Mouse nondiploid X human nondiploid. Mouse parent: thymidine kinase deficient; human parent: hypoxanthine phosphoribosyl transferase deficient. Hybrid has both enzymes and can grow in the presence of hypoxanthine, amethopterin and thymidine (HAT medium) while parents cannot.	Matsuya and Green, 1969
	Chinese hamster nondiploid X Chinese hamster nondiploid. One parent requires glycine; the other parent requires hypoxathine. Hybrids can grow without glycine and hypoxanthine while parents cannot.	Kao *et al.*, 1969
3. Single (or "half") selective medium is used to prevent reproduction of one parent. The other parent grows slowly or is inoculated in small numbers. The hybrid overgrows or may be isolated from mixed culture.	Mouse nondiploid X human diploid (Fig. 11-2 and 3). Mouse parent: thymidine kinase deficient; human parent grows slowly as a thin monolayer. Hybrids and human parent can grow in the presence of hypoxanthine, amethopterine and thymidine but mouse parent cannot. Hybrids pile up against a background of human cells and can be cloned.	Weiss and Green, 1967
4. The frequency of cell fusion is increased to such an extent that selection against the parents is not necessary.	Human HeLa nondiploid suspension culture X mouse Ehrlich ascites tumor cells in suspension. Addition of UV-inactivated Sendai virus (a myxovirus) produces rapid cell fusion.	Harris and Watkins, 1965
	Human KB nondiploid cell fusion following addition of UV-inactivated hemagglutinating virus of Japan (HVJ).	Yamanaka and Okada, 1968

No field of biology arises *de novo* but follows naturally from biological experiences, thoughts and observations, often many centuries old. The knowledge of animal chromosomal hybrids produced in nature led investigators to assume that cell fusion could be accomplished in the laboratory. In nature, chromosome hybridization between different members of one species (example in lizards: Gorman and Atkins, 1968) is usually more common than hybridization between species, although examples of the latter are well documented, such as the mule (Benirschke *et al.*, 1962). *In vitro* nuclear transplantation producing nucleocytoplasmic hybrids, notably in amphibians, also established precedence for mammalian hybridization experiments (Gurdon, 1968).

Geneticists have been particularly interested in the possibility of mammalian somatic cell crosses for genetic analysis and have

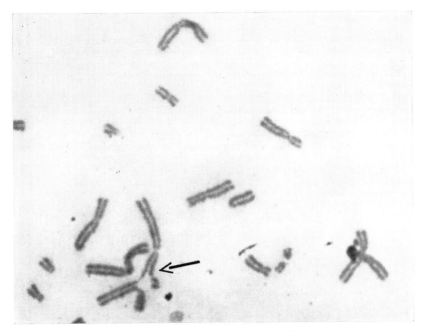

Figure 11-1. A quadriradial configuration (arrow) found in a mitosis prepared from peripheral blood of a patient with Bloom dwarfism, a rare, recessively inherited syndrome of congenital defects in humans (see Chap. 3). The close association of two different chromosomes is considered to be evidence for somatic pairing.

looked for *in vivo* evidence of such crosses at gene and chromosomal levels (Lengerova, 1967). Such evidence is of several types. In laboratory rodents, reports of rare instances of animals heterozygous for a recessive coat-color gene but showing patches of fur with the recessive phenotype led to speculation that somatic crossing-over exists, although other explanations are possible. The finding of quadriradial configurations (Fig. 11-1) in human peripheral blood leukocytes in short-term culture (German, 1964) may be interpreted as cytological evidence of somatic crossing-over. Radiation chimeras* may be considered a sort of tissue culture *in vivo;* there is clear evidence in them for both cell fusion (mating) and somatic crossing-over (gene exchange between chromosomes), both events producing new types of cells (recombinants).

Genetically different diploid human cells have been successfully hybridized *in vitro* (Siniscalco *et al.,* 1969). The potential information to be gained, if experimental human diploid cell crosses can be maintained, is indeed great. Human cells in culture could be mated for the purpose of genetic analysis.

PROOF THAT HYBRIDIZATION HAS OCCURRED

Evidence of several types is provided to verify a new cell type distinct from either parent of a mixed culture (Table 11-IV). Cell morphology of the hybrid may be different from the parent; the original mouse-mouse cell mixing of Barski, Sorieul and Cornefert (1960) produced hybrid cells of distinct morphology. In the mouse-human hybridization experiments of Weiss and Green (1967) the human parent cells in monolayer culture appeared elongated with parallel orientation, in contrast to the mouse parent cells with less fusiform shape, more refractility and random orientation (Fig. 11-2). In pure culture the hybrid cells, while refractile, showed a degree of orientation intermediate between

---

*Radiation chimeras are created by injecting healthy hematopoietic and lymphoid cells into animals (mice are commonly used) previously irradiated with a dose of ionizing radiation which would ordinarily be lethal. The foreign cells repopulate the radiation depleted host tissues, during a relatively short period of active cell proliferation. Genetic markers in different donor cells can be studied for evidence of fusion or gene exchange between mixed donor cells.

the two parents. The hybrid cells were also noted to pile up against a monolayer of one parent (human), once selective medium was used to eliminate the other parent (mouse).

Chromosome analysis may provide definitive evidence for the presence of chromosomes from two parents in the hybrid (Fig.

TABLE 11-IV

WAYS TO SHOW THAT HYBRIDIZATION HAS OCCURRED

1. Cell morphology of the hybrid may be different from the parents.
2. Chromosome analysis may provide evidence for chromosomes from two parents in the hybrid.
3. The heterokaryons from parents with morphologically distinct nuclei can show different types of nuclei.
4. If tritiated thymidine labeling of one but not the other parent results in heterokaryons with both labeled and unlabeled nuclei, two sources for the nuclei are suggested.
5. Polymorphic enzymes may be studied to demonstrate in hybrid cells the presence of proteins characteristic of both parents.
6. Different nutritional deficiency markers in cell parents will complement each other in the resulting hybrids.
7. X chromosomes from both parents can be functionally active in the hybrid cell.
8. Immunologic properties of both parents can be demonstrated in the hybrid.

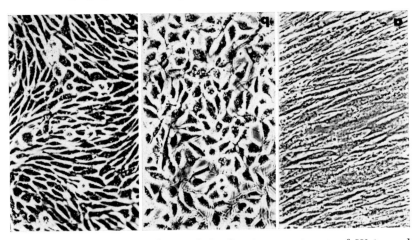

Figure 11-2. In the mouse-human hybridization experiments of Weiss and Green (1967), the morphology of the hybrid cells (left) is intermediate between the morphologies of both parents (diploid human on right and nondiploid mouse in the middle). Phase contrast photomicrographs. Courtesy of Dr. Howard Green, *Proc Nat Acad Sci USA*, 58:1105, 1967.

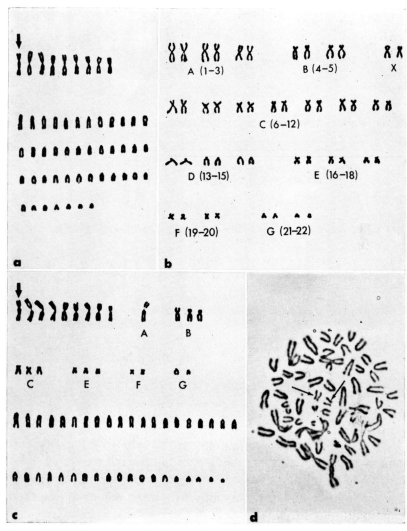

Figure 11-3. Karyotypes of the nondiploid mouse parent (a), diploid human parent (b), and hybrid (c) from the mouse-human hybridization experiments of Weiss and Green (1967). Chromosomes from both parents can be recognized in the hybrid karyotype. A mitosis from a hybrid cell cultured for a prolonged period of time is shown in (d). Very few human chromosomes are still recognizable (2 are indicated by arrows). Courtesy of Dr. Howard Green, *Proc Nat Acad Sci USA*, 58:1106, 1967.

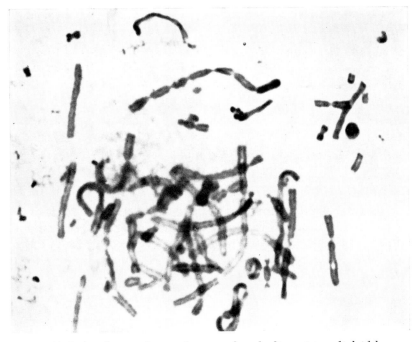

Figure 11-4. An abnormal metaphase produced after mixing diploid human and nondiploid Chinese hamster cells. The species of origin of the chromosomes are difficult to identify because of the abnormalities (including fragments, broken and multicentric chromosomes) and because a number of chromosomes are difficult to distinguish between the Chinese hamster and human complements.

11-3). The cells analyzed are preferably cloned, or grown up from a single cell. If a mixed culture is analyzed it may be possible to identify all three chromosomal cell types, both parents and the hybrid. In some situations the chromosomes may be too abnormal to identify definitively or the parent chromosomes may not be distinctive (Fig. 11-4). In nondiploid parents, marker chromosomes such as translocations may be useful for proving mixed parentage in the hybrid. A reason for the usefulness of one mouse parent in human hybridization studies is the presence in the mouse karyotype of a long series of acrocentric chromosomes, many being distinguishable from the human complement. The same may be said for one bovine parent.

In heterokaryons from parents with morphologically distinct nuclei, the different types of nuclei can be identified in the hybrid. For example, when the nucleus of a mature hen erythrocyte is introduced into the cytoplasm of a HeLa cell by treatment with inactivated Sendai virus, the two types of nuclei are readily identified in the new cell (Fig. 11-5) (Harris, 1967). Additional proof of different sources for the nuclei in heterokaryons in furnished by labeling nuclei of one parent with tritiated thymidine and demonstrating, by means of single cell autoradiography, the presence of both labeled and unlabeled nuclei in the heterokaryon (Harris, 1966).

Polymorphic enzymes may be studied to demonstrate in hybrid cells the presence of proteins characteristic of both parents. Weiss and Ephrussi (1966) showed both rat and mouse lactic dehydrogenase (LDH-5) in rat-mouse hybrids. In addition, new LDH-5 electrophoretic bands appeared in the hybrid, suggesting the production of hybrid LDH-5 isoenzymes. Mouse-Chinese

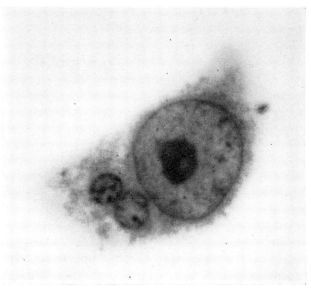

Figure 11-5. A heterokaryon containing one large HeLa nucleus and two smaller mature hen erythrocyte nuclei. Courtesy of Professor Henry Harris, Sir William Dunn School of Pathology, University of Oxford, England.

hamster crosses (Scaletta *et al.*, 1967) produced cells with beta-glucuronidase characteristic of both parents.

When different nutritional dependency markers in cell parents complement each other in the resulting hybrids, genes from both parents must be present and functioning in the hybrid. The examples of double selective medium given in Table 11-III, section 2 are evidence for this type of gene complementation. In the hybrid each parental mutant gene is "supplemented" by a normal (wild-type) homologous gene from the other parent.

Human diploid cell crosses, each male parent carrying deficiency mutations at different X-linked loci (glucose-6-phosphate dehydrogenase and hypoxanthine-guanine phosphoribosyl transferase), show that both X chromosomes are functionally active in the hybrid cells (Siniscalco *et al.*, 1969) (also see Table 11-VI).

Antigenic differences resulting from immunogenetic variation within and between species can be among the most specific and clearly demonstrable markers of cell identity in culture (Larkin, 1965). For instance, in mouse-mouse hybrids a study of H-2 antigens verified the descent of somatic matings from genetically different parents (Spencer *et al.*, 1964).

LOCALIZATION OF GENES ON CHROMOSOMES

Much needs to be known about the localization of human genes on chromosomes. Humans are poorly suited for classical types of genetic analysis since they provide no opportunity for experimental matings and have very few offspring. Although genes localized to the X chromosome (X-linked) are well known because of association with another clear marker (sex), very little is known about genes on autosomes. Somatic cell hybridization provides a potentially powerful tool for relating gene functions to particular chromosomes. The experience to date with chromosomes in hybrid cells, particularly human-animal cell crosses, shows that there is loss of parental complements, a process known for some time to geneticists and called somatic reduction. If the loss of particular human chromosomes can be correlated with loss of specific gene functions, a step would be taken towards gene localization. If, say, a specific enzyme function is lost one still does not have proof for loss of a structural gene; some regulatory gene might be lost, for instance. A refinement of this type of analysis would then be to show loss of function of one allelic gene but not the other in a heterozygote hybrid cell; if correlated with loss of one chromosome from a pair but not the other, location of the structural gene on the lost chromosome is suggested. Ideally the replacement of both chromosome and function is desirable but thus far procedures for isolating chromosomes and returning them to a functional state *in vitro* have not been developed.

In human cell hybridization, one problem has been the rapid loss of too many human chromosomes from human-animal cell hybrids in serial culture. Furthermore only a fraction of the human chromosomes have been represented initially in human diploid cell crosses with other animal cells. One method used to overcome this chromosome instability was to start with a non-diploid human HeLa parent (Matsuya and Green, 1969). In the resulting hybrids many more human chromosomes were retained (Fig 11-6). The selective loss of human chromosomes is puzzling and difficult to control or reproduce; present evidence concerning gene localization from this type of analysis may be conflicting or of a negative type (Table 11-V).

DIFFERENTIATION IN HYBRID CELLS

Hybridization studies have resulted in interesting observations concerning the expression of differentiation in cultured cells. In experiments involving allelic proteins, each present in one parent cell, both may be demonstrated in the hybrid (Fig. 11-7). When two cells with different biochemical markers are fused, the markers can be followed in the hybrids (Table 11-VI). In other situations involving parental differentiated activities, the appearance in hybrids may be absent (as with some morphological differentiation and pigment production, Table 11-VII, 1 and 2) or intermediate between parents (as with collagen and folate reductase production, Table 11-VII, 3 and 4). In the hybrid, production of a parental characteristic may be lost as parental chromosomes are lost following hybridization (Table 11-VII, 5) or the characteristic of only one parent may be manifest after

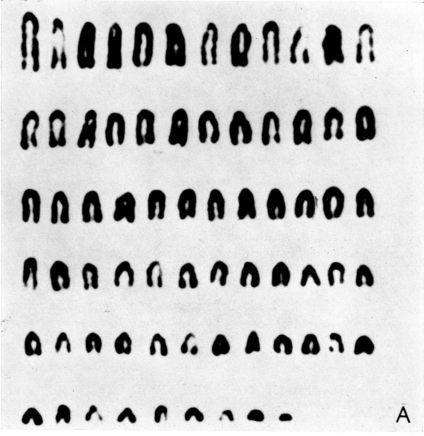

Figure 11-6. (A) Karyotype of a nondiploid mouse cell parent containing 69 telocentric chromosomes. (B) Karyotype of a nondiploid human HeLa cell parent. (C) Karyotype of a hybrid cell. Thirty-eight chromosomes in the hybrid (top three rows) have been classified as human and 137 (bottom seven rows) as mouse. Courtesy of Drs. Howard Green and Yutaka Matsuya, *Science, 163*:697, 1969. Copyright 1969 by the American Association for the Advancement of Science.

hybridization (Table 11-VII, 6). An exciting discovery is the appearance of new variants of an enzyme, termed "hybrid-enzyme" (or heteropolymeric enzyme), in a fused cell (Table 11-VII, 7). In this situation enzyme subunits of quite different parent cells, such as rat and mouse or mouse and human, when present in a combined cell are able to associate to produce heteropolymeric enzymes.

B

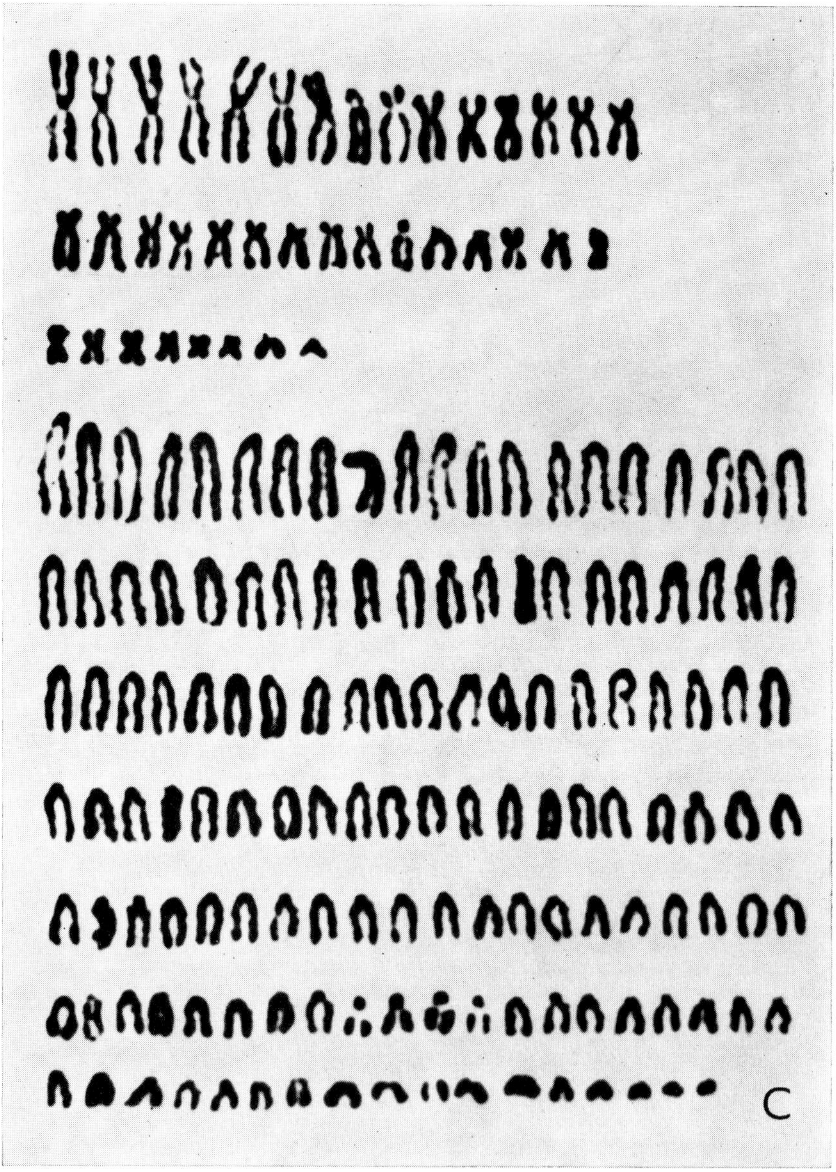
C

TABLE 11-V

EXAMPLES OF STAGED REDUCTION OF THE CHROMOSOME
COMPLEMENT IN HUMAN-ANIMAL CELL SOMATIC
HYBRID CELLS, FOR THE PURPOSE OF
MAPPING HUMAN CHROMOSOMES

Example	*Reference*
The gene for thymidine kinase is located on an E group chromosome.	
Loss of human chromosomes from nondiploid mouse X diploid human hybrid cells was studied. Loss of thymidine kinase activity was consistently associated with loss of an E group chromosome.	Matsuya *et al.*, 1968
In nondiploid mouse X diploid human hybrid cells most of the mouse genome was retained but only a single human chromosome (a submetacentric E group chromosome) was retained. This human chromosome provided thymidine kinase activity for the hybrid cell. Electrophoretic migration on starch gel and heat sensitivity of the enzyme in hybrid cells showed it to be similar to human rather than mouse enzyme.	Migeon *et al.*, 1969
8-azaguanine (8-AZG) resistance is man is X-linked; human lactate dehydrogenase (LDH) A and B genes are not linked and are not located on an F group chromosome.	
Unequivocal identification of the human X chromosome in nondiploid mouse X human leukocyte hybrids was impossible; however, the data were consistent with linkage between 8-AZG resistance and glucose-6-phosphate dehydrogenase. Because there were hybrid clones containing all LDH patterns which lacked F-type chromosomes, the LDH genes were presumably not on an F group chromosome. The existence of hybrid clones with human A but not B subunits suggested that the genes controlling these subunits were not on the same chromosome.	Nabholz *et al.*, 1969
Genes for lactate dehydrogenase (LDH), malate dehydrogenase (MDH), isocitrate dehydrogenase (IDH), and glucose-6-phosphate dehydrogenase (G6PD) are not linked in man.	
Nondiploid mouse X diploid human hybrid cells were analyzed for the enzymes LDH, MDH, IDH, and G6PD. Electrophoretic studies of hybrid cells showed both parental and also "hybrid-enzyme" activity for all the enzymes studied. There were no restrictions on formation of the "hybrid enzymes" (heteropolymeric enzymes) in the hybrid cells. Initial chromosome studies of hybrid cells were reported, providing further evidence for selective loss of human chromosomes. It was expected that further chromosome analysis of clones of hybrid cell populations would allow more genes for particular enzymes to be assigned to specific human chromosomes or chromosome groups.	Boone and Ruddle, 1969

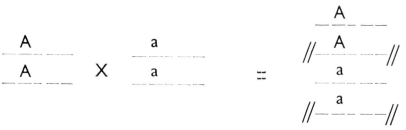

Figure 11-7. The allelic protein coded by gene A is present in one parent and the allelic protein coded by gene a is present in the other parent. Both proteins are present in the hybrid provided at least one locus for gene A and one locus for gene a is maintained in the hybrid.

FUSION OF CELLS WITH MYXOVIRUSES

The low rate of spontaneous cell fusion following mixing of genetically different cells (or genetically similar cells, for that matter) necessitated some method to increase the fusion rate. Okada (1962) had reported that one strain of the parainfluenza I

TABLE 11-VI

EXAMPLES OF HYBRIDIZATION OF TWO HUMAN CELL STRAINS
WITH DIFFERENT BIOCHEMICAL MARKERS

Two male diploid fibroblast-like cell strains, each carrying mutations at different X-linked loci (glucose-6-phosphate dehydrogenase and hypoxanthine-guanine phosphoribosyl transferase) have been successfully hybridized. The resulting mononucleated hybrid cells synthesized both normal gene products, indicating that both X chromosomes were functionally active in the hybrid cells.	Siniscalco *et al.*, 1969
A hybrid cell line of clonal origin was obtained by cocultivation of two biochemically marked human cell strains. One parental strain was diploid and derived from a male infant with orotic aciduria, a recessive deficiency involving the final two enzymes in the biosynthetic pathway leading to uridylic acid. This strain also had type B glucose-6-phosphate dehydrogenase (G6PD). The other parental strain was nondiploid and deficient for inosinic acid pyrophosphorylase. It had type A G6PD. The cloned hybrid cells showed genetic traits of both parents: (a) intermediate levels of enzymes deficient in orotic aciduria; (b) intermediate levels of inosinic acid pyrophosphorylase; (c) both A and B G6PD bands.	Silagi *et al.*, 1969

TABLE 11-VII

THE STUDY OF DIFFERENTIATED FUNCTION BY SOMATIC CELL HYBRIDIZATION

Observations	*References*

1. *Morphologic differentiation of one parent may be lost in the hybrid.*

A mouse testicular teratocarcinoma was found to maintain in long-term culture the potential for producing different types of tissue when reinoculated *in vivo,* including embryonal carcinoma, yolk sac epithelium, neuroepithelium, mesenchyme, and cartilage. After hybridization with a morphologically undifferentiated mouse established line, the multipotentiality of the teratocarcinoma cells was lost.

Finch and Ephrussi, 1967

2. *Pigment production by one parent may be lost in the hybrid.*

Hybrids were made between cells of an established Syrian hamster melanoma line and each of three unpigmented established mouse lines. These hybrids remained unpigmented under conditions resulting in heavy pigmentation in the melanoma parent cells. The hybrids and unpigmented parent lines showed no dopa oxidase activity while the pigmented parent cells showed activity.

Davidson *et al.,* 1966

3. *Intermediate levels of the enzyme folate reductase are found in hybrids between cells with high and low levels of enzyme production.*

Clonal sublines of baby hamster kidney cells in culture were selected for resistance to amethopterin. These resistant cells contained up to 125 times as much folate reductase as normal (wild-type) cells. When high and low enzyme producing cells were hybridized, the levels of reductase activity became intermediate in the hybrids.

Littlefield, 1969

4. *Intermediate levels of collagen and hyaluronic acid are produced by hybrids between cells producing larger and smaller amounts of these substances.*

Crosses were made between established mouse fibroblast-like cells in culture, with different rates of production of collagen and hyaluronic acid. Hybrids produced intermediate amounts of both collagen and hyaluronic acid.

Green *et al.,* 1966

5. *Virus induced antigens in one parent are preserved in the hybrid but are lost as the chromosomes of the same parent are lost from the hybrid.*

Long after infection with simian virus 40 (SV40), human fibroblast-like cells in serial culture can be shown to produce virus-induced T-antigens, although they do not shed infectious virus. These human parent cells were crossed with an established line of mouse cells never exposed to SV40. The T-antigen present in the human parental cells

Weiss *et al.,* 1968

TABLE 11-VII (Continued)

Observations	References
before hybridization was expressed in the hybrid and was then lost from the hybrid cells concurrently with the loss of human chromosomes.	
The hypothesis of integration of SV40 genome in the chromosomes of human transformed cells is supported. Further, it was shown that hybrid cells which lost T-antigen were capable of synthesizing this antigen upon infection with SV40, suggesting that loss of viral antigen from the hybrid was not due to loss of some cellular gene required for expression of the viral genome.	Weiss, 1970

6. *The ribosomal RNA species of only one parent may be found in hybrid cells.*

In crosses between diploid human and nondiploid mouse cells in serial culture, only mouse-type 28S RNA could be detected even in hybrids with up to 35 human chromosomes per cell. Although several explanations are possible, the most likely was thought to be that in hybrids transcription of human ribosomal genes is repressed.	Eliceiri and Green, 1969

7. *New isoenzymes may appear in the hybrid, having different physical properties from the homologous parental isoenzymes.*

Rat-mouse somatic hybrids were found to contain lactic dehydrogenase (LDH-5) from both species, as well as "hybrid-isoenzymes," presumably formed by association of rat and mouse enzyme subunits (as studied by cellulose acetate electrophoresis).	Weiss and Ephrussi, 1966
Nondiploid mouse X diploid human hybrid cells were analyzed for the enzymes lactate dehydrogenase, malate dehydrogenase, isocitrate dehydrogenase, and glucose-6-phosphate dehydrogenase. Electrophoretic studies of hybrid cells showed both parental and also "hybrid-enzyme" activity for all the enzymes studied.	Boone and Ruddle, 1969

8. *After hybridization, DNA and RNA synthesis may be resumed in a differentiated nucleus no longer synthesizing DNA and RNA in vivo.* (also see Table 11-VIII)

Heterokaryons were formed through fusion of mouse neurons with an established line of green monkey kidney fibroblast-like cells, in the presence of inactiviated Sendai virus. DNA synthesis was reactivated in the neurons.	Jacobson, 1968
When the nucleus of a mature hen erythrocyte was introduced into the cytoplasm of a HeLa cell the hen nucleus resumed synthesis of DNA and RNA. (Viral fusion technique was used).	Harris, 1967

TABLE 11-VII (Continued)

Observations	References
9. *Fusion of cells permissive and nonpermissive to viral infection can make the nonpermissive nucleus susceptible to infection in the resulting heterokaryon.*	
UV-Sendai virus was used to fuse Hep-2 (human nondiploid line) with BHK-21 (baby hamster kidney line). Before fusion the Hep-2 cell supported replication of adenovirus types 2 and 12, while the BHK-21 did not. After fusion a relatively high incidence of viral inclusion bodies were found in BHK-21 nuclei of the heterokaryons infected with adenovirus. It was concluded that the presence of permissive Hep-2 nucleus or cytoplasm in heterokaryons was essential for induction of viral inclusion bodies in nonpermissive BHK-21 nuclei.	Weber and Stich, 1969
10. *Malignancy can be suppressed when malignant cells are fused with certain nonmalignant ones.*	Harris *et al.*, 1969
or	
Fusion of a cancer and a noncancer cell may give a malignant hybrid.	Ephrussi *et al.*, 1969a

group of myxoviruses caused animal cells in suspension to clump together and fuse. Harris and Watkins (1965) applied this knowledge to increase hybridization rates of mixed cells. The prolonged cultivation of some hybrid cells thus fused was then quickly achieved (Scaletta and Ephrussi, 1965).

A strain of myxovirus (usually Sendai) is titrated for hemagglutination activity and infectivity is inactivated by ultraviolet light. Virus particles or fractions and suspended cells to be fused are mixed and shaken at 4°C for about twenty minutes. During this time the initial clumps of cells undergo varying degrees of fusion. Type of medium, and virus and parent cell concentrations must be adjusted to control the average number of nuclei per heterokaryon and the proportion of each kind of nucleus. Fused cells are subsequently studied or carried in culture, usually as monolayers (Table 11-VII, 8 through 10; 11-VIII and 11-IX). No differences have been found between the properties of hybrids obtained after ultraviolet-inactivated Sendai virus treatment and those obtained from untreated mixed cultures of parental cells (Coon and Weiss, 1969). The mechanism of virus-induced fusion is a matter of intensive investigation. Okada and Murayama

(1968) have shown that those sites where cell fusion occurs must absorb a threshold number of virus particles or virus envelopes.

The examples given in Table 11-VII, section 8 illustrate how the synthesis of DNA and RNA may be studied by autoradiography when large numbers of viral-fused cells are available. Harris (1966) produced heterokaryons containing nuclei and cytoplasm from both parents (as HeLa-HeLa, HeLa-rabbit macrophage or HeLa-rat lymphocyte combinations) or containing the cytoplasm of only one parent (as HeLa-hen erythrocyte). The results are summarized in Table VIII. From these results he concluded that (a) if either parent normally synthesizes RNA or DNA, then RNA or DNA synthesis takes place in both types of nuclei in the heterokaryon; (b) if no parent normally synthesis DNA, then no synthesis of DNA takes place in the heterokaryon; (c) in no case does the inactive cell suppress synthesis in the active partner, but the active cell may initiate synthesis in the inactive partner.

The conclusions given in Table 11-IX illustrate how cell cycle events may be studied by the technique of viral-fusion (also see Chap. 12 on cell cycle events).

TABLE 11-VIII

DNA AND RNA SYNTHESIS IN HETEROKARYONS
PRODUCED FROM VARIOUS PARENTS
(from Harris, 1966)

	Synthesis in Nuclei	
Parental Cell Types	RNA	DNA
HeLa	+	+
rabbit macrophage	+	0
rat lymphocyte	+	0
hen erythrocyte	0	0
Heterokaryon Combinations		
HeLa-HeLa	++	++
HeLa-rabbit macrophage	++	++
HeLa-rat lymphocyte	++	++
HeLa-hen erythrocyte	++	++
rabbit macrophage-rabbit macrophage	++	0 0
rabbit-macrophage-rat lymphocyte	++	0 0
rabbit macrophage-hen erythrocyte	++	0 0

TABLE 11-IX

CONCLUSIONS ABOUT CELL CYCLE EVENTS DERIVED FROM
STUDIES OF VIRAL-FUSED HYBRID SOMATIC CELLS

Rao and Johnson, 1969
Hybrid studied: HeLa homokaryon; synchronization prior to fusion: nitrous oxide and excess thymidine

Fusion of S & G2 nuclei did not result in induction of DNA synthesis in the G2 nucleus or inhibition of DNA synthesis in the S nucleus.

Fusion of S nucleus with G1 induced DNA synthesis in G1 nucleus but no inhibition in S nucleus.

Fusion of G2 with G1 delayed (slightly) the initiation of DNA synthesis in G1 nucleus.

Nuclei in the multinucleate cell were found to be highly synchronous in entry into mitosis.

When a nucleus in an advanced phase was fused with another in an earlier phase of the cell cycle, the advanced nucleus was delayed until the earlier was ready to enter mitosis; however the rate of progress of a multinucleate cell towards mitosis was dependent on the ratio of advanced nuclei to early ones.

Johnson and Harris, 1969
Hybrid studied: HeLa homokaryons; no synchrony prior to fusion

Maximal synchrony of DNA synthesis and mitosis in the resultant multinucleate cells was achieved within 2 days.

Synchrony was maintained at least 5 days between the nuclei in a binucleate cell; cells with more nuclei lost synchrony by the 3rd day.

Hybrid studied: HeLa-chick erythrocyte heterokaryons (Fig. 11-5)

Erythrocyte nuclei resumed DNA synthesis, in synchrony with HeLa nuclei; for at least 2 days there was no interference with DNA synthesis in the HeLa nucleus.

Hybrid studied: HeLa-Ehrlich heterokaryons

DNA synthesis or mitosis was not synchronized between the nuclei. A form of asynchrony was observed in which most of the Ehrlich nuclei synthesized DNA and most of the HeLa nuclei did not. The patterns of synthesis were determined by the proportions of the two kinds of nuclei.

REFERENCES

General

Ephrussi, B., and Weiss, M. C.: Hybrid somatic cells. *Sci Amer, 220* (4):26, 1969a.

The Wistar Institute Symposium Monograph No. 9: Heterospecific Genome Interaction. Philadelphia, Wistar Institute Press, 1969.

Specific

Barski, G.; Sorieul, S., and Cornefert, F.: Production dans des cultures *in vitro* de deux souches cellulaires en association, de cellules de caratere "hybride." *C R Acad Sci (Paris), 251:*1825, 1960.

Benirschke, K.; Brownhill, L. E., and Beath, M. M.: Somatic chromosomes of the horse, the donkey and their hybrids, the mule and the hinny. *J Reprod Fertil, 4*:319, 1962.

Boone, C. M., and Ruddle, F. H.: Interspecific hybridization between human and mouse somatic cells: Enzyme and linkage studies. *Biochem Genet, 3*:119, 1969.

Coon, H. G., and Weiss, M. C.: A quantitative comparison of formation of spontaneous and virus-produced viable hybrids. *Proc Nat Acad Sci USA, 62*:852, 1969.

Davidson, R. L.; Ephrussi, B., and Yamamoto, K.: Regulation of pigment synthesis in mammalian cells, as studied by somatic hybridization. *Proc Nat Acad Sci USA, 56*:1437, 1966.

Eliceiri, G. L., and Green, H.: Ribosomal RNA synthesis in human-mouse hybrid cells. *J Molec Biol, 41*:253, 1969.

Ephrussi, B.; Davidson, R. L., and Weiss, M. C.: Malignancy of somatic cell hybrids. *Nature (London), 224*:1314, 1969a.

Ephrussi, B., and Weiss, M. C.: Hybrid somatic cells. *Sci Amer, 220* (4):26, 1969b.

Finch, B. W., and Ephrussi, B.: Retention of multiple developmental potentialities by cells of a mouse testicular teratocarcinoma during prolonged culture *in vitro* and their extinction upon hybridization with cells of permanent lines. *Proc Nat Acad Sci USA, 57*:615, 1967.

German, J.: Cytological evidence for crossing-over *in vitro* in human lymphoid cells. *Science, 144*:298, 1964.

Gorman, G. C., and Atkins, L.: Natural hybridization between two sibling species of anolis lizards: Chromosome cytology. *Science, 159*:1358, 1968.

Green, H.; Ephrussi, B.; Yoshida, M., and Hamerman, D.: Synthesis of collagen and hyaluronic acid by fibroblast hybrids. *Proc Nat Acad Sci USA, 55*:41, 1966.

Gurdon, J. B.: Transplanted nuclei and cell differentiation. *Sci Amer, 219*(6): 24, 1968.

Harris, H.: Hybrid cells from mouse and man: A study in genetic regulation. *Proc Roy Soc (Biol), 166*:358, 1966.

Harris, H.: The reactivation of the red cell nucleus. *J Cell Sci, 2*:23, 1967.

Harris, H.; Miller, O. J.; Klein, G.; Worst, P., and Tachibana, T.: Suppression of malignancy by cell fusion. *Nature (London), 223*:363, 1969.

Harris, H., and Watkins, J. F.: Hybrid cells derived from mouse and man: Artificial heterokaryons of mammalian cells from different species. *Nature (London), 205*:640, 1965.

Jacobson, C. -O.: Reactivation of DNA synthesis in mammalian neuron nuclei after fusion with cells of an undifferentiated fibroblast line. *Exp Cell Res, 53*:316, 1968.

Johnson, R. T., and Harris, H.: DNA synthesis and mitosis in fused cells. I.

HeLa homokaryons. II. HeLa-chick erythrocyte heterokaryons. III. HeLa-Ehrlich heterokaryons. *J Cell Sci,* 5:603, 1969.

Kao, F.; Johnson, R. T., and Puck, T. T.: Complementation analysis on virus-fused Chinese hamster cells with nutritional markers. *Science,* 164:312, 1969.

Larkin, E. P.: A simple method for species differentiation of cell cultures by immunofluorescence. *Growth,* 29:201, 1965.

Lengerova, A.: Radiation chimeras and genetics of somatic cells. *Science,* 155:529, 1967.

Littlefield, J. W.: Selection of hybrids from matings of fibroblasts *in vitro* and their presumed recombinants. *Science,* 145:709, 1964.

Littlefield, J. W.: Hybridization of hamster cells with high and low folate reductase activity. *Proc Nat Acad Sci USA,* 62:88, 1969.

Matsuya, Y., and Green, H.: Somatic cell hybrid between the established human line D98 (presumptive HeLa) and 3T3. *Science,* 163:697, 1969.

Matsuya, Y.; Green, H., and Basilico, C.: Properties and uses of human-mouse hybrid cell lines. *Nature (London),* 220:1199, 1968.

Migeon, B. R.; Smith, S. W., and Leddy, C. L.: The nature of thymidine kinase in the human-mouse hybrid cell. *Biochem Genet,* 3:583, 1969.

Nabholz, M.; Miggiano, V., and Bodmer, W.: Genetic analysis with human-mouse somatic hybrids. *Nature (London),* 223:358, 1969.

Okada, Y.: Analysis of giant polynuclear cell formation caused by HVJ virus from Ehrlich's ascites tumor cells. *Exp Cell Res,* 26:98, 1962.

Okada, Y., and Murayama, F.: Fusion of cells by HVJ: Requirement of concentration of virus particles at the site of contact of two cells for fusion. *Exp Cell Res,* 52:34, 1968.

Rao, P. N., and Johnson, R. T.: Initiation of DNA synthesis and mitosis in multinucleate HeLa cells obtained by fusing cells from different phases of the cell cycle. *J Cell Biol,* 43:110a, 1969.

Scaletta, L. J., and Ephrussi, B.: Hybridization of normal and neoplastic cells *in vitro. Nature (London),* 205:1169, 1965.

Scaletta, L. J.; Rushforth, N. B., and Ephrussi, B.: Isolation and properties of hybrids between somatic mouse and Chinese hamster cells. *Genetics,* 57:107, 1967.

Silagi, S.; Darlington, G., and Bruce, S. A.: Hybridization of two bio-chemically marked human cell lines. *Proc Nat Acad Sci USA,* 62:1085, 1969.

Siniscalco, M.; Klinger, H. P.; Eagle, H.; Koprowski, H.; Fujimoto, W. H., and Seegmiller, J. E.: Evidence for intergenic complementation in hybrid cells derived from two human diploid strains each carrying an x-linked mutation. *Proc Nat Acad Sci USA,* 62:793, 1969.

Spencer, R. A., Hauschka, T. S.; Amos, D. B., and Ephrussi, B.: Codominance of isoantigens in somatic hybrids of murine cells grown *in vitro. J Nat Cancer Inst,* 33:893, 1964.

Teplitz, R. L.; Gustafson, P. E., and Pellett, O. L.: Chromosomal distribution in interspecific *in vitro* hybrid cells. *Exp Cell Res,* 52:379, 1968.

Weber, J., and Stich, H. F.: Response of somatic cell hybrids to exposure to adenovirus type 2 and 12. *Exp Cell Res,* 56:319, 1969.

Weiss, M. C.: Further studies on loss of T-antigen from somatic hybrids between mouse cells and SV 40-transformed human cells. *Proc Nat Acad Sci USA,* 66:79, 1970.

Weiss, M. C., and Ephrussi, B.: Studies of interspecific (rat X mouse) somatic hybrids. II. Lactate dehydrogenase and B-glucuronidase. *Genetics,* 54:1111, 1966.

Weiss, M. C.; Ephrussi, B., and Scaletta, L. J.: Loss of T-antigen from somatic hybrids between mouse cells and SV 40-transformed human cells. *Proc Nat Acad Sci USA,* 59:1132, 1968.

Weiss, M. C., and Green, H.: Human-mouse hybrid cell lines containing partial complements of human chromosomes and functioning human genes. *Proc Nat Acad Sci USA,* 58:1104, 1967.

Yamanaka, T., and Okada, Y.: Cultivation of fused cells resulting from treatment of cells with HVJ. II. Division of binucleated cells resulting from fusion of two KB cells by HVJ. *Exp Cell Res,* 49:461, 1968.

Chapter Twelve

THE SIGNIFICANCE OF CELL CYCLE EVENTS

CELL LIFE CYCLE PHASES

T he cell life cycle is properly studied in cells grown outside of the whole organism (Fig. 12-1). If the cell is one unit of biological activity, then the cell cycle encompasses all of the parameters of this activity. The period of mitosis (M) has been of interest to biologists for a long time because the chromosomes become distinctly visible by light microscopy at this time. During the period of DNA synthesis (S) chromosomes are occupied with the important activity of self-replication, as well as coding for RNA. RNA and protein synthesis also go on during the period

MAMMALIAN DIPLOID CELL LIFE CYCLE

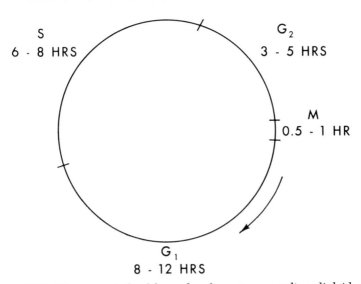

Figure 12-1. Diagram of the life cycle of most mammalian diploid cells. The approximate length of each phase of the cycle is indicated in hours. The direction of progression is indicated by the arrow.

227

between M and S (GI), during S, and during the period between S and the next M (G2). The expressions G1 and G2 originally came from the words gap-1 and gap-2, at a time when mitosis and DNA synthesis were defined as distinct events and little was known about what went on in between. All phases or divisions of the cell life cycle are matters of intensive investigation (Prescott, 1968) because contained within them are answers to such important questions as what controls DNA replication, what regulates cell growth, and what brings about condensation of chromosomes until they are visible by light microscopy during mitosis.

Cultured cells differ considerably in regard to the ease of cell cycle analysis and the results of such analysis. Table 12-I summarizes the range of duration of cell cycle phases in most mammalian cell lines (at 37°C), compared to most human diploid

TABLE 12-I

RANGE OF DURATION OF THE CELL LIFE CYCLE PHASES
FOR MOST MAMMALIAN CELL LINES GROWN AT 37°C,
COMPARED TO MOST HUMAN DIPLOID LINES

Phase	Mean Duration (Hours) Human Diploid	Other Mammalian	General Comments
G1	about 7-9	0-30	Usually the most variable period. RNA synthesis occurs.
S	about 8	4-9	Late replicating chromosomes start and finish synthesis later in this period.
G2	about 4	2-5	DNA synthesis stops, RNA synthesis continues.
M	less than 1	0.2-1.0	Includes prophase, metaphase, anaphase, telophase and nuclear membrane reformation.
Total mean cycle time (generation time)	about 20-22		Individual cells differ considerably from the mean figure.

TABLE 12-II

COMPARISON OF LIFE CYCLE DISTRIBUTION OF CHINESE HAMSTER
OVARY CELLS GROWN IN SUSPENSION CULTURE WITH THAT
OF S3 HELA CELLS GROWN AS MONOLAYERS
(Puck *et al.*, 1964)

Total Generation Time/Phase Time

Phase	*S3 HeLa* (Total Generation Time 20.10 hrs)	*Chinese Hamster Ovary* (Total Generation Time 12.4 hrs)
Mitosis	0.055	0.065
G2	0.22	0.23
S	0.29	0.33
G1	0.41	0.38

lines. Table 12-II compares two cultured cell lines with different total generation times. In this comparision all divisions of the cell cycle occupy similar proportions of the total generation time in both cell types. However, some investigators find the absolute length of G1 to change more than the absolute lengths of the other phases, with changing length of total generation time (Sisken and Kinosita, 1961). The effect of variable environment on cell cycle divisions seems to depend on what varies, whether pH or temperature and so forth (Sisken *et al.*, 1965). Examples of temperature effects are summarized in Table 12-III. G1 arrest is considered to be the main mechanism for temporary cessation of the cell cycling pattern. For instance, the circulating human lymphocyte, when induced by phytohemagglutinin to divide *in vitro*, first moves into S and on to mitosis (Bender and Prescott, 1962). When thyroxine is administered to nondiploid human monolayer cells (kidney origin) the life cycle is reduced from twenty-seven to twenty hours; the shortening is due to reduced time in G1 and other phases appear to be virtually unchanged (Burki and Tobias, 1970).

Some methods to study cell life cycle divisions are listed in Chapter 2, Table 2-III (also see Fig. 2-2, 2-3, and 2-4). Most of these methods determine a mean figure for the culture population. Individual cells differ considerably from the mean figures, a striking deviation being cells with long total generation times as

TABLE 12-III

EXAMPLES OF TEMPERATURE EFFECTS ON
CELL CYCLE PHASES

The effect of moderate changes in temperature on the length of
each part of the cycle for human nondiploid amnion cells in
monolayer culture was studied by cinemicrography. Each part of
the cycle except anaphase had a U-shaped temperature response
curve. (Decrease in length with increasing temperature until an
optimum temperature; then increase in length of the phase with
further temperature increase). At temperatures below optimum,
G1 and metaphase were most sensitive and G2 plus prophase and
anaphase the least sensitive to changes. At temperatures above
optimum, metaphase was again most sensitive; G1, S, and G2 plus
prophase had moderate and similar sensitivities, and anaphase
seemed completely insensitive. All responses were quick to change
with temperature.

Sisken *et al.*,
1965

HeLa human nondiploid cells were studied in suspension culture.
After a shift in temperature, the population kinetics of HeLa
cells did not immediately reach a steady state characteristic of
the new temperature. Of four life cycle periods, the period before
DNA synthesis reached its steady-state value fastest (compared
to DNA synthesis, the period after DNA synthesis and mitosis).
Exponential growth of the culture was maintained only from 33°C
through 40°C. The period of mitosis was the most temperature-
sensitive period of the life cycle. At subnormal temperatures
(26°C through 31°C) there was an accumulation of cells in
mitosis and mitotic indices as high as 0.44 could be obtained. The
duration of mitosis was a function both of the temperature and
of the time which the cell spent at this temperature.

Rao and
Engelberg,
1965

Variability in the duration of mitosis as a function of temperature
was studied by time-lapse cinemicrography of HeLa (wild-type)
cells. Mean mitotic duration ranged from 36 to 80 min. between
32.7°C and 39.6°C. Minimum duration was in the vicinity of
37.5°C.

Rao and
Engelberg,
1968

demonstrated by cinemicroscopy (Sisken and Morasca, 1965). It
is important to keep in mind the variability of individual cell
behavior within a culture population. All cells cannot be expected
to respond identically to synchronization procedures or to other
types of manipulation such as introduction of drugs or labeled
compounds (see Chap. 2).

Phytohemagglutinin-stimulated human peripheral blood lymphocytes may deviate from the generalized patterns of cell cycle
behavior listed in Table 12-I. In one study, a mean length of the

first S + G2 was found to range from sixteen to seventeen hours (minimal 6 to 9 hours; maximal over 24 hours) (Steffen and Stolzmann, 1969). The time between PHA stimulation and entrance into the first *in vitro* DNA synthesis period was also found to vary considerably in length, being as long as seventy-two hours for some cells. In six long-term lymphocyte cell lines derived from normal human subjects and from patients with malignant diseases, population doubling times ranged from twenty-six to sixty-seven hours (Aoki and Moore, 1970). In this study, the G2 stages of the various cell lines were of almost the same duration; the length of the G1 state was the primary determinant of the length of the cell cycle (also see Chap. 1, on short- and long-term peripheral blood cultures).

Gradient centrifugation has been used to study events of the life cycle of cultured cells (Warmsley *et al.*, 1969). Cells in G1 were at the top of the gradient, S cells in the middle, and G2 near the bottom.

INTERPRETATION OF CELL LIFE CYCLE EVENTS

Some conclusions about the significance of specific cell cycle phases, confirmed in cultured human cells, are summarized in Table 12-IV. "The patterns of enzyme synthesis can be classified into two broad groups, depending on whether or not synthesis is continuous during the cycle. . . . Most of the enzymes that have been examined are synthesized discontinuously at a particular stage of the cycle which is characteristic for each enzyme." (Mitchison, 1969, p. 657; also see Chap. 4 on enzyme synthesis in relation to the cell cycle, and Fig. 4-4). In synchronized human lymphoid cell lines, production of immunoglobulins G and M was greatest during late G1 and S phases of the cell cycle (Matalon *et al.*, 1969). Little immunoglobulin appeared immediately before, during, and immediately after mitosis; thus transcription of immunoglobulin took place during a limited part of the mitotic cycle. In synchronized human fetal diploid cells, collagen synthesis appears to be continuous, at least during S phase (Davies *et al.*, 1968).

TABLE 12-IV

SOME CONCLUSIONS ABOUT THE SIGNIFICANCE OF SPECIFIC CELL CYCLE PHASES,
CONFIRMED IN CULTURED HUMAN CELLS

Conclusion	Culture Type	Human Tissue of Origin	Reference
G1			
In cells that are arrested in G1 for an extended period of time, the return to proliferative activity begins with a continuation of G1 between the application of the proliferative stimulus and the first round of DNA synthesis. In subsequent cycles G1 becomes shorter.	Short-term peripheral blood culture	Lymphocyte, PHA stimulated	Bender and Prescott, 1962
The rate of RNA synthesis is constant (or increases only slightly) during G1.	HeLa, monolayer established line	Cervical carcinoma	Pfeiffer and Tolmach, 1968
S			
Initiation of DNA synthesis requires the synthesis of both RNA and protein. Thus it is suggested that a particular protein must be made which controls the initiation of replication.	KB, suspension, established line	Oral carcinoma	Taylor, 1965
Mammalian cells treated during S with inhibitors of protein synthesis undergo a rapid decline in DNA synthesis.	HeLa, monolayer established line	Cervical carcinoma	Young, 1966
Although there is no consistent evidence that synthesis of known enzymes concerned with DNA synthesis must be done before the S period, thymidine kinase does show cyclic behavior in relation to the S phase.	HeLa, monolayer established line	Cervical carcinoma	Stubblefield and Mueller, 1965
Synthesis of various species of RNA occurs throughout interphase, but undergoes a two-fold increase in rate during the first half of S, which is dependent on the duplication of DNA.	HeLa, monolayer established line	Cervical carcinoma	Pfeiffer and Tolmach, 1968; Pfeiffer, 1968

TABLE 12-IV (Continued)

Conclusion	Culture Type	Human Tissue of Origin	Reference
The long fibers (DNA molecules) composing chromosomal DNA are made up of tandemly joined replication sections or units. During S phase adjacent units initiate replication at the same time and proceed in opposite directions from each initiation point. (See Fig. 12-2)	HeLa, monolayer established line	Cervical carcinoma	Huberman and Riggs, 1968
Histones are synthesized on small cytoplasmic polyribosomes when DNA is replicated (during S phase). Except for this histone messenger RNA-ribosome complex, the other cytoplasmic factors requisite for histone synthesis are present throughout the cell cycle.	HeLa, monolayer established line	Cervical carcinoma	Pederson and Robbins, 1970
G2			
Some new protein molecules must be synthesized within a 30-60 minute period prior to metaphase, for division to occur.	Fermandes, monolayer, established line	Amnion	Donnelly and Sisken, 1967
Cells maintain the average G2 rate of RNA synthesis until mitosis.	HeLa, monolayer, established line	Cervical carcinoma	Pfeiffer and Tolmach, 1968
M			
Mitosis is delayed by X-irradiation of cells in G2 and S. Irradiation during G1 delays mitosis less or not at all.	T cell, monolayer, established line	Kidney	Bootsma, 1965

234   *Human Cell Culture in Diagnosis of Disease*

< — >   < — >   < — >

Figure 12-2. Adjacent tandem replication units in a DNA fiber (molecule) initiate replication at the same time and proceed in opposite directions as indicated by the arrows.

REFERENCES

General

Baserga, R.: Biochemical events in the cell cycle. *Nat Cancer Inst Monogr,* 30:1, 1969.
Mueller, G. C.: Biochemical events in the animal cell cycle. *Fed Proc, 28:* 1780, 1969.
Prescott, D. M.: Sequential events of the cell life cycle. In *Exploitable Molecular Mechanisms and Neoplasia. A Collection of Papers Presented at the Twenty-Second Annual Symposium on Fundamental Cancer Research.* Baltimore, Williams and Wilkins, 1968, p. 359.

Specific

Aoki, Y., and Moore, G. E.: Comparative study of mitotic stages of cells derived from human peripheral blood. *Exp Cell Res,* 59:259, 1970.
Bender, M. A., and Prescott, D. M.: DNA synthesis and mitosis in cultures of human peripheral leukocytes. *Exp Cell Res,* 27:221, 1962.
Bootsma, D.: Changes induced in the first post-irradiation generation cycle of human cells studied by double labeling. *Exp Cell Res,* 38:429, 1965.
Burki, H. J., and Tobias, C. A.: Effect of thyroxine on the cell generation cycle parameters of cultured human cells. *Exp Cell Res,* 60:445, 1970.
Davies, L. M.; Priest, J. H., and Priest, R. E.: Collagen synthesis by cells synchronously replicating DNA. *Science,* 159:91, 1968.
Donnelly, G. M., and Sisken, J. E.: RNA and protein synthesis required for entry of cells into mitosis and during the mitotic cycle. *Exp Cell Res,* 46:93, 1967.
Huberman, J. A., and Riggs, A. D.: On the mechanism of DNA replication in mammalian chromosomes. *J Molec Biol,* 32:327, 1968.
Matalon, R.; Dorfman, A.; Dawson, G., and Sweeley, C. C.: Limited periods of gene expression in immunoglobulin-synthesizing cells. *Science,* 164:1524, 1969.
Mitchinson, J. M.: Enzyme synthesis in synchronous cultures. *Science, 165:* 657, 1969.
Pederson, T., and Robbins, E.: Absence of translational control of histone synthesis during the HeLa cell life cycle. *J Cell Biol,* 45:509, 1970.
Pfeiffer, S. E.: RNA synthesis in sychronously growing populations of HeLa S3 cells. II. Rate of synthesis of individual RNA fractions. *J Cell Physiol,* 71:95, 1968.

Pfeiffer, S. E., and Tolmach, L. J.: RNA synthesis in synchronously growing populations of HeLa S3 cells. I. Rate of total RNA synthesis and its relationship to DNA synthesis. *J Cell Physiol, 71*:77, 1968.

Prescott, D. M.: Sequential events of the cell life cycle. In *Exploitable Molecular Mechanisms and Neoplasia. A Collection of Papers Presented at the Twenty-Second Annual Symposium on Fundamental Cancer Research.* Baltimore, Williams and Wilkins, 1968, p. 359.

Puck, T. T.; Sanders, P., and Petersen, D.: Life cycle analysis of mammalian cells. II. Cells from the Chinese hamster ovary grown in suspension culture. *Biophys J, 4*:441, 1964.

Rao, P. N., and Engleberg, J.: HeLa cells: Effects of temperature on the life cycle. *Science, 148*:1092, 1965.

Rao, P. N., and Engelberg, J.: Mitotic duration and its variability in relation to temperature in HeLa cells. *Exp Cell Res, 52*:198, 1968.

Sisken, J. E., and Kinosita, R.: Timing of DNA synthesis in the mitotic cycle *in vitro*. *J Biophys Biochem Cytol, 9*:509, 1961.

Sisken, J. E., and Morasca, L.: Intrapopulation kinetics of the mitotic cycle. *J Cell Biol, 25*:179, 1965.

Sisken, J. E.; Morasca, L., and Kibby, S.: Effects of temperature on the kinetics of the mitotic cycle of mammalian cells in culture. *Exp Cell Res, 39*:103, 1965.

Steffen, J. A., and Stolzmann, W. M.: Studies on *in vitro* lymphocyte proliferation in cultures synchronized by the inhibition of DNA synthesis. I. Variability of S plus G2 periods of first generation cells. *Exp Cell Res, 56*:453, 1969.

Stubblefield, E., and Mueller, G. C.: Thymidine kinase activity in synchronized HeLa cell cultures. *Biochem Biophys Res Commun, 20*:535, 1965.

Taylor, E. W.: Control of DNA synthesis in mammalian cells in culture. *Exp Cell Res, 40*:316, 1965.

Warmsley, A. M.; Bergeron, J. J., and Pasternak, C. A.: The use of gradient centrifugation to study events in the life cycle of cultured cells. *Biochem J, 114*:64P, 1969.

Young, C. W.: Inhibitory effects of Acetoxycycloheximide, Puromycin, and Pactamycin upon synthesis of protein and DNA in asychronous populations of HeLa cells, *Molec Pharmacol, 2*:50, 1966.

Chapter Thirteen
THE SIGNIFICANCE OF HETEROCHROMATIN;
SEX CHROMATIN

From the time of the 19th-century cytologists, odd assortments of densely staining flecks, blobs, rods, and agglomerations have been seen in the cell nuclei of various species of plants and animals. Modern insight began in 1928 when Heitz first saw the true relationship of these puzzling structures to the chromosomes, called them heterochromatin, and proposed that heterochromatin had special genetic attributes (Brown, 1966, p. 417) (Tables 13-I and 13-II).

TABLE 13-I

DEFINITIONS OF TERMS CONCERNED WITH HETEROCHROMATIN

Chromatin	Areas of a cell nucleus that stain in some manner with a DNA stain.
Chromocenter	A block of heterochromatic material.
Euchromatin (euchromatic)	Relating to areas of the nucleus that do not stain "differently" with DNA stains.
Facultative heterochromatin (facultative heterochromatization)	The heterochromatic material has certain characteristics: it becomes heterochromatic early in development; the heterochromatized (inactivated) chromosomes contain as many genes (?) as their noninactivated homologues. Example: inactivated mammalian X chromosomal material.
Heterochromatin (heterochromatic; heterochromatization)	Relating to areas of the nucleus that stain "differently" with DNA stains.
Negatively heterochromatic (negatively heteropyknotic)	Staining less. (See definition of heterochromatic.)
Positively heterochromatic (positively heteropyknotic)	Staining more. (See definition of heterochromatic.)
Sex chromatin (Barr body; female sex chromatin)	A characteristic area of heterochromatin in the nucleus, composed of X chromosome material that stains heavily with a DNA stain.
Sex chromatin negative (chromatin negative)	The female sex chromatin body is not present in a cell nucleus.
Sex chromatin positive (chromatin positive)	The female sex chromatin body is present in a cell nucleus.
Structural or constitutive heterochromatin (structural or constitutive heterochromatization)	The heterochromatic material has certain characteristics: a fixed time of appearance in development is not identified; the genes of both homologous chromosomes are inactivated. Example: some (or most?) inactivated mammalian autosomal material.

236

TABLE 13-II

SOME CHARACTERISTICS OF HETEROCHROMATIN

1. Greater (or different) affinity for DNA stains, by light microscopy.
2. Closeness (packing) of DNA fibers, by electron microscopy.
3. Genetic inactivity; depressed formation of RNA.
4. Self-replication late to finish; takes less total time for replication (as compared to euchromatin).

Since mammalian heterochromatin is visible in many kinds of interphases and may be well demonstrated in cells taken directly from the individual, what is the value of cell culture? A partial answer to this question may be stated simply: cells in culture can be studied while alive; they can be manipulated to obtain optimal morphology and to answer questions about the mechanism of heterochromatization.

The purpose of this chapter is to point out the special uses of cell cultures and what has been learned from them about all types of human heterochromatin. The terms heterochromatin and heterochromatic material are used interchangeably here but it should be emphasized that these terms both refer to a state (of DNA).

SEX AND AUTOSOMAL HETEROCHROMATIN

In phase contrast the nuclei of many cultured living female cells contain a dark particle, about 1-2μ in diameter closely attached to the nuclear membrane (Schwarzacher, 1963). This particle is sometimes very similar in size and shape to the sex chromatin body seen in fixed and Feulgen stained nuclei, although it may appear as a bent or folded thread ½-1μ thick and about 3-5μ long. Thus there is no doubt the the sex chromatin can be seen in living human female cells. The fact that the sex chromatin attains different degrees of optical density in different cells within the same culture may be a reflection of the state of condensation of the sex chromatin-forming X chromosome. The location is not always peripheral. The female sex chromatin mass in living cells examined by phase contrast is related to the number of X chromosomes, being present in XX and XXY human cells but not in XO or XY (DeMars, 1962); this rule of one less female sex chromatin mass than X chromosome was confirmed in the same cells after fixation. Examples of two sex chromatin masses per cell in skin cultured from an XXX female are given in Figures 13-1, a. and b.

Y chromosome material can also be identified in fixed human interphase nuclei. The distal portion of the human Y chromosome fluoresces brightly when stained with fluorescent acridine derivatives. Cultured skin fibroblast-like cells growing on microscope slides, lymphocytes from short-term peripheral blood culture and cells taken directly by buccal smear were examined for fluorescence (Pearson *et al.*, 1970). In lymphocyte metaphases the distal half of the long arm of the Y chromosome included the largest and brightest site of fluorescence. XY interphase nuclei also showed a brightly fluorescent body about 0.25μ in diameter, either single or double in structure. No similar structures were seen in XX cells but two were seen in some XYY cells. The physical dimensions of the male chromatin body are similar to those of the fluorescent region of the Y chromosome. This observation implies that at least part of the Y chromosome is condensed in the interphase nucleus and in this respect is analogous to the second X chromosome in XX interphases. The rule for the male chromatin body is, however: the same number of male sex chromatin masses as Y chromosomes.

Both nucleolus-associated and scattered areas of heterochromatin are also seen in human interphase nuclei, either XX or XY (Lima-de-Faria *et al.*, 1965). Since there is no relation to sex chromosomes, the term autosomal heterochromatin is used. The correspondence of this type of heterochromatin with chromosome segments is obtained at late prophase of human peripheral blood cultures, where several positively heterochromatic (darkly staining) regions belonging to the autosomes are found scattered throughout the nucleus (Lima-de-Faria *et al.*, 1965).

STRUCTURE, ARRANGEMENTS IN THE NUCLEUS, AND REPLICATION OF HETEROCHROMATIN

The appearance of heterochromatin by light microscopy is mentioned in the first section of this chapter. It was assumed that

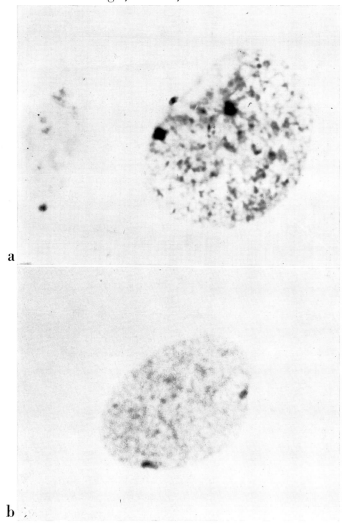

a

b

Figure 13-1. (a) Two sex chromatin masses are present in a fibroblast-like cell grown from skin primary explant of a female child. All of the metaphases examined in both peripheral blood cultures and monolayer serial cultures showed an XXX sex chromosome complement. Interphase nuclei for sex chromatin analysis were prepared from the serial cultures by growing the cells on coverglasses, rinsing, fixing and staining with thionin. (100X oil emersion objective.)

(b) Fibroblast-like cells in serial culture from the same XXX child were trypsinized, fixed as a button, air dried on microscope slides and stained with thionin. Techniques of preparation change the morphology of the two sex chromatin bodies as compared to Figure 13-1a above. 100X oil emersion objective.

greater affinity of heterochromatin for DNA stain would be equated with greater localization (concentration) of DNA. Studies of human cultured cells by electron microscopy confirm the presence of DNA fibers in female sex chromatin bodies of greater density (compactness) than in the surrounding areas of the nucleus but of less density than in metaphase chromosomes. The fibers of female sex chromatin bodies found lying away from the nuclear periphery appear to be organized more compactly than the fibers of the sex chromatin bodies found at the nuclear periphery (Wolstenholme, 1965). As with the living cell, the different degrees of compactness of sex chromatin DNA fibers are probably a reflection of the state of condensation of the sex chromatin-forming X chromosome.

A rule may be firmly stated that heterochromatin is late replicating as compared to euchromatin (Lima-de-Faria and Jaworska, 1968). Light microscope autoradiography with tritiated thymidine (see Chap. 2, on labeling of cells with tritiated compounds) reveals a definite sequence of DNA replication in cultured human cells. Heterochromatin labels later in the DNA synthesis period but incorporates label over a shorter time and thus replicates faster as compared to euchromatin (Comings, 1967a; Priest, 1968) (Table 13-III). The full significance of this late but faster replication and its relation to genetic inactivity in heterochromatin is still to be clarified.

TABLE 13-III

A SUMMARY OF THE REPLICATION CHARACTERISTICS OF
HUMAN HETEROCHROMATIN IN SERIAL CULTURE
(from Priest, 1968)

1. The human C group chromosomes late to start and finish replication in asynchronous and in FUdR synchronized cell lines are X chromosomes (Fig. 13-2).

2. These same chromosomes are heterochromatic during interphase, forming sex chromatin.

3. During metaphase these "differently" replicating X chromosomes cannot be identified simply by metaphase position or morphology and show a wide range of measurements for arm ratio, centromere index and total length. Thus without autoradiography they are not readily distinguishable from other chromosomes within the C group.

Table 13-III (Continued)

4. Replication in the "differently" replicating X chromosomes starts in the short arm and extends over the entire chromosome during the second and third hrs. of S until by the fourth hr. distinction from other members of the C group cannot be made by means of the labeling pattern.

5. When these "differently" replicating X chromosomes start replication the pattern of H₃TdR label over interphase sex chromatin and other "nonspecific" heterochromatin shifts from unlabeled to labeled in FUdR synchronized human cell lines (Fig. 13-3, a and b). Specific label of heterochromatin is characteristic of the last one-third of S phase.

6. The overall time required for replication of the "differently" replicating X chromosomes is less than that for the other chromosomes in both asynchronous and FUdR synchronized cells.

7. It can be postulated that there is a direct relation between the delay of onset of replication in heterochromatin and its degree of interphase condensation.

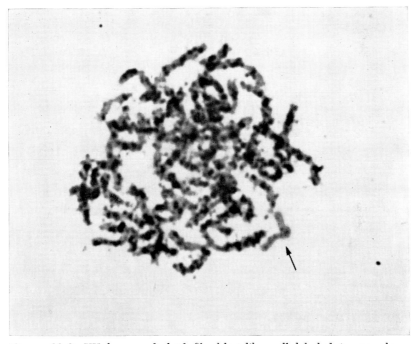

Figure 13-2. XX human diploid fibroblast-like cell labeled in monolayer culture. A late prophase reveals the peripheral location of an unlabeled X chromosome late to start its replication (arrow). Later in mitosis (midmetaphase) the peripheral position is usually not identified. This mitosis was labeled with H₃TdR during the first 30 minutes of the previous DNA synthesis period. This X chromosome corresponds to the sex chromatin during interphase. Ilford L-4 emulsion. Giemsa stain. 100X oil emersion objective.

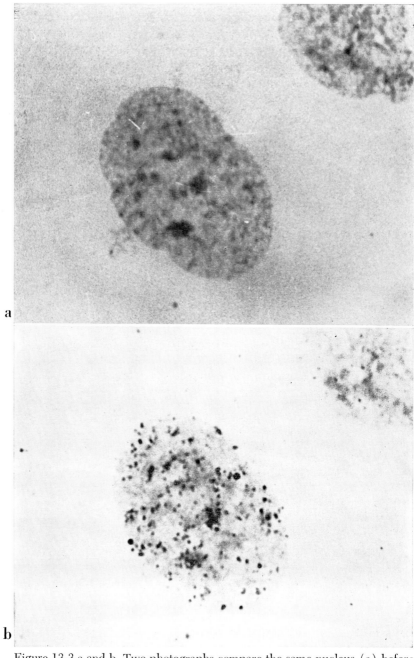

a

b

Figure 13-3 a and b. Two photographs compare the same nucleus (a) before and (b) after application of NTB-2 emulsion to reveal the pattern of H_3TdR label over heterochromatin. The label was applied later in S phase when localization is apparent over late replicating sex and "non-specific"

→

Greater resolution of heterochromatin and euchromatin is obtained with electron microscopy (EM). Nucleic acid synthesis has been studied by EM autoradiography using short-term *in vitro* label of human lymphocytes treated with phytohemagglutinin (PHA) (Milner and Hayhoe, 1968). The lymphocytes were pulse labeled at forty-eight hours following introduction of PHA into the culture, when the cells enlarge and the nucleus changes in appearance from heterochromatin-rich to euchromatin-rich (see Chap. 1, on short-term peripheral blood cultures and Figs. 1-4 and 1-5). At this time DNA and RNA synthesis also start. In many nuclei there are still substantial areas of heterochromatin (denser DNA fibers), particularly adjacent to the nucleolus and apposed to the nuclear membrane. In these nuclei tritiated thymidine and uridine label is localized at the junction between euchromatin and heterochromatin. On the other hand, some nuclei are wholly euchromatic (sparse DNA fibers) and label over these nuclei is scattered. The localization of both thymidine and uridine uptake at the junction between heterochromatin and euchromatin suggests that during the process of PHA stimulation of the lymphocyte, DNA and RNA are synthesized at newly decondensed DNA template sites.

If DNA replicates only as euchromatin all heterochromatin must decondense at some stage of interphase. In the (PHA-stimulated) lymphocyte there is a stage during the S phase when all the nuclear chromatin is in the decondensed form. It may be suggested that at this stage all the nuclear chromatin has replicated or is available for replication if other necessary conditions are fulfilled. An alternative pattern for replication of heterochromatin might be localized and short-lived decondensation of small areas of heterochromatin so that no stage of total decondensation is reached (Milner, 1969, p. 71).

Although the data from PHA- stimulated lymphocytes suggest an entirely euchromatic stage (in some cells), data from thymidine labeled human normoblasts in short-term bone marrow cultures suggest that the normoblast heterochromatin decondenses, replicates and then recondenses during a single interphase. No labeled nuclei with a totally decondensed pattern are seen (Milner, 1969). The EM normoblast data would therefore fit a

---

heterochromatin. This cell was grown in culture from an XXX individual. Two discrete sex chromatin bodies are visible as well as less discrete autosomal heterochromatin. (a) Thionin stain (b) restained with Giemsa. 100X oil emersion objective.

replication pattern for heterochromatin that involves localized and short-lived decondensation. The evidence from light microscopy of human cultured cells, limited by low magnification and low resolution, also suggests localized and short-lived decondensation of heterochromatin at the time of its replication; note that the sex chromatin body by light microscopy can be both present and labeled by tritiated thymidine (Klinger *et al.*, 1967) and uridine (Comings, 1966).

RELATION OF SEX CHROMATIN TO CULTURE CONDITIONS AND CELL CYCLE

Changes in the character of sex chromatin in relation to culture conditions such as cell density, and in relation to the cell cycle are important for the interpretation of any analysis of sex chromatin in cultured cells. Changes in heterochromatin with the cell cycle also have bearing on basic principles of DNA replication (see the previous section on replication of heterochromatin).

In cultured human XX cells, maximal (saturation) density populations have a higher percent of sex chromatin positive cells than do rapidly proliferating cultures containing fewer cells (Table 13-IV) (also see Table 13-V, 2.). The extremes of 90 to 95 percent chromatin positive cells in maximal density cultures and 10 percent chromatin positive cells in rapidly proliferating cultures have been reported (DeMars, 1964). Analysis of frequency of chromatin positive cultured cells, for clinical diagnosis, should be performed at a time when the normal XX cells would show the greatest percent of positive cells; thereby, the discrimination of chromatin positive mosaicism and chromatin negative situations is facilitated. Deviations from the rule that frequency analysis of sex chromatin positive cells is performed best on confluent cultures are dictated by special conditions of investigation. For instance, if sex chromatin is to be studied in synchronized cells, some types of synchronization are not possible on confluent cultures.

TABLE 13-IV

SEX CHROMATIN IN RELATION TO CULTURE CONDITIONS

Observations	Reference

A. *Subculture*

DNA synthesis of cultured human fibroblast-like cells may be partially synchronized when cells are transplanted into a new culture vessel. A peak in mitosis frequency frequently occurs 24 hours after subculture. In cultures from XX humans, sex chromatin positive cells are less frequently observed just after this mitotic peak. (Also see Table 13-V.)	Schnedl, 1969

B. *Cell Density*

In cultures of XX females, the frequency of sex chromatin positive nuclei increases linearly from about 35-60% at cell densities of less than one cell per 0.01 mm² of culture surface, to 90-100% at densities of 20-125 cells per 0.01 mm². This frequency-to-density relationship is independent of the mitotic rate and the rate at which cell density increases. When large variations in cell density are produced intentionally on the same glass coverslip, frequency of sex chromatin positive cells is related to the density of cells in any one area of a coverslip and is independent of the cell density in other parts of the coverslip. These observations can indicate that there is a relation between sex chromatin formation and metabolic state of the cell.	Klinger *et al.*, 1968

C. *Culture Age*

A decrease in percent of sex chromatin positive cells has been reported in relation to age of the culture and number of subcultures. (In human XX diploid cells it is possible that this decrease could be accounted for by decrease in cell density as a culture with finite life-expectancy grows old.)	Orsi *et al.*, 1961

TABLE 13-V

SEX CHROMATIN AND THE CELL CYCLE

Observations	Reference

1. *Morphology*

When cells with identifiable sex chromatin pass through DNA synthesis, this region becomes more diffuse (though still identifiable by light microscopy) during the last third of S phase, at which time H₃TdR label is also localized to it.	Ockey, 1966

TABLE 13-V (Continued)

Observations	*Reference*
The sex chromatin becomes more dense again early in G_2. (Sex chromatin size and DNA content are not discussed in this study.)	
The condensed X chromosome can be seen at prophase in XX cells. Although it appears larger than most of the sex chromatin bodies present in neighboring interphase nuclei, the condensed X seen in each daughter nucleus of telophase corresponds quite well in size to the interphase sex chromatin body. Thus a female somatic cell enters into and emerges from interphase with an X chromosome condensed.	Ohno, 1963
The sex chromatin body (condensed X chromosome) becomes obscured for a short period after telophase as the other chromosomes uncoil.	Ockey, 1966

2. *Frequency*

There is an increase in frequency of sex chromatin positive cells during the cell cycle when early G1, late G1, and G2 nuclei are compared.	Schnedl, 1969

However;

in cultures in logarithmic growth, sex chromatin negative cells are found in all three intermitotic phases (G1, S, and G2) but with a statistically higher frequency in early interphase than in late interphase. In cultures in post-logarithmic growth, the majority of cells are in G1 and sex chromatin positive.	Therkelsen and Lamm, 1966

3. *DNA Content and Size*

Three types of nuclei may be defined by light microscopy on the basis of H_3TdR label and DNA content determined photometrically: (a) unlabeled nuclei with low DNA content (G1); (b) labeled nuclei with intermediate DNA values (S); (c) unlabeled nuclei with double the low DNA content (G2 and a few tetraploid nuclei). DNA content of sex chromatin thus varies with the cell cycle and also varies directly with nuclear DNA content.	Klinger *et al.*, 1967
The area of the sex chromatin body is closely related to its DNA content and increases in size following DNA replication.	Comings, 1967b

Observations concerning the relation of human sex chromatin to the cell cycle are summarized in Table 13-V (also see Chap. 12, on significance of cell cycle events). Frequency of positive cells, sex chromatin morphology and DNA content are all influenced by position of the cell in the cell cycle.

Fluctuations in incidence of chromatin positive cells have been reported in relation to the menstrual cycle, when interphases are examined in direct preparations (say, in buccal smears). If the cause is hormonal, one reasonable study might involve application of various hormones to cultured cells. However, fluctuations in the frequency of cells containing sex chromatin bodies, in relation to other culture conditions should be kept in mind during any studies of effects of a specific substance introduced into the culture.

MECHANISM AND EFFECTS OF HETEROCHROMATIZATION IN CULTURED CELLS

There is agreement that heterochromatin is associated generally with genetic inactivity and decreased RNA production. Many specific problems remain to be answered. One, the spatial mechanics of nucleic acid synthesis, has already been discussed in this chapter in the section on replication of heterochromatin. There is evidence to support the hypothesis of localized and short-lived decondensation of heterochromatin, accompanied by both DNA and RNA synthesis at the junction between heterochromatin and euchromatin.

Another problem, the mechanism to bring about condensation and decondensation of DNA fibers is not solved satisfactorily. It has frequently been proposed that a variation in the relative content of lysine-rich, moderately lysine-rich, and arginine-rich histones might provide a mechanism by which specific portions of the genome may be genetically regulated. This possibility was investigated by comparing the electrophoretic pattern of these three fractions in cells differing markedly in their content of genetically active and genetically inactive chromatin. Three models were used: heterochromatin versus euchromatin; metaphase cells versus interphase cells, and mature lymphocytes versus phytohemagglutinin-stimulated lymphocytes. In no case was there a significant difference in the histone patterns of these constrasting models. It is concluded that, although histones may act as a generalized repressor and structural component of chromatin, factors other than a variation in histone pattern may be responsible for repression or depression of specific segments of the genome (Comings, 1967c, p. 699).

Why are some cells cultured from normal human females

chromatin negative? Several studies have been designed to answer this question (Comings, 1967b; Klinger *et al.*, 1967). Table
13-VI summarizes possible answers and reasons against most of
them, but favoring one: that sex chromatin negative cells have
lost only the condensation of their sex heterochromatin (compactness of DNA fibers).

TABLE 13-VI

THE PROBLEM OF CHROMATIN NEGATIVE CELLS

(from Comings, 1967b)

Hypothesis

1. A cell may be sex chromatin negative because it has lost the inactive
X chromosome.

Against

a. The percentage of cells with a sex
chromatin body approaches 100%
in confluent culture.

b. A significant number of XO cells
are absent in metaphases from cultures of normal human fibroblast-
like cells.

2. The inactive X chromosome may
have become reactivated perma-
nently or during some portion of
the cell cycle.

Against

a. Studies of the incidence of sex
chromatin positive cells in relation
to the cell cycle do not document
a clear time of sex chromatin
negativity.

b. A second G6PD band is absent in
cloned AB fibroblasts. The clones
are either A or B, making it un-
likely that a significant number of
cells contain a reactivated X.

3. Sex chromatin negative cells might
be explained by the possible neces-
sity of sex chromatin to decondense
to undergo DNA replication.

Against

a. The sex chromatin body, by light
microscopy, can be both present
and labeled by tritiated thymidine.

b. The frequency of sex chromatin
positive cells does not clearly decrease during S phase of the cell
cycle.

c. The frequency of nuclear H_3TdR
labeling is no greater for sex chromatin negative compared to sex
chromatin positive cells.

4. The sex chromatin body may not
be visible in some cells due to

Against

The presence of a sex chromatin in

TABLE 13-VI (Continued)

Hypothesis

factors related to the geometry of the cell.

5. Sex chromatin negative cells represent the loss of condensation of heterochromatin without the loss of genetic inactivation.

virtually all cells of a confluent culture suggests that nuclei have no hiding places.

For

a. There is evidence that condensation of DNA can be lost without loss of genetic inactivation or loss of delayed DNA replication.

b. Partially decondensed sex chromatin bodies seen in cell cultures (by phase contrast) are probably less extreme examples of sex chromatin negative cells.

REFERENCES

General

Brown, S. W.: Heterochromatin. *Science, 151*:417, 1966.

Miles, C. P.: The sex chromatin in cultured cells. In Moore, K. L. (Ed.): *The Sex Chromatin.* Philadelphia, W. B. Saunders, 1966, chap. 12.

Priest, J. H.: *Medical Technology Series: Cytogenetics.* Philadelphia, Lea & Febiger, 1969, chap. 10: Sex Chromatin.

Schmid, W.: Heterochromatin in mammals. *Arch Klaus Stift Verebungsforsch, 42*:1, 1967.

Specific

Brown, S. W.: Heterochromatin. *Science, 151*:417, 1966.

Comings, D. E.: Uridine-5-H^3 radioautography of the human sex chromatin body. *J Cell Biol, 28*:437, 1966.

Comings, D. E.: The duration of replication of the inactive X chromosome in humans based on the persistence of the heterochromatic sex chromatin body during DNA synthesis. *Cytogenetics (Basel), 6*:20, 1967a.

Comings, D. E.: Sex chromatin, nuclear size and the cell cycle. *Cytogenetics (Basel), 6*:120, 1967b.

Comings, D. E.: Histones of genetically active and inactive chromatin. *J Cell Biol, 35*:699, 1967c.

DeMars, R.: Sex chromatin mass in living, cultivated human cells. *Science, 138*:980, 1962.

DeMars, R.: Sex chromatin formation during the interphase of human fibroblasts. *Science, 146*:424, 1964.

Klinger, H. P.; Davis, J.; Goldhuber, P., and Ditta, T.: Factors influencing mammalian X chromosome condensation and sex chromatin formation.

I. The effect of *in vitro* cell density on sex chromatin frequency. *Cytogenetics (Basel)*, 7:39, 1968.

Klinger, H. P.; Schwarzacher, H. G., and Weiss, J.: DNA content and size of sex chromatin positive female nuclei during the cell cycle. *Cytogenetics (Basel)*, 6:1, 1967.

Lima-de-Faria, A., and Jaworska, H.: Late DNA synthesis in heterochromatin. *Nature (London)*, 217:138, 1968.

Lima-de-Faria, A.; Reitalu, J., and O'Sullivan, M. A.: Replication of autosomal heterochromatin in man. *Chromosoma (Basel)*, 16:152, 1965.

Milner, G. R.: Changes in chromatin structure during interphase in human normoblasts. *Nature (London)*, 221:71, 1969.

Milner, G. R., and Hayhoe, F. G. J.: Ultrastructural localization of nucleic acid synthesis in human blood cells. *Nature (London)*, 218:785, 1968

Ockey, C. H.: Behavior of the sex-chromatin X and heterochromatin in the human female. In Darlington, C. D., and Lewis, K. R. (Eds.): *Chromosomes Today*. Edinburgh, Oliver & Boyd, 1966, vol. I.

Ohno, S.: Dynamics of the condensed female X chromosome. *Lancet, 1*:273, 1963.

Orsi, E. V.; Wallace, R. E., and Ritter, H. B.: Changes in incidence of sex chromatin in subcultured cells. *Science, 133*:43, 1961.

Pearson, P. L.; Borrow, M., and Vosa, C. G.: Technique for identifying Y chromosomes in human interphase nuclei. *Nature (London), 226*:78, 1970.

Priest, J. H.: The replication of human heterochromatin in serial culture. *Chromosoma, 24*:438, 1968.

Schnedl, W.: Sex Chromatin and nuclear size during the cell cycle. *Chromosoma, 27*:421, 1969.

Schwarzacher, H. G.: Sex chromatin in living human cells *in vitro. Cytogenetics (Basel), 2*:117, 1963.

Therkelsen, A. J., and Lamm, L. U.: Difference in the frequency of sex chromatin positive cells in the different intermitotic phases of human cells in tissue culture. *Exp Cell Res, 44*:636, 1966.

Wolstenholme, D. R.: Electron microscopic identification of sex chromatin bodies of tissue culture cells. *Chromosoma, 16*:453, 1965.

Chapter Fourteen
CONTROL MECHANISMS

S ome understanding has been gained of regulatory mechanisms as they operate in bacteria. The information on mechanisms of regulation in mammalian cells is much more complex, but progress is sufficient to indicate that there are important differences in the controls identified in bacteria and higher organisms (Wyngaarden, 1970, p. 105) (Table 14-I).

Regulation of specific enzymes appears to play a major role in mammalian cells (Table 14-II) and will be the concern of this chapter. Examples of some parts of the outline shown in Table 14-II, but not all parts, are available with respect to human cultured cells. Some examples involve more than one type of regulation or stimulus. Many observations are difficult to classify at the present stage of our knowledge; the distinction in types of enzyme regulation, between regulation of synthesis, catabolism or activity is particularly difficult. The molecular basis for enzyme regulation in mammalian cells is under intensive study (Table 14-III) (Wyngaarden, 1970). These molecular mechanisms will not be discussed further in this chapter.

TABLE 14-I

DIFFERENCES IN MECHANISMS OF REGULATION BETWEEN
BACTERIA AND MAMMALIAN CELLS
(from Wyngaarden, 1970)

Bacteria	Mammalian Cells
1. *Capacity to Adjust Rapidly to Environmental Change*	
Synthesis of labile, specific messenger RNAs is controlled to regulate the production of stable proteins.	Messenger RNAs are quite stable and enzymes relatively labile; control of enzyme activity involves regulation of rate of enzyme synthesis, degradation, activation and inhibition.
2. *Regulation of Transcription*	
Repressor mechanism of regulation	Repressor mechanism is not well

251

TABLE 14-I (Continued)

Bacteria	*Mammalian Cells*
of transcription is well documented.	documented; other regulatory mechanism(s) probably provide for switching off of the genome.

3. *Relationships Between Transcription and Translation*

Protein synthesis appears to occur on a complex of DNA with messenger RNA, ribosomes, enzymes, and other substances involved in peptide bond formation; translation of the genetic message into protein may influence its transcription from DNA to RNA.	Excepting limited nuclear protein synthesis, transcription of the genetic message from DNA into RNA is physically separated by the nuclear membrane from its translation from RNA into protein; transcription and translation may therefore be regulated (more) independently of one another.

4. *Complexity*

	About 1000 times more of everything (DNA, RNA, ribosomes, protein).

TABLE 14-II

REGULATION OF SPECIFIC ENZYMES IN MAMMALIAN CELLS

    A. Types of regulation
        1. Regulation of enzyme synthesis
           a. Increased rate
           b. Decreased rate
           c. Qualitatively different enzyme
        2. Regulation of enzyme catabolism
           a. Increased rate
           b. Decreased rate
        3. Regulation of enzyme activity
           a. Activation
           b. Inhibition

    B. Stimuli
        1. Nutritional change
        2. Drug or chemical exposure
        3. Changes in oxygen tension, temperature, pH
        4. Alteration of hormone level or action
        5. Changes in substrate concentration
        6. Inherited genetic mutations
        7. Cell differentiation

TABLE 14-III

POSSIBLE MECHANISMS OF ENZYME INDUCTION IN
MAMMALIAN CELLS

(from Wyngaarden, 1970)

1. Specific gene amplification (DNA synthesis)
2. Increased rate of gene transcription
3. Increased rate of messenger RNA transport
4. Messenger stabilization
5. Translational control
    Regulation of chain initiation, propagation,
    or termination
    Regulation of nascent chain folding

TYPES OF REGULATION—REGULATION OF ENZYME SYNTHESIS

One type of control over gene expression involves repression of genes on all but one of the X chromosomes in somatic cells of mammals, sometimes referred to the other way around, as the single active-X hypothesis (also see Chap. 13, on sex heterochromatin). In any one XX cell the repression involves either the maternally or paternally derived X chromosome, not both. The mechanism is still unsettled. However, since human cell strains in culture from heterozygous XX females carry X-linked mutations that show this type of regulation of enzyme synthesis, these cultures may help to solve the problem of how this genetic control works. Two examples of these X-linked mutations carried in culture are glucose-6-phosphate dehydrogenase (G6DP) deficiency (Davidson *et al.*, 1963) and hypoxanthine-guanine phosphoribosyl transferase (HGPRT) deficiency (Salzmann *et al.*, 1968) (also see Chap. 4, on metabolic defects).

ENVIRONMENTAL STIMULI FOR ENZYME REGULATION

When human fibroblast-like diploid cells or nondiploid HeLa cells were grown anaerobically for one or two passages (5 to 10 cell generations), both cell types showed significantly less cytochrome oxidase as compared to control cells grown aerobically (Hakami and Pious, 1967). Using this study as an example, Table 14-IV illustrates methodology to study regulation of enzyme activity in cultured human cells. In this example a final answer is not obtained.

The effect of oxygen-induced changes in lactic dehydrogenase (LDH) isoenzymes was investigated in human cultured lymphocytes stimulated by PHA (Hellung-Larsen and Andersen, 1969). LDH isoenzyme pattern was dependent on the oxygen

TABLE 14-IV

AN EXAMPLE OF METHODOLOGY TO STUDY REGULATION OF
ENZYME ACTIVITY IN CULTURED HUMAN CELLS
(ENZYME: CYTOCHROME OXIDASE)

Hypothesis	*Test of the Hypothesis* (and whether the answer is for or against)
1. Enzyme deficient genetic variants are selected by anaerobic conditions.	*Against* Anaerobic effect is quickly reversible.
2. Anaerobic growth induces synthesis of an inhibitor of enzyme activity.	*Against* Mixing of aerobically and anaerobically grown cells gives no evidence of an inhibitor.
3. Lack of oxygen causes conformational changes in the enzyme molecule to render it inactive.	*Against* Enzyme "inactivated" by anaerobic growth was not "reactivated" by *in vitro* exposure to oxygen (isolated mitochondria incubated with oxygen and nitrogen).
4. Anaerobic growth stops synthesis of mitochondria (and synthesis of cytochrome oxidase since it is a mitochondrial enzyme.)	*Against* Loss in enzyme activity under anaerobic conditions is too rapid. Gain in activity under aerobic conditions is exponential with no initial lag as would be expected if mitochondria were involved. Morphologic studies show no reduction in number of mitochondria associated with reduced enzyme activity.
5. Availability of oxygen regulates the cellular content of cytochrome oxidase rather than its activity. a. Rate of synthesis is regulated. b. Rate of degradation is regulated.	*For* These are the remaining possibilities that need further investigation.

tension in the culture. Within the range employed in this study (0-70% O_2), the proportion of M subunits of LDH increased progressively with decreasing pO_2. Since total LDH activity was unaffected by pO_2 (within the range of 5-20% O_2), it was concluded that the oxygen tension regulated activity of both H and M subunits. When oxygen tension was changed during culture, forty-eight hours were necessary for complete adaptation of the isoenzyme pattern to the new pO_2.

A temperature sensitive glucose-6-phosphate dehydrogenase (G6PD) has been found in mutant cultured human diploid cells (DeMars, 1968). A single cell technique to detect enzyme-normal and enzyme-deficient cells showed that the slightly deficient mutants could not be distinguished from normals under ordinary conditions. However, when the cells were preheated to 55°C for five minutes, mutant cells could be distinguished by their deficient activity.

Other culture conditions influence production of specific enzyme by the cells. Catalase has been extensively studied in this regard (Pan and Krooth, 1968) (also see Chap. 4, on metabolic defects). The specific catalase activity of human diploid cell strains increases with progressive growth of the culture and falls again following subculture. It should be stressed here that this pattern for catalase is not necessarily the same for other enzymes studied. Alkaline phosphatase is another enzyme found to vary with changing population densities occurring during growth *in vitro* (Miedema, 1968) (also see the section in this chapter on alkaline phosphatase activity and substrate concentration).

Steroids are being studied intensively regarding their role in enzyme regulation. A study was made of adrenal glucosteroid effect on cell membrane preparations from HeLa-S_3 sublines (S_3G and S_3K) (Melnykovych *et al.*, 1969) and activity of two esterases, alkaline phosphatase and 5′nucleotidase was measured. In cells with low constitutive enzyme activity (see definition in Table 14-V), steroid effect increased the levels of activity; in cells with high constitutive enzyme activity, the levels were decreased.

TABLE 14-V

DEFINITIONS CONCERNED WITH SUBSTRATE REGULATION
OF SPECIFIC ENZYMES

Descriptive Term Applied to Cultured Cells	*Definition**
Constitutive	Relatively high enzyme activity in the absence of substrate (for the enzyme).
Noninducible (noninduction)	No measurable enzyme activity even after treatment with substrate.
Inducible (induction)	Appearance of enzyme activity when small amounts of substrate are introduced.
Self-inducible (self-induction)	Increasing specific activities of enzyme (in cultures maintained for long periods of time without change of medium).
Repressible (repression)	Low enzyme activity (under conditions keeping activity low, such as removal of substrate or media change).
Derepressible (derepression)	Higher enzyme activity (under conditions keeping activity high, such as introduction of substrate or growth without media change).

*These terms may also be applied in other situations of enzyme regulation.

SUBSTRATE CONCENTRATION AND REGULATION OF SPECIFIC ENZYMES

Activity of alkaline phosphatase in lysates of human fibroblast-like cultured cells was found to vary according to substrate concentration (Cox and Pontecorvo, 1961). Most cell strains had no measurable alkaline phosphatase activity unless permitted to grow in the presence of small amounts of putative substrates (usually phenyl phosphate). Two unusual cell types were noted: "constitutive" strains that demonstrated relatively high enzyme activity in the absence of substrate and "noninducible" strains that had no measurable activity even after treatment with substrate (Table 14-V). Increasing specific activities of alkaline phosphatase were also observed in cultures maintained for long periods of time without change of medium, "called self-induction."†

†Note that the behavior of catalase specific activity described by Pan and Krooth, 1968, may be an example of "self-induction" but is not called such by the authors, nor does the term rule out multiple stimuli for the change in enzyme activity (see section, this chapter on environmental stimuli for enzyme regulation).

However, additional histochemical studies of alkaline phosphatase in twelve strains of diploid human fibroblast-like cells derived from newborn foreskins revealed marked variation of activity within all populations of cells, whether classified as constitutive or inducible (Martin, 1964) (Table 14-V).

INHERITED GENETIC MUTATIONS AND REGULATION OF SPECIFIC ENZYMES

Inherited genetic mutations may be regarded as stimuli for enzyme regulation (Table 14-VI) (also see Chap. 4). It is obvious from this table that distinction in types of enzyme control, between regulation of synthesis, catabolism or activity is difficult at the present stage of our knowledge.

TABLE 14-VI

INHERITED GENETIC MUTATIONS AS STIMULI FOR REGULATION
OF SPECIFIC HUMAN ENZYMES IN CULTURED CELLS

Type of Mutation and its Expression	Possible Type of Regulation	Reference
Galactose-1-phosphate (product) inhibits galactokinase activity in both normal and galactosemic cell strains, whereas other glycolytic intermediates have no effect.	Several possibilities: feedback effect resulting in decreased rate of enzyme synthesis, increased catabolism or inhibition.	Tedesco and Mellman, 1969
In cells from patients with orotic aciduria, activities of two sequential enzymes in pyrimidine biosynthesis (orotidylate pyrophosphorylase and decarboxylase) are decreased but may be increased by administration of 6-azauridine.	Several possibilities: increased rate of enzyme synthesis (by 6-azauridine); decreased rate of enzyme catabolism; enzyme activation.	Pinsky and Krooth, 1967
Temperature sensitive G6PD mutants in human diploid cells.	Synthesis of qualitatively different enzyme: difference is brought out by environmental stimulation.	DeMars, 1968
Heterozygous X-linked mutations, when they occur on the inactive-X chromosome are not expressed.	Decreased rate of synthesis of an enzyme that may or may not be qualitatively different.	

TABLE 14-VI (Continued)

Type of Mutation and its Expression	Possible Type of Regulation	Reference
G6PD deficiency		Davidson *et al.*, 1963
HGPRT deficiency		Salzmann *et al.*, 1968
HGPRT deficient cells (from patients with X-linked hyperuricemia) have a block in conversion of hypoxanthine to inosinic acid but paradoxically there is hypernormal *de novo* synthesis of hypoxanthine.	Removal of feedback repression resulting in increased rate of enzyme synthesis (?) to produce hypoxanthine. Regulation of enzyme catabolism or activity is also possible.	Felix and DeMars, 1969
Deficient fibroblast-like cells show low but significant levels of hypoxanthine-quanine phosphoribosyl transferase (PRTase) but this mutant enzyme is more heat labile than normal enzyme.	Synthesis of qualitatively different enzyme.	Fujimoto and Seegmiller, 1970

Often the tertiary or quaternary structure of an enzyme, and therefore its activity, relates to the concentrations of surrounding small molecules, including substrate, co-enzyme, inhibitor, activator and stabilizer molecules. Occasionally it should prove possible to raise the activity of a mutant enzyme *in vivo* by manipulating the concentration of the appropriate small molecule . . . Doubtless the enzymatic inactivity of each inborn error of metabolism can be caused by a variety of lesions in the structure and regulation of that enzyme. Cell cultures from individual patients may be useful in pinpointing the molecular defect peculiar to each kindred, and perhaps in determining if this defect can indeed be ameliorated by changing the concentration of one of the small molecules that modify the structure or amount of the enzyme concerned (Littlefield, 1968, pp. 413-414).

CELL DIFFERENTIATION AND REGULATION OF SPECIFIC ENZYMES

When human diploid cells were studied from primary explants of adult individuals, fetal acid phosphatase isoenzyme (C) was detected in the cultured cells (Beckman *et al.*, 1968). The investigators postulated that growth of the cells in culture caused them to revert, enzymatically, to an earlier developmental stage (a process termed dedifferentiation by some authors). The enzyme regulation may involve derepression of the genome, in other words, renewed expression of genes normally acting early but not later in development. A similar process may also explain the presence in HeLa (human nondiploid) cells of a fetal-like alkaline phosphatase (Elson and Cox, 1969). Another example involves variations in napthylamidase isoenzymes studied in human cultured cells (Beckman *et al.*, 1967). Cultured diploid cells from skin regularly showed isoenzyme components not present in skin biopsies examined directly.

At a fixed time in embryonic development repression of genes on all but one of the X chromosomes occurs in somatic cells of mammals (see earlier in this chapter, the section on regulation of enzyme synthesis). Whatever the mechanism, it is certainly an important developmental event in humans and represents a regulation of specific enzymes in cell differentiation.

Differences in transfer RNAs have been reported in human leukemia (Gallo, 1969). In these studies lymphocytes were obtained from patients with acute and chronic lymphocytic leukemia. Cells were grown in culture to obtain the quantity needed. Approximately 500 grams each of normal and leukemic cells were used for the study, and tRNAs for twenty amino acids were compared between lymphocytes and lymphoblasts. Differences were found, but the significance and reproducibility of the differences are unsettled. A discussion of the significance runs as follows:

> The normal immature leukocyte differentiates: this process involves the selective synthesis of new (mature cell) proteins and is accompanied by inactivation of DNA. The fully mature leukocyte does not synthesize DNA or divide and contains a complement of proteins different from that in the immature cell. In leukemia there is accumulation of a cell population that retains the capacity to synthesize DNA and to divide and that does not appear to contain the full complement of mature leukocyte protein. On the other hand, these cells apparently contain greater amounts of "immature cell protein." An alteration in protein synthesis (via altered tRNA) could result in inability to synthesize the full complement of mature cell protein. The same disorder of protein synthesis might also lead to an insufficient or abnormal repressor protein. The consequence could be the undifferentiated cell (Gallo, 1969, p. 149).

REFERENCES

General

Littlefield, J. W.: Control mechanisms in animal cell cultures. *Arch Biochem, 125*:410, 1968.

Wyngaarden, J. B.: Genetic control of enzyme activity in higher organisms. *Biochem Genet, 4*:105, 1970.

Specific

Beckman, L.; Beckman, G.; Bergman, S., and Lundgren, E.: Isozyme variations in human cells grown *in vitro*. II. Acid phosphatase. *Acta Genet (Basel), 18*:409, 1968.

Beckman, L.: Bergman, S., and Lundgren, E.: Isozyme variations in human cells grown *in vitro*. I. Amino acid naphthyl amidase. *Acta Genet (Basel), 17*:304, 1967.

Cox, R. P., and Pontecorvo, G.: Induction of alkaline phosphatase by substrate in established cultures of cells from individual human donors. *Proc Nat Acad Sci USA, 47*:839, 1961.

Davidson, R. G.; Nitowsky, H. M., and Childs, B.: Demonstration of two populations of cells in the human female heterozygous for glucose-6-phosphate dehydrogenase variants. *Proc Nat Acad Sci USA, 50*:481, 1963.

DeMars, R.: A temperature-sensitive glucose-6-phosphate dehydrogenase in mutant cultured human cells. *Proc Nat Acad Sci USA, 61*:562, 1968.

Elson, N. A., and Cox, R. P.: Production of fetal-like alkaline phosphatase by HeLa cells. *Biochem Genet, 3*:549, 1969.

Felix, J. S., and DeMars, R.; Purine requirement of cells cultured from humans affected with Lesch-Nyhan syndrome (hypoxanthine-quanine phosphoribosyltransferase deficiency). *Proc Nat Acad Sci USA, 62*:536, 1969.

Fujimoto, W. Y., and Seegmiller, J. E.: Hypoxanthine-quanine phosphoribosyltransferase deficiency: Activity in normal, mutant, and heterozygote-cultured human skin fibroblasts. *Proc Nat Acad Sci USA, 65*:577, 1970.

Gallo, R. C.: Transfer RNAs in human leukemia. *J Cell Physiol, 74 (Supp 1)*:149, 1969.

Hakami, N., and Pious, D. A.: Regulation of cytochrome oxidase in human cells in culture. *Nature (London), 216*:1087, 1967.

Hellung-Larsen, P., and Andersen, V.: Kinetics of oxygen-induced changes in lactic dehydrogenase isoenzymes of human lymphocytes in culture. *Exp Cell Res, 54*:201, 1969.

Littlefield, J. W.: Control mechanisms in animal cell cultures. *Arch Biochem, 125*:410, 1968.

Martin, G. M.: Variation of alkaline phosphatase activity among cells of inducible and constitutive strains of human fibroblasts. *Proc Soc Exp Biol Med, 116*:490, 1964.

Melnykovych, G.; Swayze, M. A., and Bishop, C.: Effects of prednisolone on esterases in heteroploid cells of human origin. *Biochim Biophys Acta,* *184*:672, 1969.

Miedema, E.: Regulation of alkaline phosphatase in human cell cultures independent of hydrocortisone and sensitivity to population density changes. *Exp Cell Res, 53*:488, 1968.

Pan, Y. -L., and Krooth, R. S.: The influence of progressive growth on the specific catalase activity of human diploid cell strains. I. Effect of cellular genotype: Homozygous strains. *J Cell Physiol, 71*:151, 1968.

Pinsky, L., and Krooth, R. S.: Studies on the control of pyrimidine biosynthesis in human diploid cell strains. I. Effect of 6-azauridine on cellular phenotype. *Proc Nat Acad Sci USA, 57*:925, 1967.

Salzmann, J.; DeMars, R., and Benke, P.: Single-allele expression at an X-linked hyperuricemia locus in heterozygous human cells. *Proc Nat Acad Sci USA, 60*:545, 1968.

Tedesco, T. A., and Mellman, W. J.: Galactose-1-phosphate uridyltransferase and galactokinase activity in cultured human diploid fibroblasts and peripheral blood leukocytes. I. Analysis of transferase genotypes by the ratio of the activities of the two enzymes. *J Clin Invest, 48*:2390, 1969.

Wyngaarden, J. B.: Genetic control of enzyme activity in higher organisms. *Biochem Genet, 4*:105, 1970.

APPENDIX

CELL CULTURE METHODOLOGY

CELL CULTURE METHODOLOGY

I. LONG-TERM CULTURE OF HUMAN MONOLAYER CELLS

A. Cells in Culture Bottles (stationary)

1. Assemble medium,* 0.25% trypsin solution, mammalian cell balanced salt solution† and canisters of Pasteur pipettes, 5- and 10-ml serological pipettes. Use sterile technique throughout.

2. Take a confluent 8-oz prescription bottle to be subcultured and decant medium. With 5-ml pipette add about 5 ml mammalian cell balanced salt solution. Put pipette aside. Rotate the bottle so that top and sides, as well as bottom, are washed. Decant fluid.

3. Repeat washing with salt solution.

4. With Pasteur pipette and 1-ml sterile rubber bulb, add 1 ml trypsin and discard Pasteur pipette. Make sure trypsin comes in contact with entire bottom of bottle. Allow to stand at room temperature for one min.; then decant trypsin. Cap and incubate at 37°C for three to five min. Check with inverted microscope to insure that cells are removed from bottom surface.‡

5. For 8-oz prescription bottles add 9 ml medium to each of two new labeled bottles (1:2 split) or to each of four new labeled bottles (1:4 split), using the same 10-ml serologi-

---

*Mammalian cell media are available commercially or may be prepared from standard formulations. A partial list includes: Dulbecco and Vogt's modification of Eagle's medium (D & V), medium 199, NCTC 109, Ham's F-10 or F-12, and Waymouth's medium. Serum supplement is required, often 15 percent fetal calf serum.

†Balanced salt solutions for mammalian cells are available commercially or may be prepared. A partial list includes: phosphate buffered saline (deficient in calcium and magnesium), Earle's solution, and Hank's solution.

‡If cells are not removed, continue incubation for five min. and recheck. If cells remain attached, add 1 ml trypsin and reincubate five or more min.

cal pipette. Set pipette aside. Make sure medium is pink-orange in color (pH about 7.4 with phenol red indicator). If it is bright pink, run CO_2 into gas phase above medium until color is pink-orange.

6. With 5-ml pipette add medium to cells to a total of 2 ml if subdivision is 2:1, or 4 ml of medium if 4:1. With same pipette suspend cells well, and pipette 1 ml into each bottle set up in step five. Cap loosely and place in CO_2 incubator. Alternatively, run CO_2 into bottle as needed, being sure to direct gas flow in gas phase of bottle, not into medium; cap tightly and place in nongas flow incubator.

General

1. When fluid is decanted from bottle, the mouth of the bottle should be flamed when the cap is removed and after decantation.
2. Fluid decanted from a bottle should be poured down funnel into flask, and funnel should subsequently be washed down with 1:10 dilution of bleach (Clorox®) from a wash bottle to decrease the risk of cross-cell contamination.
3. A pipette that has been introduced into a bottle containing cells should never be returned to stock bottles of medium, salt solution, or trypsin.
4. Never subculture all of your cells on the same day. Set up a routine for subculturing on alternate days, using red-coded medium, salt solution, and trypsin on odd days and blue-coded on even days.
5. Blow out cotton plugs from each serological pipette as soon as possible after using, and place tip up in soaking solution. Used pipettes should not be allowed to dry out.
6. Use your own bottle of medium, trypsin, and salt solution. Never use anyone else's.
7. When you return a bottle of medium to the refrigerator for reuse, always make sure the cap is tight. Check color of medium before you put it on cells. If pH is too alkaline (bright pink color), medium will need to be gassed with CO_2 for one min. until color is right.

8. It is unwise to economize by retaining an old bottle to use as one of the new bottles. The main problems with this method are (a) accumulation of debris and old medium, and (b) splitting of cells is not exact.

9. For routine cell maintenance, at least two new bottles should always be started. Then on the next subculture, one can be subcultured and the other held in reserve, in case of contamination or growth problems. It is usually wise to keep in reserve several of these older bottles dating back for more than one subculture. To keep more than three bottles from different old subculturing is usually unnecessary and wastes incubator space.

10. Disposable sterile plastic tissue culture flasks (250 ml) and serological pipettes are useful (made by Falcon Plastics). Fluid volumes in the protocol will need to be adjusted for the size of the culture containers.

B. Cells in Roller Bottles

Monolayer cells can be grown in large quantities in roller bottles. The apparatus to roll the bottles at controlled and variable speeds and either permanent or disposable glass bottles are available from Bellco Biological Glassware and Equipment, Vineland, N.J. Procedures for culture differ in quantity but not in quality from those for standard culture bottles. General suggestions for human diploid cells are listed here.

1. Initial cell inoculation should not be less than 2×10^6 cells for a bottle of 840 cm^2 growth area. Higher cell inoculations or repeated inoculations will result in more rapid confluency.

2. Cells grow well in volumes of medium not less than 50 ml per 840 cm^2 bottle. Volume between 50 ml and 150 ml are usual. Medium changes are indicated as the medium becomes acid.

3. Bottles may be gassed to the appropriate CO_2 concentration if caps are tight.

4. Bottles should be rolled at the lowest speed. A more rapid

speed is used for trypsinization and for about one hour following inoculation of new cells or medium change.

5. Rinses with balanced salt solution prior to trypsinization should be no less than 100 ml volume. Trypsin (0.25%) is added in quantities of about 5 ml. Cell dispersion takes approximately the same time as for standard bottles. It is a good idea to roll the bottles fairly rapidly during trypsinization.

6. The usual yield for human diploid cells at confluency is not less than 2 x 10^7 cells per bottle of 840 cm^2 growth area.

II. PRIMARY EXPLANTS

A. Pinch Skin Biopsy Technique

1. Scrub the skin well with 70% ethanol or with 0.02% iodine in 70% ethanol (1 ml 2% iodine tincture in 99 ml 70% ethanol), followed by 70% ethanol. The inside of the forearm is a good area for persons of all ages because this area is less sensitive to pain, is easily accessible, and is free of hair.

2. With a long-tipped sterile forceps obtain a pinch of skin about 10 mm long and 1 to 1.5 mm wide. Apply increasing pressure with the forceps and hold until the skin becomes white. The individuals will feel uncomfortable pressure. It is best to ask them not to watch and proceed quickly with the skin excision at this point in the procedure. The pinch is good anesthesia for the exclusion.

3. Use a sterile scissors with fine blades. Snip quickly along the two points of the forceps. The specimen should be about 4 to 5 mm long and 1 mm wide. The exact size will vary from one person to another. The ease of obtaining dermis will also vary but will be uniformly accomplished if the pinch and excision are as large as just described. Pinpoint bleeding at the site of the excision is an indication that mesodermal tissue has been obtained.

4. Drop the specimen immediately into a small Petri dish containing balanced salt solution. Process within several hours (up to 24 hr.).

5. Lift up the tissue with a fine forceps and cut off pieces no larger than 1 x 1 mm. Sterile disposable needles may be used to transfer the small fragments to the culture container.

6. Sterile 30 ml plastic tissue culture flasks (Falcon Plastics) are excellent for starting primary explants for serial culture. The fragments can be inserted through the narrow neck and placed as far in as desired. Include one to three tissue pieces in each container. At least two and preferably three containers are recommended.

7. Allow the fragments to dry out *briefly*. During this period the tissue sticks slightly to the plastic surface.

8. Carefully let 1 drop of culture medium plus 20 percent to 25 percent fetal calf serum fall from a Pasteur pipette over each fragment. On the plastic surface, a drop will "bead" and will serve the function of a "clot" to hold the fragment. About 0.25 to 0.5 ml medium may also be added directly to another portion of the flask for humidification, but care must be taken to keep this amount from running into the area of the fragments.

9. Gas gently to the proper pH and cap tightly. Also place in a dry desiccator or gas flow incubator at the proper concentration of CO_2. This additional precaution insures proper pH even if the cap of the culture container leaks. Primary explants are extremely sensitive to changes of pH.

10. Incubate at 37°C for about two days, undisturbed. Look at the color of the medium, if possible without moving the culture containers. Only if the pH is wrong should the cultures be manipulated at this time. Re-gas if necessary.

11. After this period, the flasks may be checked under an inverted microscope for signs of evaporation or undue amount of precipitated material in the medium. Several more drops of medium may be added with a Pasteur pipette.

12. When new epithelial-like or fibroblast-like growth first appears at the edge of the primary explant (after about

four days, with a range of about two to ten), the explant is less susceptible to "floating" away from the surface. Nevertheless, care must still be taken when medium is added. Thirty-ml plastic tissue culture flasks (Falcon Plastics) will hold about 3 ml. Subsequently change medium every four to five days.

13. Do not be in a hurry to make the first subculture. A good halo of fibroblast-like cells covering an area larger than the primary explant should be present. Some explants will show rings of epithelial-like growth before the fibroblast-like cells appear. These epithelial-like cells cannot be subcultured by the usual procedures for monolayer fibroblast-like cells.

14. Cells from the first trypsinization may be transferred to a 250-ml plastic flask or 8-oz prescription bottle in about 10 to 15 ml of medium plus 15 percent or 20 percent serum. Gently run 1 ml balanced salt solution over the primary explant, using a Pasteur pipette. Aspirate. Discard fluid. Repeat 2X. Add 0.5 ml of 0.25 percent trypsin, making sure the area of fibroblast-like growth is covered. Incubate at 37°C until the cells detach (not longer than about 20 min.).

15. Rinse 1 ml of medium gently over the cells. Aspirate and add to the new bottle. Repeat several times. Add new medium to the primary explant.

16. Return cultures to the incubator at proper pH and humidified 37°C.

17. Allow the first subculture to reach near-confluency and subculture to two bottles. Keep a culture record.

18. Consider freezing a portion of the cells as soon as possible for prolonged storage in liquid nitrogen.

19. Primary explants may be trypsinized repeatedly at intervals after new outgrowth occurs.

B. Human Surgical Specimens, Autopsy Tissues, Fetal Tissues
Surgical Specimens

1. Specimens must be handled with sterile technique and

processed as quickly as possible after removal from the patient.

2. In general, they may be established according to the method, or its modifications, described in detail for skin biopsies. Several rinses in balanced salt solution may be indicated particularly to remove red blood cells.

3. In general, fibroblast-like cells will grow out, and chromosome complement of the primary explant will be maintained throughout the lifetime of the human cell culture (50 ± 10 population doublings). An occasional exception is the culture from a human tumor which may have a nondiploid or unstable chromosome complement in culture.

4. Dense tissues may require *in vitro* trypsinization prior to culture.

5. Foreskin is an excellent source from which to establish long-term cultures. The skin preparation recommended for skin biopsies is also recommended for circumcisions to be used for tissue culture.

Autopsy Tissues

1. The chance of contamination increases. Autopsy skin may be prepared with iodine and alcohol as described for skin biopsies of living tissues. Internal organs should be dissected with sterile instruments, or else the interior of large organs may be dissected out by sterile technique. Only small pieces of tissue are needed for culture. Follow the rules already described for skin biopsies. Include several rinses in balanced salt solution.

2. Thymus in children makes a good primary explant. Small round cells will be present initially before the fibroblast-like cells overgrow the culture. Initiation of the monolayer fibroblast-like culture may be shorter for thymus than for other tissues.

3. Gonad cultures may be indicated in cases of sex chromosome malformations, intersexes, or chromosomal mosaicism. Again, the fibroblast-like cell will grow. Mitotic chromosomes are obtained, not meiotic chromosomes.

4. At autopsy, multiple tissue sampling may be performed for the evaluation of chromosomal mosaicism.

Fetal Tissues

1. The same culturing principles apply as for skin biopsies. In general, the new outgrowth occurs more rapidly.
2. Once fetal tissues are established, they may grow more rapidly (slightly shorter means cell cycle time), although this rule is not absolute. The culture life is longer by about ten population doublings.
3. Fetal fibroblast-like cells may be slightly more difficult to trypsinize and obtain as single cell suspensions for subculture than are cultures of adult tissue origin. Again, this rule is not absolute.

III. LONG-TERM STORAGE OF CELLS

A. Preparation of Cells for Freezing

1. Trypsinize monolayer cells in the usual manner for subculturing. Cells should not be overly confluent.
2. When cells are removed from the bottom surface, add medium and suspend well. They should be single, and without clumps.
3. Centrifuge at 600 to 800 rpm for ten min.
4. Remove supernatant.
5. Resuspend in medium with 10 percent final concentration of sterile glycerin. Amount of medium should be adjusted to make the cell count not less than 2×10^6/ml.
6. Add 2 ml of cell suspension to labeled sterile freezing ampules.
7. The technique of sealing the ampules is very important. If a small leak is present after sealing, liquid nitrogen can enter the ampule when it is frozen, and the ampule will explode when it is thawed, due to rapid expansion of the liquid nitrogen. Some investigators place the sealed ampules in a dye solution prior to freezing, to check for leaks.

B. Freezing Cells

Detailed instructions accompany the freezing equipment,

and these instructions should be read carefully. An electronic recorder is necessary to record the rate of cooling of the cells in the freezing chamber. A separate controller unit regulates the entry of liquid nitrogen from the main tank into the freezing chamber. The controlled drop of 1°C/min. should be followed to −40°C then the temperature may be reduced quickly to −80°C. At this point the ampules are transferred rapidly to racks which are inserted into the canisters in the liquid nitrogen refrigerator.

IV. CLONING

A. Single Cell Plating for Cloning

Culture No. _____ Date _____

Select a bottle of cells that is nearly confluent.

Trypsinize by usual routine.

Add 10 ml of medium plus 15 to 20 percent serum. Suspend cells well with Pasteur pipette and perform cell count.

Counts Per Large
Corner Squares

1 Side of Chamber	8 squares	Divide by 8	x $10^4 =$
1　2　3　4			
Other Side of Chamber			cells/ml $= n$
1　2　3　4			

Solve for ml:

$$\frac{n}{1} = \frac{1 \times 10^6}{ml}$$

Use dispo 1-ml pipettes whenever possible, for cell transfers.

Use 10-ml dispo-plastic tubes.

Add _____ ml to make 10 ml suspension in medium plus serum (1×10^6 cells/10 ml).

Add 0.2 ml of cell suspension to 9.8 ml medium plus serum (2×10^4 cells/ml).

Add 1.0 ml of cell suspension to 9.0 ml medium plus serum (2×10^3 cells/10 ml) (200 cells/ml).

Be sure cells are well suspended before each dilution.

Add 10 ml medium plus serum to each 100 x 20-mm plastic tissue culture Petri dish.

To _____ Petri dishes labeled one hundred cells, add 0.5 ml of cell suspension and agitate gently.

To _____ Petri dishes labeled fifty cells, add 0.25 ml of cell suspension.

To _____ Petri dishes labeled forty cells, add 0.2 ml of cell suspension. (optional)

To _____ Petri dishes labeled twenty cells, add 0.1 ml of cell suspension.

Place dishes (level) in humidified desiccator or incubator at 37°C.

Adjust pH with the proper CO_2 concentration.

Dishes should not be disturbed for about three days.

B. Ring Method from Single Cell Platings

1. When clones have formed from single cell platings (after 1 to 2 weeks, depending on the growth rate of the cells), select the number of clones to be subcultured. Examine the plate under an inverted microscope. Select clones that are isolated, compact, and composed of approximately one hundred or more cells. With a wax pencil, place a ring on the bottom of the Petri dish to mark the exact position of the clone. More than one clone may be taken from each dish.

2. Decant the medium from the Petri dish, add 5 ml balanced salt solution and pour off; repeat the rinse. Aspirate the last drops of salt solution with a Pasteur pipette.

3. Using sterile technique and a round wooden applicator, place silicone grease on one side of a cloning ring. This ring should have an outside diameter of about 1.5 cm and an inside diameter of about 0.5 cm (the dimensions may be smaller but not larger). Height should be about 1.0 cm. The rings may be cut from solid Teflon® rods; the material used should withstand autoclaving.

4. Place ring over the wax mark on bottom of Petri dish, using a sterile forceps. Press the ring down firmly. If too much silicone grease is used, it will spread over the clone and prevent removal of the cells. Check placement of the

ring under an inverted microscope. The clone should be centered in the ring.

5. Place 1 drop of 0.25% trypsin from a Pasteur pipette into the center of the ring. Incubate about two min. at 37°C or until the cells appear round on microscopic examination. (Trypsin may be left on about 10 min. at room temperature. Longer trypsinization time at this point may prevent the cells from growing after subculture.)

6. A 2-oz or 4-oz prescription bottle may be used for subculture. Add 10 ml medium plus at least 15 percent serum (20% may be used). With a Pasteur pipette, add just enough medium from the 2-oz or 4-oz bottle to fill the cloning ring (about 0.5 ml). Place the end of the pipette lightly against the bottom of the center hole in the ring and rinse the medium up and down several times. Check carefully to make sure the ring is not leaking. If it is, the clone will need to be discarded. Add medium and cells to the subculture bottle. Repeat the rinsing of cells from inside the ring once or twice more. Check under the inverted microscope to make sure the ring is empty.

7. Incubate the bottle at 37°C with the proper pH adjustment.

8. At least one re-cloning is recommended for established cell lines. Human cells are difficult to reclone.

V. SHORT-TERM CULTURE OF HUMAN PERIPHERAL BLOOD

A. Macromethod

Equipment and Reagents

1. 10-ml plastic disposable syringe with No. 20 needle, sterile.
2. Sodium heparin, aqueous solution, 1000 USP units/ml, sterile.
3. Phytohemagglutinin (a dried preparation is available from Burroughs Wellcome & Co., London, England). Reconstitute with sterile triple distilled water. An extract of red kidney beans may be prepared, but different lots will vary in mitogenic activity.

4. Tissue culture vessel. Two-oz prescription bottles which are made of soft glass and are disposable are very satisfactory. They should be rinsed with triple distilled water prior to use and autoclaved. Siliconization is not necessary.

5. Tissue culture medium. Several types of defined medium for mammalian cells can be made from standard protocols, or are available commercially. Puck's F-10 or F-12, Dulbecco and Vogt's medium, Medium 199, Waymouth's medium, NCTC-109 are all satisfactory. Serum must be added and is available commercially from the companies that supply medium. A concentration of 15 percent fetal calf serum is recommended. The medium should contain phenol red indicator. Antibiotics are optional.

Procedure

1. Wet 10-ml syringe with heparin. Draw 10 ml blood, clear needle, and stand syringe on plunger for ½-2 hr. When plasma has cleared of RBCs, bend needle and extrude plasma into sterile tube.

or

Draw 10 ml blood in plain syringe. Add to tube containing 0.2 to 0.5 ml of heparin. Allow RBCs to settle out. Aspirate plasma from RBCs with sterile Pasteur pipette.

2. A leukocyte count *may* be made on plasma, using a standard procedure for WBC count, in a hemocytometer. Total cell count should be at least 2×10^6/ml.

3. Add 0.5 to 1.0 ml plasma to culture medium in 2-oz culture container. Total volume should not exceed about 10 ml.

4. Add 0.1 to 0.2 ml phytohemagglutinin, shake culture, and incubate at 37°C. Gastight containers should be gassed with CO_2 (10% for D & V medium, 5% for most others). If gas exchange is allowed, the containers should be placed in a humidified, gasflow incubator with the appropriate concentration of CO_2 (5% or 10%). It is very important to maintain the cultures at the correct pH. The color of phenol red indicator should be pink-orange (pH 7.4).

5. During incubation for about three days (72 hr.) the cultures may be shaken three times daily.

B. Micromethod

Procedure

1. Prepare culture medium plus 15% fetal calf serum and container as described for macromethod.
2. Add about 0.4 ml heparin to about 10 ml medium in 2-oz container.
3. Add 0.1 to 0.2 ml phytohemagglutinin.
4. Allows three to four drops of blood to drip from a finger prick or a heel stab into culture container, which is shaken gently to prevent clotting.
5. Incubate as for macromethod.

or

1. Obtain 0.1 to 0.2 ml sterile capillary or venous blood in a 1-ml plastic syringe wet with heparin.
2. Inoculate blood directly into medium in 2-oz container.
3. Add 0.1 to 0.2 ml phytohemagglutinin.
4. Incubate as for macromethod.

VI. LONG-TERM CULTURE OF HUMAN PERIPHERAL BLOOD

1. Peripheral blood should be cultured within two hrs. or as soon as possible.
2. An initial inoculation of 4-5 x 10^6 cells per ml in media supplemented with fetal calf serum is recommended. Serum concentration varies between different cultures and ranges from 5-30 percent.
3. Agitation of the cultures twice a day may be desirable to prevent the cells from piling up in small areas. The cells do not adhere to the lower surface of the container but will "hover."
4. Medium renewal must be performed on the basis of changes in pH and cell population (and even in the absence of growth) at appropriate intervals. As a general rule small amounts of medium are added every forty-eight

hr. for the first week; then about 20 percent of the existing volume is added each week, and about 80 percent of the medium is replaced monthly. Usually the medium is replaced (90%) when cultures are combined.

5. Total cell counts and cell viability (dye exclusion) are determined at ten days. Usually the viable cell population drops to about 1.5×10^6 per ml after ten days in culture. Cell viability will vary from 20-90 percent. Cell counts are repeated at twenty days and cultures combined if the cell population is below 5×10^5 per ml. Cultures are combined following centrifugation; 90 percent of the medium is replaced.

6. When cells begin to grow rapidly, partial medium changes or subcultures are required every 48-72 hrs. In contrast to the initial period of slow growth, the cells will grow in different types of suspension and stationary cultures with high viabilities, provided the cell population is maintained above 5×10^5 per ml. Large volume production units may be used.

INDEX